When Buckminster Fuller came to Canada, he kept asking the same question: ‘Have you ever really considered how much your buildings actually weigh?’

The Canadians took this very seriously. (Hey, we never thought of it that way!)
He showed them plans of domed cities, cities with no basements, no foundations.
Cities that could be moved in a minute.

Portable cities.
Portable towns.

He said: Think of it as camping out.
He said: Think of it as one big tent.

He said:
Think of it as
The Big Top

...spinning
...lightweight
...portable

37786
AIR FORCE

He said:
Think of it as
The Big Top.

...spinning
...lightweight
...flyaway

FOX
STUDIOS
AUSTRALIA

He said:
Think of it as
The Big Top.

- Laurie Anderson

DESIGNING LIGHTNESS

STRUCTURES FOR SAVING ENERGY

ADRIAAN BEUKERS
ED VAN HINTE

nai010 publishers

FOREWORD

Design, for all its well-meant idealism and big claims of changing the world for the better, has so far failed to show its true potential for achieving a more sustainable world. The climate crisis is upon us, we are losing biodiversity at an alarming rate, and yet the design community seems at a loss about how to respond. And so, at the start of 2020, we are celebrating incense holders that were inspired by volcanic eruptions (designer José Bermúdez), cute chairs 'based on intimate parts of the body' by Adam Nathaniel Furman and a robot (Rollbot) developed by Charmin's GoLab that delivers a fresh toilet roll to those who are out of paper, just to name a few.

Perhaps it is a paucity of vision? A lack of a foundational principle, something to hold on to? Many of these rather useless and unsustainable designs aren't the result of bad thinking or bad design, but if a project is based on the wrong starting point, nothing good will come of it. Lightness is the right starting point.

In fact, it is not even a starting point – it is much more. The authors are too modest when they claim that this book is about designing 'maximum value for minimum amount of mass'. I believe lightness is a mindset, a mentality, a way of designing and perhaps even a way of living. The basic idea of sustainability, after all, is that we should walk lightly on the earth. Let lightness be our guide.

As with all good guides, *Designing Lightness* makes you curious without immediately giving away the clue. The book's playful design, fascinating titles (Changsha Fast, The Limping Pharaoh), rich visuals and tongue-in-cheek humour keep you engaged. As you progress through the text you slowly begin to grasp the logic of lightness, the intricacies of designing with and for lightness, and finally, how lightness can (and should) pervade economies and societies. Much to its credit, *Designing Lightness* doesn't shun technical details and patiently explains basic mechanical concepts like bending, buckling, creep and torsion. It also provides the necessary guidebook wisdoms: 'Poor structural design will always remain poor.'

The collaboration between Adriaan Beukers, professor emeritus of Design & Production of Composite Structures at TU Delft and Ed van Hinte, writer, researcher and teacher, has proved to be most fruitful. The first book they wrote together, *Lightness*, sold out quickly and made it to four editions. *Designing Lightness* expands and deepens their unique take on the world. Read this book! It will help you discover new methods, principles, ideas and paths for truly sustainable designs. Travel safely.

– Conny Bakker
Professor of Design Methodology for Sustainability and Circular Economy, Delft, University of Technology

URGENCY

1.
WHY SKYSCRAPERS AND ALL WE MAKE SHOULD BE LIGHT

Treehouse in New Guinea

Humans put far too much effort into moving stuff around, including themselves. Goals need to be set to limit environmental side effects, resource depletion and atmospheric degradation. It is an established fact that we must avoid overloading the living environment at all costs. One way of achieving this, the weight reduction aspect, is often overlooked, despite its potential. For the sake of simplicity in advocating lightness we will start with a slightly flawed, but certainly indicative comparison. Let us take two contemporary classics: the extremely high tower of Burj Khalifa in Dubai and the largest existing passenger airplane to date, the Airbus A380. On second thoughts, we can better narrow it down to a more universal example: an average skyscraper and a normal passenger carrier.

A standard 50-storey building would weigh about 250,000 tonnes and would serve 5000 people working or living there. So we are dealing with a weight of 50 tonnes per person. An average airplane, such as an Airbus A220-300, can carry a maximum of 164 people and weighs about 55 tonnes, including fuel to enable it to move. This means that, even just before take-off, it weighs only 0.34 tonnes (likely to become less in the future) per person on board.

Now, we are not saying buildings should be replaced by planes. An aircraft is a

Airbus A380 and Burj Khalifa, Dubai

vehicle that carries passengers over considerable distances at high speed, and is equipped with wings, engines and landing gear. It also flies at high altitudes where temperatures are about -50°C. And it has its own dynamics of evolution. A high rise on the other hand needs no flying gear whatsoever, and protecting people against such extremely cold meteorological conditions would be exceptional. One would think that its main job is to provide comfortable space to live and work at a given location. Its evolution mainly seems to concern height, slenderness and being different. The question then is: why do skyscrapers, and most other buildings and civil structures for that matter, need to be so awkwardly heavy?

The answer is that weight is hardly a consideration in building and construction. Heaviness happens to be a traditional quality that comes with a gut feeling of trustworthiness and pride. Buildings are supposed to be stationary objects that provide a comfortable protective interior environment, these days preferably in a sustainable way, showing off their 'zero-emission' label.

Heaviness comes with a gut feeling of trustworthiness and pride.

A building itself is not a vehicle, but the fact that constructing it usually requires moving gargantuan quantities of materials is simply ignored. All this steel, glass and concrete (one tonne of CO_2 emission is required to produce one tonne of concrete) needs to be brought on site and erected using mighty trucks and cranes, together with tools and heavy energy devouring machinery. In addition, these high rises are not being built now and again. Each year about 150 buildings with 50 floors or more are produced worldwide, never mind the thousands of less-tall ones and millions of houses, as if these wouldn't require a massive injection of material and energy.

Moreover, we mustn't overlook the fact that after use there may be demolition and the transportation of debris, or of reusable parts to different locations if the building is to be part of the circular economy. Circularity doesn't happen by itself and requires energy. On top of that, it is meant to be about far more than just one cycle, with all the logistical consequences.

Circularity doesn't happen by itself and requires energy.

A similar observation occurs when the plane is compared to a normal car, which would typically weigh over 1.2 tonnes, or double that for SUVs. The average car claiming rate is 1.42, which specifies the average number of people per trip. This implies that an average car user is accustomed to claiming no less than 0.84 tonnes or 840 kilograms of a regular vehicle.

1.1 CHANGSHA FAST, VERY FAST

This skyscraper is called Mini Sky City, after plans for the record-breaking Sky City tower (838 m) in Changsha in the middle of China were ditched in 2016 due to safety issues. Using the original principles for its much taller unbuilt big brother the 57-storey steel and glass modular structure was built in 19 working days in 2015. Admittedly prefabrication took several months. Some think that building in this way will lead to urban uniformity. On the environmentally positive side, this way of constructing can save close to a staggering 15,000 trucks of concrete.

Top left: Structure by Richard Horden (p40). Top right: The changing position of the sun during one year is called Analemma
Bottom: Top-heavy crane

1.2 SCRAPE FROM ABOVE

Ambitions can reach far beyond sky high. In 2018, Clouds Architecture Office in New York designed the Analemma tower concept for what could be considered an ultra-light 27-kilometre-high tower. The tower's name is also the name of the diagram in the shape of a number 8 that traces the position of the sun in the sky as seen from one location during an entire year. The skyscraper would be ultra-light in the sense that it is not designed to rest on the Earth's surface. Instead it is suspended from an asteroid in geosynchronous orbit, implying that it would describe a 10,000-kilometre orbit in 24 hours, so that the speed of the low end (5 kilometres above the Earth's surface) is similar to the cruise speed of a jet airplane. There will be drag.

Conditions inside are fully controlled and quite special: 'Devotional activities are scattered along the highest reaches, while surface transfer points take advantage of topographic height. The size and shape of windows changes with height to account for pressure and temperature differentials. The amount of daylight increases by 40 minutes at the top of the tower due to the curvature of the earth.'

Analemma would of course be solar powered. The thing could be built in Dubai. It may prove difficult to convince an asteroid of the right size to choose a convenient orbit. The main killjoy, however, is likely to be the cable. In theory the strongest kind of fibre is carbon nanotube, with a breaking length of about 6,000 kilometres. This is defined as the length of fibre at which it will break just holding its own weight while it hangs, say from an asteroid. Given the fact that so far the longest nanotube was about 0.5 metres, it will require some extremely serious developmental effort to reach 50,000 kilometres. Be patient.

Burj Al Babas in Turkey is a luxury resort that went broke before it was completed

Now, why would car users need over ten times their own weight in car mass (or at least 20 times in a SUV) to travel from one place to another? It seems as though cars are mainly interested in transporting themselves.

Again, cars are hardly a rare commodity. It is estimated that worldwide 1.3 billion cars are currently on the move, implying that every day 1.6 billion tonnes of mostly steel are cruising roads from A to B and back, when not held up in traffic jams. Part of why we behave this way is that such car weight gives a feeling of safety, reassurance, homeliness and self-esteem. Apparently, we humans need the illusion of being free in our very own playroom, with superfluous space and empty chairs to accommodate potential fellow travellers. Once again, the environmental side effects are taken for granted.

> *Why would car users need over ten times their own weight in car mass?*

This culture of implicit heaviness trickles down to just about everything, although there are modest signs of a growing awareness. Even some SUVs have undergone a slight (5 per cent) weight reduction and the relationship between the weight and reach of electric cars is becoming apparent. In the world of office furniture, the CEO of a manufacturing company did notice that their desks and chairs were actually quite heavy when they had to be carried up a few flights of stairs to be displayed at a fair. Weight has scarcely been a design issue. This is certainly true of furniture in general. One can purchase lightweight chairs and tables, but with very few exceptions they are meant for the camping market. Even logistics champion and home identity wizard IKEA could put much more effort into weight reduction. Understandably this is not just up to them. It is a market issue. No sooner have their customers unboxed their objects of home desire and assembled them than they'll forget about the effort it took to drag the packages inside and handle the heavy fibreboard planks. Again, mass to most is not a serious consideration.

Abundance reaches well beyond the weight of individual products. The sheer number of produced and consumed objects, knick-knacks, toys and clothes, is vast. So is the amount of food that is produced but not consumed. The mass of the increasing number of digital products is continuously becoming less in terms of functionality per unit weight. However, here we have an unexpectedly emerging caveat: data centres worldwide currently already consume an estimated 5 per cent of all energy, which is half of what air travel consumes, but it may well rise to a staggering 40 per cent in 2030, with energy consumption on the whole increasing as well.

> *Abundance reaches well beyond the weight of individual products.*

Designing Lightness seeks to address the part of abundance that is defined by the mass of individual structures of anything, from buildings to packaging and from cars and aircraft to tools. This includes their contribution to energy usage and ways to reduce it. Consequently, this book is about cultivating maximum value for minimum amount of mass. The cultivation of value is preferable over merely adding value, because it combines sustainability with the notion of time.

Sustainability has undoubtedly become a household term since the Brundtland report *Our Common Future* was published by The World Commission on Environment and Development in 1987. A lot of work has been done since then and one of the most important outcomes is the 2015 UN list of sustainable development goals.

Currently the ruling narrative of 'the solution' to achieve these goals, as far as production, consumption and economy are concerned, consists of a 'circular economy' combined with an 'energy transition'. The former is pictured in the Butterfly model promoted by the Ellen MacArthur Foundation. It defines the way in which materials are taken from resources and kept going in the value chain of use for as long as possible. Recycling is seen as the ultimate means to reboot the value

Energy requires system adaptations and equipment for conversion and storage, for which resources are limited.

potential of used materials, without the need to produce new ones. The model consists of technical cycles of mined materials and biological cycles of farmed materials. The main difference between these is that biological materials are digestible and don't require active recycling.

Both cycles are to be increasingly powered by renewable energy. This shift from fossil fuels to solar and wind power – and maybe nuclear power – is generally called the 'energy transition', with the built-in assumption that this is achievable.

As always there is this human inclination to borrow from the future. Consuming renewable energy is never a free ride. Energy has to be made available. It requires system adaptations as well as equipment for conversion and storage. The resources to produce all this are limited. In addition, the machines and devices needed are no different from any other product in that they also wear down and have a value that requires cultivating in terms of maintenance, repair and possibly functional redefinition.

Consuming renewable energy is never a free ride.

One way to try and prevent ourselves from producing and consuming more than we can handle is to minimize the mass of all the things we produce. This is by no means a simple task. Technologically the challenge is more complicated than most people think, or lightness would be a more obvious requirement. In some instances, lightness principles are counter-intuitive, such as the idea that an airship is a smarter flying machine than a jet airliner. Yet these principles can be explained and made clear: an airship goes up with very little effort, but 'up' isn't a destination, and because of its size it has to work like hell to get anywhere.

In some instances, lightness principles are counter-intuitive.

Since lightness may involve composite structures the process of recycling may be compromised, depending on the composition, the mass, the logistic control and, above all, the responsibility. This requires long-term planning. On the whole, a lightweight structure can change the idea of what something is and how it feels, because every detail will have to be reinvented. A future 50-storey building may weigh only 2500 tonnes and will no longer be a skyscraper. Evolution is at hand ■

Wind turbines and solar panels require mining

1.3 FILL HER UP, PLEASE

There once was a small company in Llandrindod Wells in Wales called Riversimple. It decided to totally redo the car and call it Rasa, short for Tabula Rasa, Latin for clean slate. It doesn't look all that progressive, but this hire car is special because it is designed to be light and efficient. It weighs 580 kilograms, and only 1.5 kilograms more with a full tank, enough for about 485 kilometres at a top speed of 100 km/h. It is so lightweight because of the composite monocoque chassis and the fact that it runs on hydrogen. The power for cruising comes from a moderate sized (8.5 kW) fuel cell. Extra power can be stored in lithium-ion capacitors, which can quickly absorb energy from the brakes or other sources and deliver it to the four wheel-mounted engines for acceleration. The company states that hydrogen is not universally perfect. Because of their weight batteries in conventional electric cars may be more efficient for short distances. Charging these batteries may be more efficient than producing and storing hydrogen. It depends on circumstances whether a battery car or a hydrogen car is preferable.

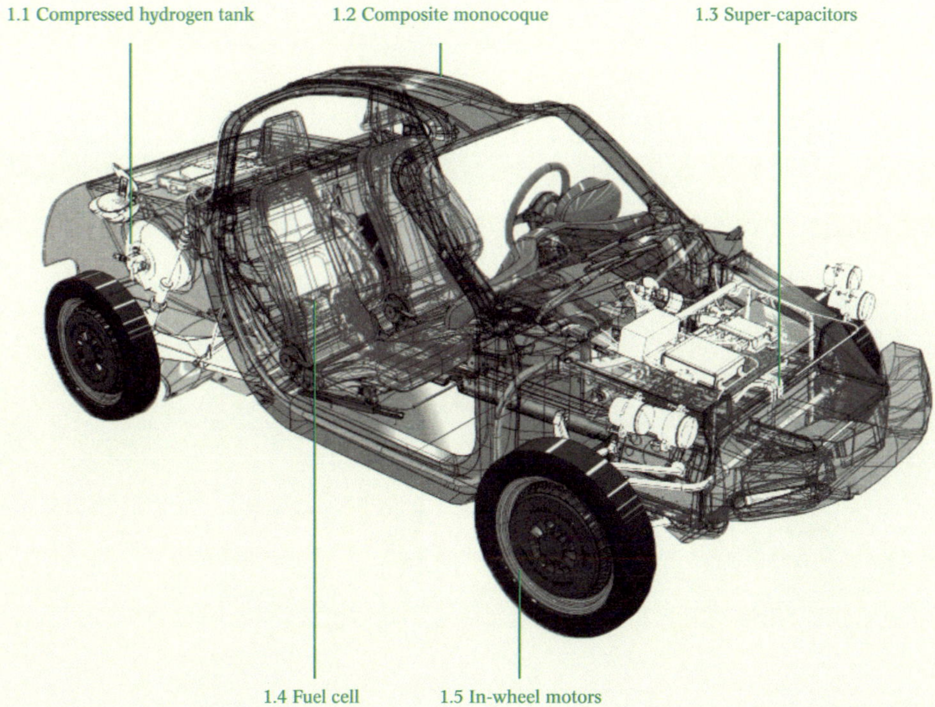
1.1 Compressed hydrogen tank
1.2 Composite monocoque
1.3 Super-capacitors
1.4 Fuel cell
1.5 In-wheel motors

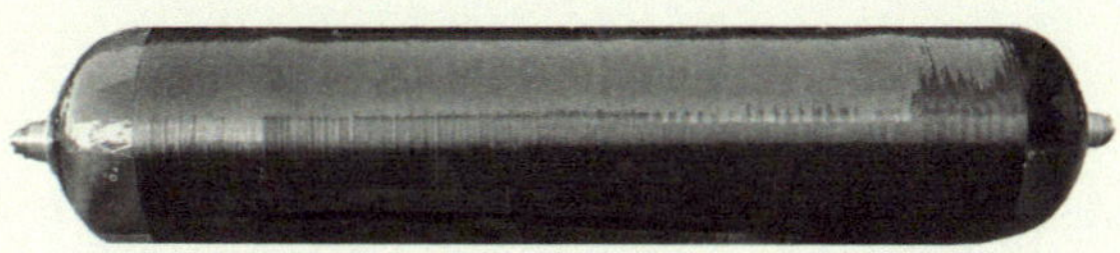

1.1

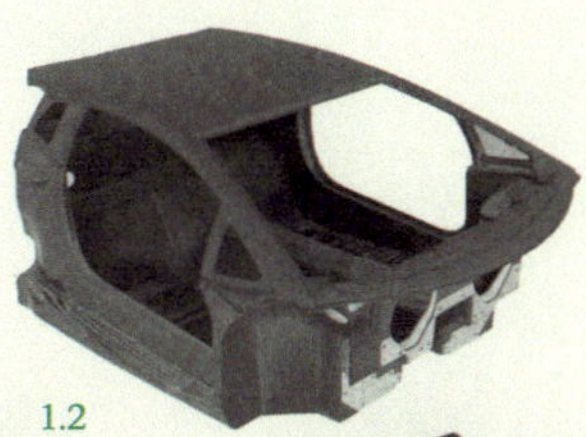

1.2

NUVERA
ORION

1.4

Green-Cap
EDLC(DB)
2.7v 100F
Green-Cap
EDLC(DB)
2.7v 100F

1.3

1.5

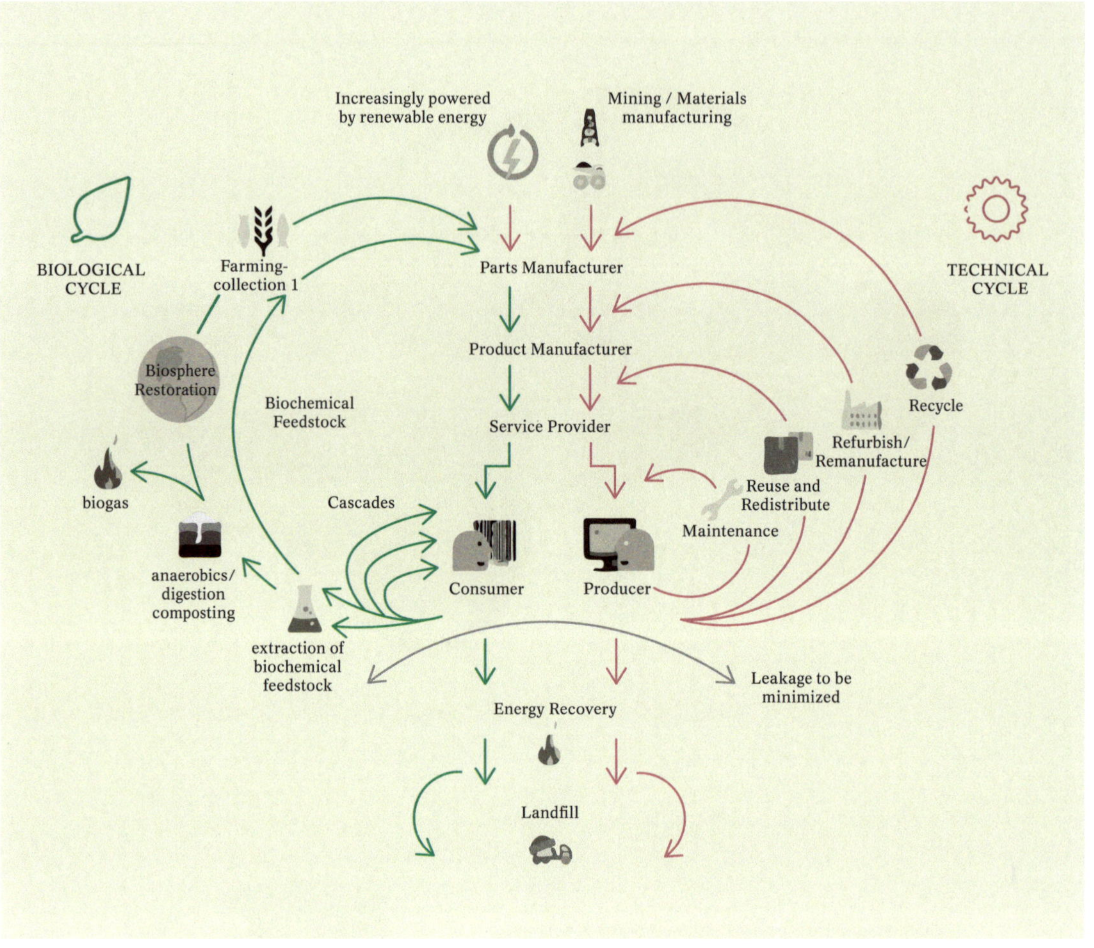

Butterfly model (Ellen McArthur Foundation)

1.4 CAREFUL CIRCLES

It took ages for humans to understand that the opportunism of continued use of old stuff – in medieval times people living in Cairo already used the surface stones from pyramids to build their houses – could develop into a system. It started with recycling aluminium, because producing it from ore takes twenty times more energy than melting and remoulding used material. It became more popular after it was discovered that you could actually save costs by recycling production waste. Later it came to light that there are flows of different kinds of materials and products that need to be managed. Production, consumption, repair, refurbishment, maintenance, recycling, waste processing: they are all part of the same continuous household cycle.

Dame Ellen MacArthur, who in 2005 broke the world speed record for single-handedly sailing around the world, launched a foundation named after her to promote the Butterfly model for Circular Economy. It consists of biological cycles on the left, for renewable materials that grow, and technical cycles on the right for materials that have to be mined and worked. The model is all about value. It is a relatively simple picture

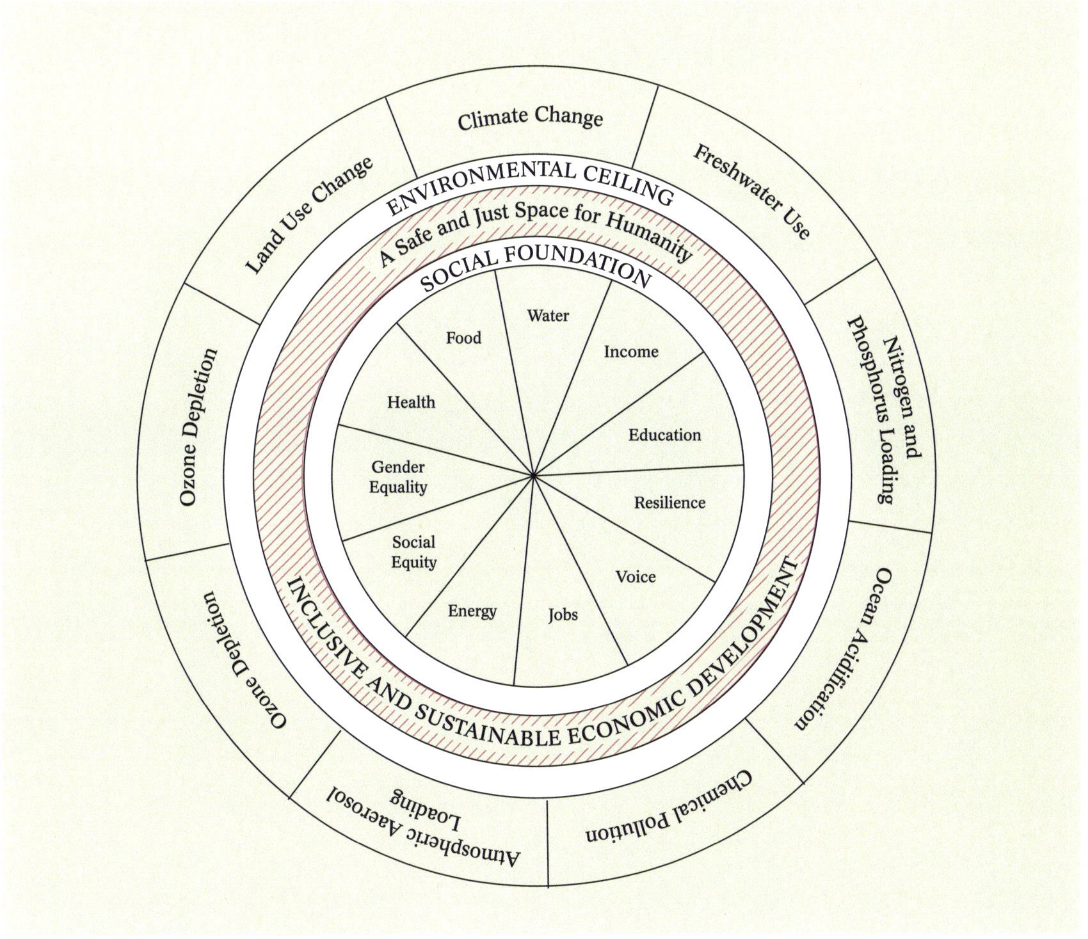

Doughnut Economics model (Kate Raworth)

in comparison with reality, because cycles are more a matter of logistic control than of material processing. Many cheap plastics would be easy to recycle if it wasn't so difficult to retrieve them from waste flows. Input of new materials, superfluous waste and energy consumption should be expressed more clearly.

An economy is not just a question of materials, value and processing. Essentially, it is about us and the benefits it brings us. We all should be able to live a healthy life, with sufficient food, water and education. A model that expresses these qualities is the 'Doughnut Economics' model developed by British economist Kate Raworth. The doughnut expresses the balance that we should aim for. In the central hole are social circumstances that need to be avoided: subminimum wages, insufficient food, obesity, lack of schooling, and so on. Outside the doughnut you will find process failings: pollution, CO_2 emission, disappearance of species. We need to make every effort to reach that doughnut balance.

These two circular propositions must inspire us to explore a richer and less primitive kind of economic thinking.

2. FAST AND EASY

It is raining heavily. Some primeval folks, let's call them the Kardashians, are slowly walking between the rocks in a mountainous area, their feet seeking out places where they can just keep their balance. The goatskins they are wearing to protect them against the weather are soaking wet and heavy. They carry their belongings: some sharp stones, bones and long pieces of wood they use for tools, some meat, berries and a big bunch of small aromatic leaves packed in large palm leaves. They use those to sleep on.

Suddenly the woman walking just behind the leader sees a promising chasm, ahead of the group, a bit to the right. She points it out and with her fellow wanderers she approaches it and they carefully go in. It is dark and not very warm, but it seems empty and safe. The group decide to stay, dry off a bit and wait to find out what the near future has in store for them.

The quickest way to create shelter is to discover it. The same holds for the potential of skins, stones, branches and bones. This example illustrates how the intelligence of trial and error can begin to make its mark. Objects in the environment seem to offer themselves for use. This is when material value comes into play.

In Xiamen, China, the rich Chinese businessman Liu Huiyan arrives home from work. He lives alone, but he knows tea will be ready and the room temperature will be perfect. He has everything under control by using a simple app on his smartphone (which didn't even exist 25 years earlier). His electric BYD silently rolls toward the garage, which opens its door in welcome. The car manoeuvres itself into a parking place and stops. Liu gets out and, while the garage door shuts, plugs in the energy connector to recharge his vehicle. The artificially intelligent house entrance recognizes its inhabitant and opens the door. In the kitchen he pours himself his fresh cup of tea and grabs some shrimp nibbles. He walks on to his living room, which is ornamented with plants, pictures and a glass case that displays a lovely collection of fingerboards. Liu used to participate in tournaments but decided to move on to real full-size skateboarding. He touches the wall to switch on the lighting. Finally, Liu sits down in his comfy chair, which then adopts Liu's ideal screen watching position. The news is on. There is a water shortage on the other side of the world. It is a disaster for thousands of people. Liu turns off the sound, grabs his smartphone and calls his friend who happens to be on a bus on its way from Interlaken to Zurich in Switzerland.

Convenience is the single most important driving force behind technological development.

These two scenes happen thousands of years apart. Yet they are very similar. Both describe people who are adapting to the convenience available to them. The main difference is the degree to which convenience has evolved over time. Convenience is the single most important

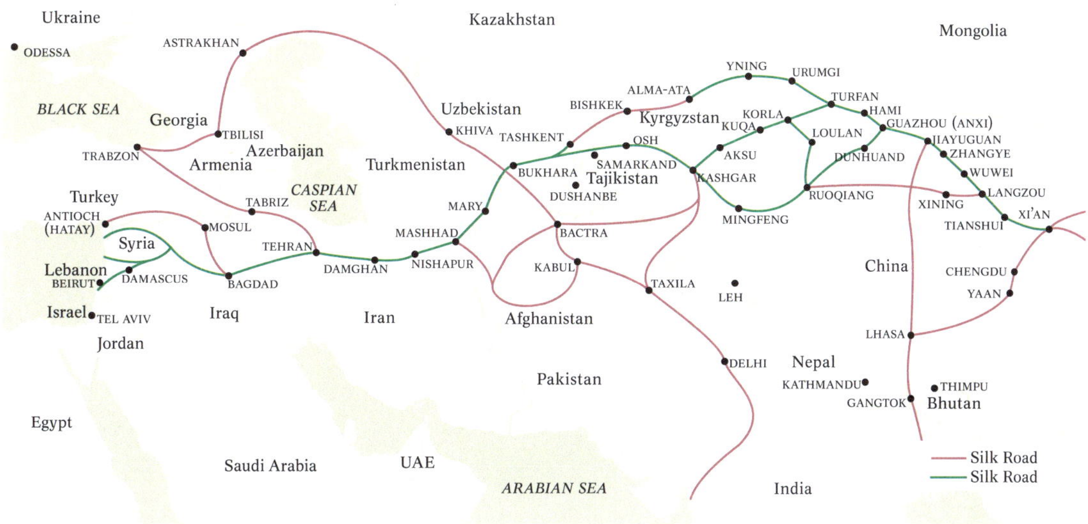

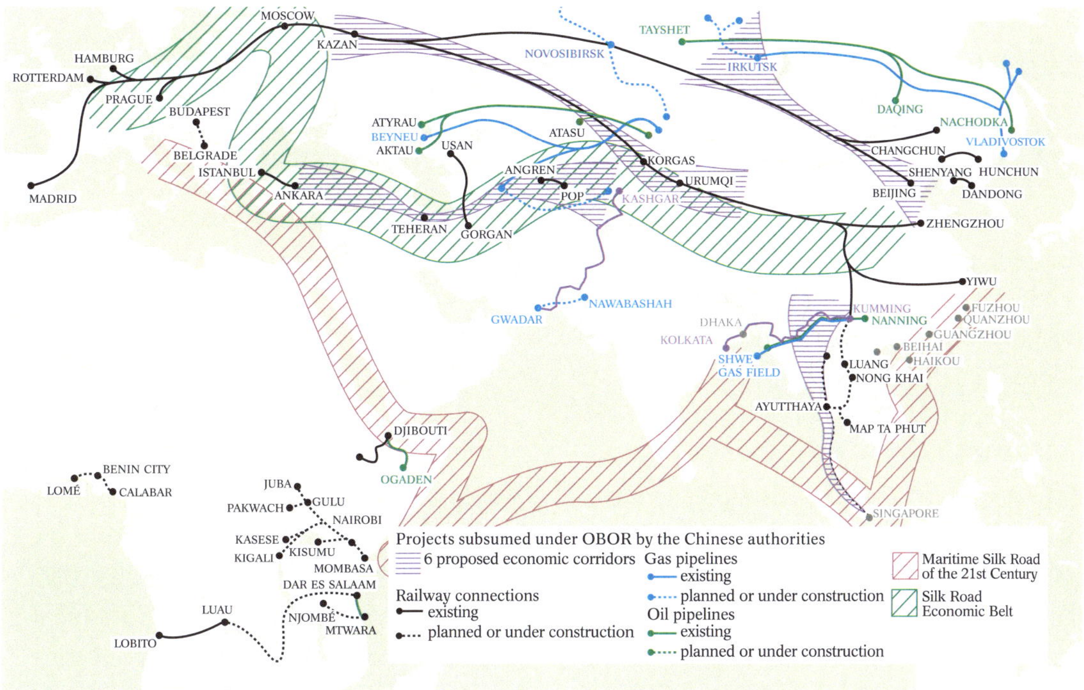

Top: Map of the ancient Silk Road. Middle: Current Silk Road in development

Thomas Thwaites tried to build a toaster from scratch by mining the raw materials

driving force behind technological development, closely followed by expression of identity. As a consequence, nowadays we have become accustomed to various degrees of the easy life.

Convenience means immediate availability of what designers and architects call 'function'. This consists of a sense of useful potential and the time within which it can be put to use.

The Kardashians' primitive shelter may have taken hours, or even days, to be discovered and become available, but once the tribe moves in, their bedding is quite convenient, although not very comfortable or clean. On the other hand, we cannot even begin to describe the level of convenience technology has reached for Liu, and us for that matter. He is probably not even aware of just how much development and effort it has taken, and still takes, to allow him to live the way he does.

There are far more chairs on this planet than there are people.

There are two sides to convenience. On the primitive side of it, we find quantities of things. Having far more than enough tools and devices at our disposal ensures that the good life is always readily available in no time. That is why there are far more chairs on this planet than there are people. That is also why in the Netherlands there are 1.3 bicycles per capita and why the average use of an electric drill is a matter of minutes rather than months during its lifetime: every family owns at least one, just in case. Convenience is also about the actual experience of buying. There is great satisfaction in acquiring something instantaneously, as soon as you want it, which doesn't necessarily mean that you need it. Particularly in the fashion industry the surplus is pretty mind-boggling. In the UK on average every person owns £200 worth of clothes items that are never worn. It won't be that different in other Western countries. This book doesn't address the functional overload side of convenience, or maybe just a little, because even reducing the weight of chairs, drills and jeans helps.

Even the simplest of implements are too smart and complicated for one person to make.

It does address the more uplifting side of convenience, which, among other elements of comfort, supports the lightness idea: because it depends on it. Whereas the first chapter was about the urgency of lightness, this one marks its technological inevitability. Speed and ease increase with weight reduction, which itself comes with structural sophistication. This can go quite far. Even the simplest of implements around Liu are too smart and complicated for one person to make, particularly if everything taken for granted in modern life, such as travel, tools, carrying bags, even sneakers, is included in the 'implement manufacturing' package. There is a wonderful TED talk (2010) and a book by artist Thomas Thwaites, both entitled 'The Toaster Project'. It is the story of how Thwaites tried to copy the cheapest toaster he could buy, from scratch. When he dismantled the object, he discovered to his dismay that even this simple appliance consisted of 400 parts of over 100 different materials. For lack of time he decided to limit his project to four basic raw substances: steel, copper, mica and plastic. All four were far more complicated to mine or produce than Thwaites expected. For instance, to turn his small portion of iron ore into steel he had to cheat by resorting to a microwave. Plastic, for the cover, had to be harvested from a landfill, because making your own from crude oil was out of the question. After months of hard work his product was put on a shelf in a shop for a great photo opportunity, at the cost of an estimated £1187.54. This Flintstone level commodity worked for about 5 seconds, which is long, considering that no electrical insulation could be used.

The point is, that the achieved level of convenience in a commercial toaster depends on a highly sophisticated industrial operation of worldwide proportions. We have learned to develop and blindly trust extremely – and I do mean extremely – complicated technology to provide us with convenience, including lightness.

Here we can make a distinction between two components of convenience: transportation and use. Transportation is the foundation. Without it we have nothing to use. It concerns either people that travel, or goods that are being moved. Transportation has a long history and there are striking similarities among all its manifestations. Commuters all over

1. Adaptor
2. Air conditioning
3. Air fryer
4. Alarm
5. Assembly line
6. Baby monitor
7. Beamer
8. Blender
9. Boiler
10. Bread maker
11. Bulldozer
12. Bus
13. Calculator
14. Camcorder
15. Car
16. Car mirror
17. Car chair
18. Car window
19. Centrifuge
20. Clock
21. Coffee grinder
22. Coffee machine
23. Computer
24. Crane
25. Cream freezer
26. Cutting machine
27. Decoder
28. Dishwasher
29. Drilling machine
30. Dryer
31. 3D printer
32. DVD player
33. Drone
34. Dynamo
35. Egg cooker
36. Electric car
37. Electric cooker
38. Electric saw
39. Electric stapler
40. Electric step
41. Electric toothbrush
42. Electric unicycle
43. Elevator
44. Escalator
45. Fan
46. Filter (air)
47. Filter (oil)
48. Flashlight
49. Flat-belt conveyor
50. Food processor
51. Freezer
52. Fryer
53. Frying pan
54. Garbage disposal
55. Garbage truck
56. Generator
57. GPS
58. Grill
59. Hair dryer
60. Handheld vacuum
61. Harvester
62. Heater
63. Helicopter
64. Hot airgun
65. Humidifier
66. Immersion blender
67. iPad
68. Iron
69. iWatch
70. Jet engine
71. Jigsaw
72. Juice extractor
73. Kettle
74. Kitchen machine
75. Lamp (LED)
76. Laptop
77. Laser
78. Lawn mower
79. Marine
80. Microwave
81. Milk Frother
82. Mincer
83. Mixer
84. Mobility scooter
85. Motorcycle
86. MP3 player
87. Nano engine
88. Oven
89. Oxygen generator
90. Phone
91. Pin device
92. Plotter
93. Power bank
94. Printer
95. Radio
96. Razor
97. Refrigerator
98. Remote control
99. Rocket
100. Rotary hammer
101. Router
102. Sander
103. Saw
104. Security camera
105. Sewing machine
106. Ski lift
107. Speaker
108. Sprinkler
109. Star engine
110. Steam engine
111. Stove
112. Toaster
113. Tractor
114. Metro
115. Fuel transfer pump
116. Vacuum cleaner
117. Washing machine
118. Water pump
119. Yacht

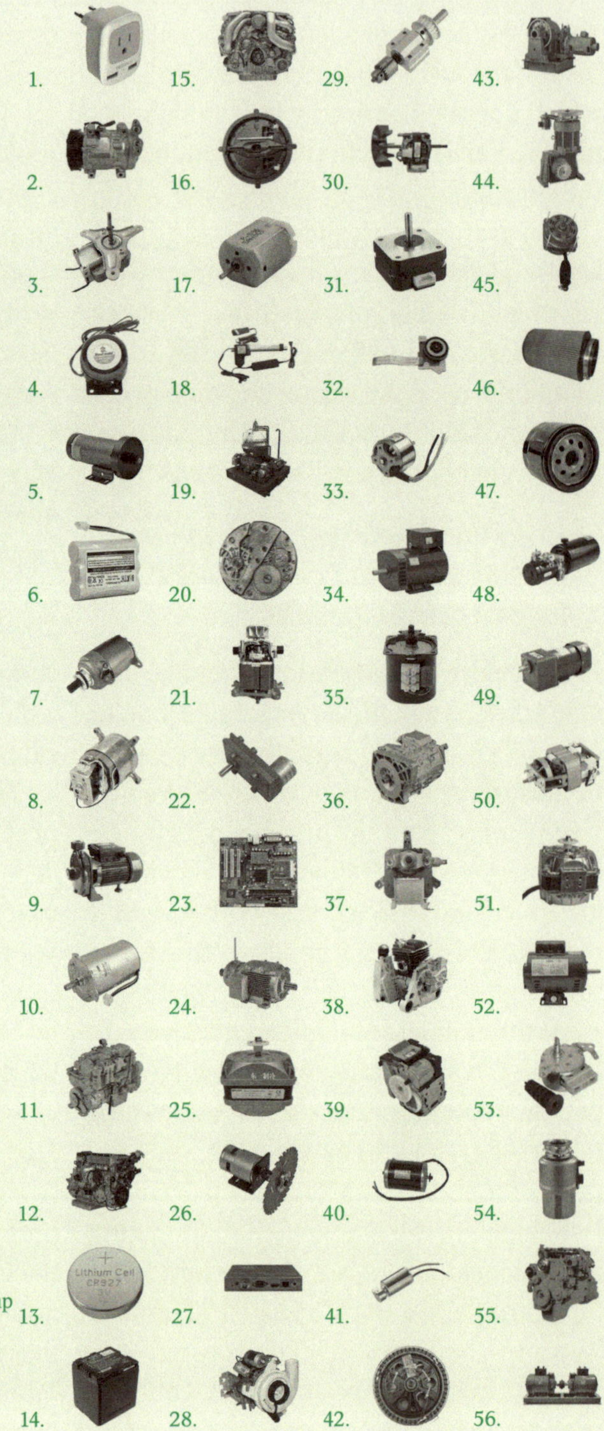

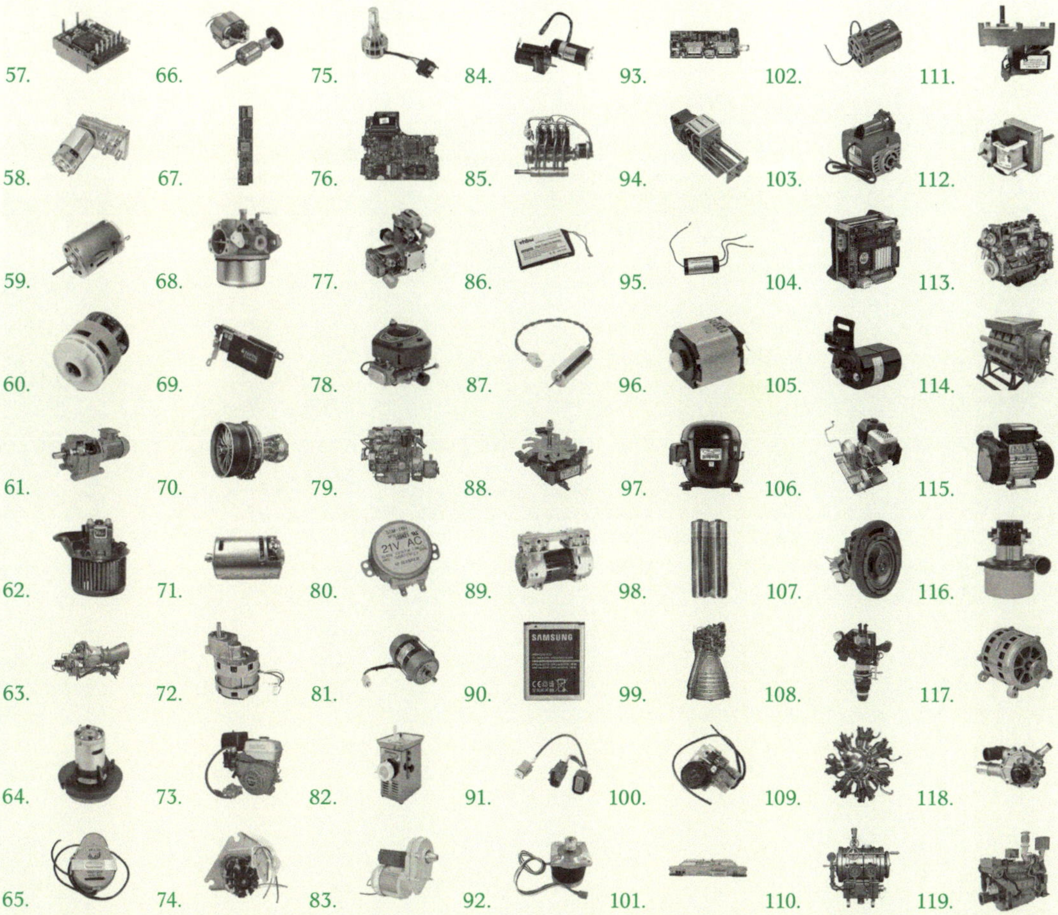

2.1 MOTORS FOR CONVENIENCE

Technological development translates hardware literally into convenience. We humans really like to be served by magic. Servants are not supposed to exist. When servants were people, they mostly lived separate lives in their own rooms. On estates there were separate working spaces for household tasks and the staff had their own corridors and stairways to serve invisibly. This desire has by no means disappeared. Digital servants such as Siri and Cortana are there to help you behind the smartphone screen. Physical help is also increasing and spreading, continuously adding to the mass we surround ourselves with. Just think of all the things you can use that have little motors in them. Or take a 2020 car. Half a century ago it was normal that a car had an engine, a starter motor and one or two windscreen wiper motors. Oh, and there may have been a little motor in the cassette player and if you were rich you had an antenna that moved in and out. These days the mirrors and windows are motorized and so are the chairs and maybe the sunroof and trunk lid. The one internal combustion engine under the hood will be replaced by a smaller electric one for each wheel. The motor in the radio has gone though. Information and music are all digital nowadays. Motors to automatically control car movements are almost with us now, waiting for sensing devices that can predict the behaviour of strangers in the night.

Left: Athens Olympics Beach Volleyball stadium
Right: Amphitheatres in Lucca (top) and Arles (bottom) are now part of the city

2.2 JUST TO MAKE SURE

A life of convenience is what we yearn for. Just to make sure, we own far more things than we can actually pay attention to in terms of time. A built-in app in everything, which registers use time, would be totally ridiculous, but also revealing. Stadiums, particularly the prestigious Olympic ones, belong to the most useless large structures humans create. They are expensive identity symbols radiating prestige, packing in crowds for no more than a couple of weeks and afterwards standing virtually idle, filled with thousands of empty plastic chairs. To collect more things, we often resort to very large convenience establishments to provide us with a wide choice of shampoos, cupboards or whatever, but they mainly provide us with choice, because that is what marketers think we want and it's also what we like to believe we can handle rationally. So, we grow obese surrounded by stuff and like to think we can conveniently lose weight effortlessly with the help of an oriental guru.

the world, for instance, spend about an hour going back and forth between home and work. This is now called Marchetti's Constant. Philosopher Bertrand Russell observed it earlier. The distance can vary, according to context and affluence. Obviously, commuters travelling by plane cover a great many more kilometres in this hour than the ones who drive, let alone those who walk. Apparently, we humans consider an hour to be acceptable.

Millions of people commute by car and the number of cars seems to be gradually levelling out. Some have observed what they call 'peak car', a point in time that may have occurred in the recent past, beyond which car use is likely to gradually decrease. Whether this peak has really shown up is not clear, since it depends on many different parameters. Currently it looks as though the growth of car use in Europe has come to an end, but the cause could just be a mixture of young people hanging fire on getting a driver's license and older pensioners picking up travelling as a hobby in the near future. Or it may just signify economic stagnation. Australia expects a future rise in car use, but that may be to favour road-building policies. In the US, covering more distance by a shift towards air travel has been announced in the past but is not likely to become big. However, there is an ongoing major shift towards using sharing platforms such as Uber and Lyft, which entails a more intense use of fewer cars rather than a decrease in overall use. In India Uber is soaring too. Then there is the growing congestion: it may tempt commuters to start using alternatives, such as public transport, scooters or bikes, including e-bikes. One final cause of a decrease in car sales (which is not the same as car use) could be the shift towards the electric car that drivers may be waiting to buy once it becomes more affordable.

Transporting goods also involves an unexpected constant: the cost of transportation in general always amounts to approximately three per cent of the total cost. This principle emerged with the appearance of the Silk Road through the deserts of Asia and Africa. The transported goods were costly, light and not voluminous. That made long distance transportation by camel affordable. Over time, however, when more and more settlements were created along the caravan trail, safety was compromised and resting and grazing the animals became quite expensive. Consequently, the Islamic justice system began subsidizing the roadhouses or 'caravanserais'. Because of this, camel drivers could keep their costs low and continue competing with sailing ships.

Currently China is developing and constructing an iron turbo version of the old Silk Road. Intended for freight trains, it connects China with the Middle East, Europe, Africa, India and Indonesia. Caravanserais are no longer needed, and now huge terminals distribute and collect enormous quantities of goods. This would be a good idea if prosperity were to just depend on quantities of products. We are now beginning to feel that there is much more to explore as regards economic growth besides producing and transporting more.

The most important ongoing change after the Second World War has been less about choosing materials than about optimizing and refining material combinations.

For one thing, products can be lightweight and more convenient as a result. This is in fact a trend in material use that Mike Ashby, chronicler of material functionality, visualized back in 1987. He designed a diagram that shows the relative importance of large groups of materials: ceramics, composites, polymers and metals. It seems there are mainly new combinations of materials these days. There happens to be a correlation between the importance of polymers and composites and our craving for lightness. In the primeval era of the Kardashians everything had to be lightweight, because they had to be able to carry all their gear themselves. For Liu Huiyan, the importance of lightness is in carrying and use. The sheer amount of functional potential he can carry is amazing, although it is less physical than it used to be. If he had to lift the 1950s equivalent of a smartphone he would end up in hospital.

The most important ongoing change after the Second World War has been less about choosing materials than about optimizing and refining material combinations for different purposes. It concerns designs of processes and concepts, often delving deep, chemically and physically, into the scale of the extremely small.

To compose a material that is strong and stiff and can be used to produce heat-resistant insulating pliers smaller than two millimetres requires research on the nanometre scale. On the other hand, procedures that have been in use for decades, and have delivered trustworthy results, may only just now turn out to be explainable at the level of nanotechnology. The materials commonly known as composites are in fact designed structures of materials put together according to certain recipes.

This fact creates a challenge for today. Putting elements together with advanced machinery in many cases needs to be a reversible process. We must be careful not to exhaust resources and not let the quantity of unmanageable waste grow way above our heads. The larger the number of certain products we manufacture, the more important it is for us to be aware that production is part of the material flow we keep going. The primeval Kardashians carried what they needed. These days we have to find out how to deal with what we don't need. This is already happening in the world of composites. We are on the brink of mass-producing composites that can be decomposed and reprocessed ■

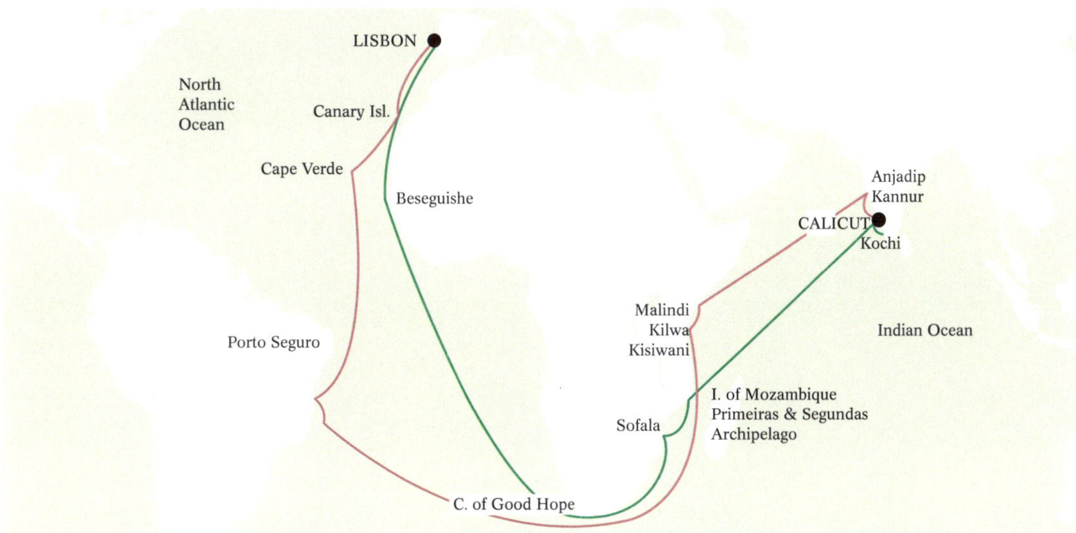

Top: Caravanserai sponsored by the Chinese government (p61). Middle right: Contemporary caravanserai (trucks). Bottom: Alternative shipping route via Brazil to avoid headwinds and bad weather, 1500

ENERGY CARRIER	ENERGY TRANSFORMER	TRANSPORT SYSTEM	STRUCTURES
Direct Before-1830	• Wood • Water • Humans • Animals • Wind	• Coaches • Barges • Walking • Camels • Horses	• Wood • Linen • Copper • Iron • Brass
Coal 1830-1900	• Steam engine	• Trains • Coaches • Ships	• Steel • Linen • Wood • Iron
1900-1940	• Electric dynamo	• Cars • Trains • Buses	• Plywood • Iron • Wood • Steel • Linen
Oil 1903 - 2003	• Piston • Turbine engines • Internal combustion engine	• Flying machines • Cars • Buses • Aluminium aircraft*	• Polymers • Iron • Aluminium • Steel • Wood • Plywood • Linen
1960-2025	• Turbine engine**	• Supersonic aircraft 2001 + • Conventional subsonic aircraft	• Titanium • Steel • Composites • Polymers • Iron • Aluminium
Nuclear 1970-1990	• Centralized electricity distribution	• High velocity trains	• Steel • Composites • Aluminium
Gas 1990-2025?	• Methane • Hydrogen • Clean and efficient energy supply	• City transport	• Advanced composites • Steel • Aluminium • Advanced alloys • Titanium • Ceramics
Hydrogen Wind Solar Oil Nuclear 2025-After	••• Fuel cell ••• Gas ••• Bio fuel ••• Direct electricity • Highest calorific value per unit	••• Smart car ••• Composite aircraft ••• BWB ••• High velocity trains ••• New train concepts ••• Buses	••• New polymers ••• New reinforcing materials ••• Fibres ••• Improved metals ••• Ceramics

* All aluminium aircraft with pressurized fuselage
** High efficient bypass turbine engines

Oil and H2: highest calorific value per unit mass

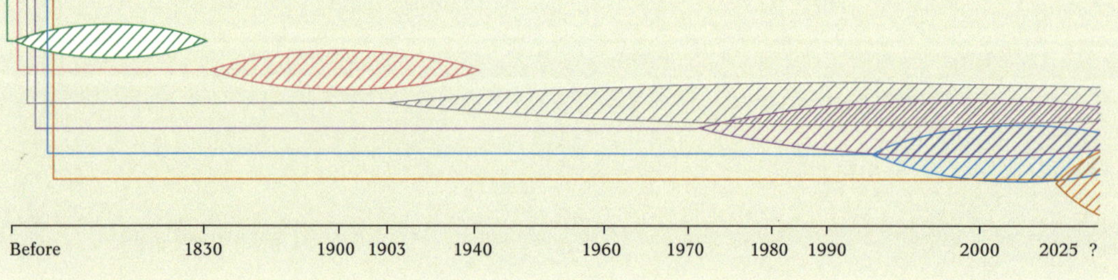

Overview of energy carriers

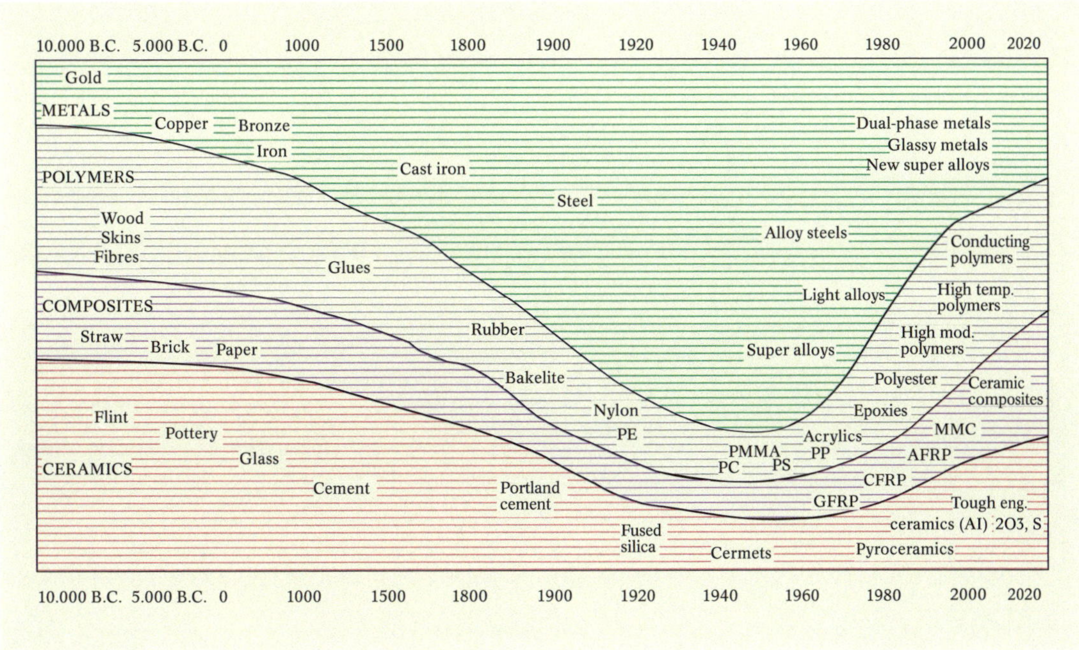

Ashby Diagram

2.3 CHARTING MATERIALS

Mike Ashby has provided us with much useful knowledge about materials by carefully mapping them according to their functional properties. He also created this diagram illustrating the relative importance in applications of metals, polymers, composites and ceramics. It shows how humans, and maybe some of their evolutionary peers, first learned to use what they found, but gradually, across the generations, figured out how they could create what they needed from those found objects and materials. They learned to build shelters from wattle and daub, and to make clothes and tools. Crucially, in mastering and passing on the art of unleashing energy by controlling fire, they became the only animal to gain an understanding of physics and chemistry, with a partially outsourced metabolism. Firing ceramics and later melting metal grew into aspects of the human household.

It is striking that, in a way, the graph shows that the emergence of metals has repressed the use of the other material groups. The discovery of both new metals and their attractive potential has for centuries caused humans to believe that progress depends on metals.

After the Second World War views gradually changed. It became more profitable to look for alternative ways of producing increasing quantities of products with less effort. Plastics promised a considerable advantage in mass production, because it took less energy and materials to manufacture more lightweight complex objects on a massive scale. Modern composites, starting with Glass Fibre and Carbon Fibre Reinforced Polymers (GFRP and CFRP), are leading the way to even more lightness. Since thermoplastics are currently colonizing composites bit by bit using mass production technologies, they reduce the need for thermosetting polymers that won't melt. In other words, they enhance recycling potential. Composites are currently entering an era of mass production. Simultaneously bio-composites are now evolving into a realistic option, including effortless degradability, provided we succeed in organizing material flows more effectively. Ashby's diagram more than anything illustrates humanity's technological learning curve. Richard Buckminster Fuller's exhortation to do 'more and more with less and less, until eventually you can do everything with nothing' may prove inevitable.

3. SHARING THE LANGUAGE

3.1 LITTLE MARBLE LIE
3.2 CONTRIVED SIMPLICITY
3.3 DIPPED IN CARBON

Tupuselei marine village, New Guinea (seen from the shore)

Fort Boyard, Ile d'Aix, France

After briefly meeting a group of ancient ancestors and one contemporary from China, we know there is a convenience driven undercurrent towards lightness. But human intuition is more complicated than that, otherwise builders, car salespeople and even airplane manufacturers wouldn't proudly show off the weight of what they can handle. The ease with which large and heavy objects can be moved is magical, and therefore attractive. Heaviness is macho. In addition, weight provides a feeling of solidity that renders heavy products preferable over lighter competitors.

Weight typically contributes to identity. Humans yearn for continuous confirmation of who they feel they are, to themselves and to others, through the things they surround themselves with. Lightness and heaviness are contradictory parts of that. Contradiction actually is quite normal within the minds of consumers. In praising products to sell more of them, the arguments used are to please identity stereotypes rather than rational judgement. Bicycle frames can boast 'hand welded' and 'laser robot graphics' simultaneously, throwing artisanry and high tech into the same hat.

We have arrived at the complex issue of human imagination, behaviour and social considerations, an issue often ignored by designers and engineers. It is about consumer behaviour, but also and more importantly for designing lightness, professional behaviour in the development and production of anything from paper napkins to retail delivery drones and office buildings. Design occurs within the context of human behaviour and we can all see what this implies.

We all have habits that can be difficult to break, and we all do things that we know we shouldn't. We operate within rigid belief systems and our behaviour is not as much based on conscious decision-making as we would like it to be.

> *We all have habits that can be difficult to break, and we all do things that we know we shouldn't.*

Intuition is the helmsman of behaviour. This is how Nobel Prize winner Daniel Kahneman described decision-making in his bestselling book *Thinking, Fast and Slow*. Occasionally reason intervenes. Designers in particular think of intuition as some special kind of creative gift, but that's not what it is. There is nothing mysterious about it. Intuition simply is an experience-based skill to quickly decide and act without thinking. It is where 'gut feeling' enters the playing field. Experience feeds the helmsman with obviousness.

Of course, experience is different for everyone, but there is also a professional part of one's background that is shared according to conventions and beliefs within a certain area of expertise. Here another motive for Designing Lightness shines through: cooperation between disciplines is crucial. This implies that professionals with different backgrounds need to understand each other, but they also need to be aware that what is obvious to them is not necessarily self-evident to colleagues in other fields.

Cooperation between disciplines is crucial.

Even the content of lightness as a category of knowledge depends on perceptions within different professional cultures. Differences in perception increase over time due to knowledge fragmentation, which is the dark side of specialization. Whereas scientists and artists used to be universalists, now we live in the heyday of specialization.

The word 'function', for example is likely to be familiar to all readers, but this doesn't imply that they understand each other when they discuss it.

Differences between specialisms are rooted in language. The word 'function', for example is likely to be familiar to all readers, but this doesn't imply that they understand each other when they discuss it. A technical engineer interprets it as a physical quality: the object's ability to withstand or handle radiation, vibrations, force, temperature change, and other physical phenomena. Architects and designers interpret function personally and socially in terms of use. Walter Gropius, director of the Bauhaus for the first five years of its brief existence (1919-1933) and one of the initiators of the functionalist movement in design and architecture, said: 'Bauen bedeutet Gestaltung von Lebensvorgängen' (Building means designing life processes). So, function in design defines what users are supposed to do: hold one hand underneath this tank to get soap, cut vegetables here, continue reading there, this is a place to sit and rest, let children play over there, and this is the way to the exit. This implies that a designer may, for example, ask a technical person if a table will be functionally 'flexible', meaning it can serve different purposes. In their reply the technologist may instead address the bending capability of the plastic table structure. Misunderstandings like this happen every day.

The word 'concept' is another tricky one. In engineering it is an optional solution to a particular problem, a combination of coherently elaborated ideas. Within a design engineering process there may be any number of concepts that can be compared and combined to get to the next stage and eventually to the one preferred solution. In the worlds of design and architecture the word concept has gradually become an idea that through elegant presenting has somehow acquired the status of worthiness. Such 'conceptual' design doesn't need to be realistic and may be supported by contemporary non-committal epithets such as 'speculative'.

'Conceptual' design doesn't need to be realistic and may be supported by contemporary non-committal epithets such as 'speculative'.

Interpretations of designs also have interestingly different priorities. This becomes clear when discussing the minimalist adage 'less is more', which is said to

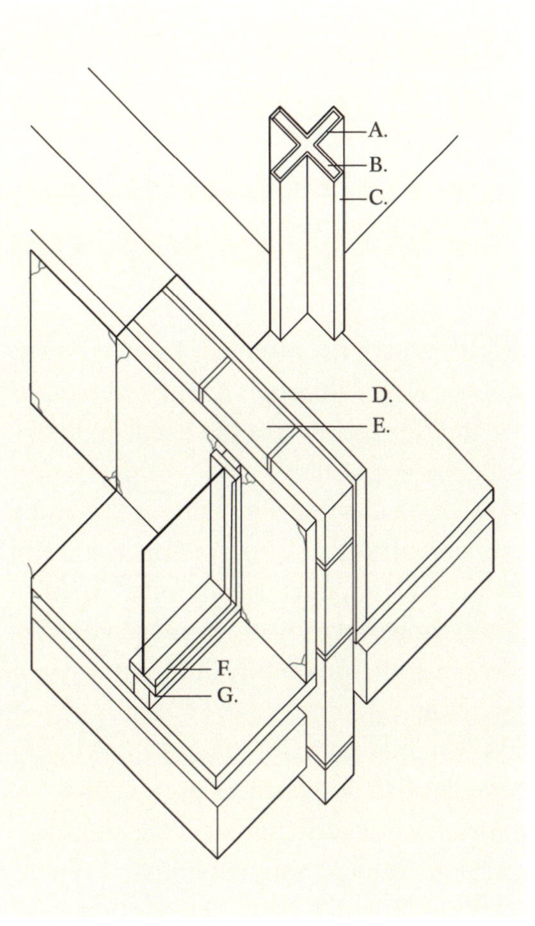

Left: Barcelona Pavilion by Ludwig Mies van der Rohe and Lilly Reich. Right: Technical drawing of a detail

3.1 LITTLE MARBLE LIE

This difference in views between architectural and technical perception is magnificently illustrated by the contrast between a description of Mies's world-famous German Pavilion in Barcelona and the technical drawing of a detail of that minimalist structure. To quote Adam Jasper (in *ArchDaily* Sep 18, 2015): '"Its role", according to an official statement by President Paul von Hindenburg, was to "present the Spirit of the New Germany: simplicity and clarity of means and intentions–everything is open, nothing is concealed"', thereby expressing Mies van der Rohe's intention. Part descriptions on the drawing say: A Chrome-plated sheet metal column cover; B. Structural column: four rolled steel angles bolted together; C Chrome plated sheet metal cover, attached with machine screws (a rare example of exposed fasteners in Mies's work); D Marble Facing. The marble is made as thin as possible to reduce expense. Only the end pieces are solid, so the entire wall appears monolithic; E Brick or concrete masonry-core wall; F Bronze glass stop, attached to base with machine screws; G Window-frame base, fabricated from two structural steel angles which are then clad with bronze sheets. With the exception of B, E and F all descriptions are about the opposite of the building's intention: concealment. There is a technical term for this: impertinent laminates. Cheap materials do all the work; the expensive ones, in minimal amounts, provide the right feeling and maximize the selling price.

Lightness is so obvious that it forgets to ring a bell in the minds of its most basic proponents.

originate with the architect Ludwig Mies van der Rohe, although the first person to use the expression was the English poet and playwright Robert Browning (1812–1899). It means that simplicity is preferable over complexity in terms of appearance or style. It's all about clarity of form. An engineer, however, is likely to perceive structures in a fundamentally different way and say, 'How can less be more? Less is always less'. Engineers are into literal thinking, whereas artistic designers prefer metaphors. It's not as if engineers are stupid and don't understand metaphors. From their functionalist point of view, however, an adage such as 'less is more' is interesting, but less important than function.

Even the word 'lightness' itself evokes confusion. Tell a culturally biased person you are writing a book on lightness and they immediately recognize the theme but are bound to come up with an idea for a title that is derived from Milan Kundera's *The Unbearable Lightness of Being*. Designers and architects are true believers in lightness, but they tend to focus on how it is perceived. They may put in some extra steel for an enhanced slender elegance.

You could say that in the world of engineering and composites the opposite happens. Lightness is so obvious as a property that it fails to ring a bell in the minds of its most ardent advocates. Composite manufacturers are so deeply involved in developing advanced material structures and applications that the effect of their efforts – minimum weight relative to performance – has somehow sunk below the horizon of their awareness. The decision to get involved in lightness to them is almost forgotten history.

Engineers are into literal thinking, whereas designers prefer metaphors.

Language reaches well into the area of image and appearance. It doesn't need that much generalization to understand that culturally oriented designers mainly create objects from the perspective of their 'look' and 'feel', whereas technically focused ones are not really all that interested in looks. They check diagrams and tables and earlier solutions and make estimates about function. The thing has to work. Both kinds of creators build models, dummies and prototypes, but they judge them from different perspectives.

This works both ways. An architect may design a hexagonal bookcase because he saw this shape in a book about lightness and figured it looked kind of 'cool', without acknowledging the reason why it was in the book in the first place.

At the same time there is an understanding. They admire and apply honeycomb panels for their minimal weight in relation to stiffness, but fail to fully understand why they have that shape. Similar things befall 'tensegrity' structures like the ones designed by the designer and visionary Richard Buckminster Fuller and his artist student Kenneth Snelson. Tensegrity is a contraction of the words tension and structural integrity that Buckminster Fuller came up with and these contraptions look intriguing and promising. So they are imitated, but not really understood in terms of the

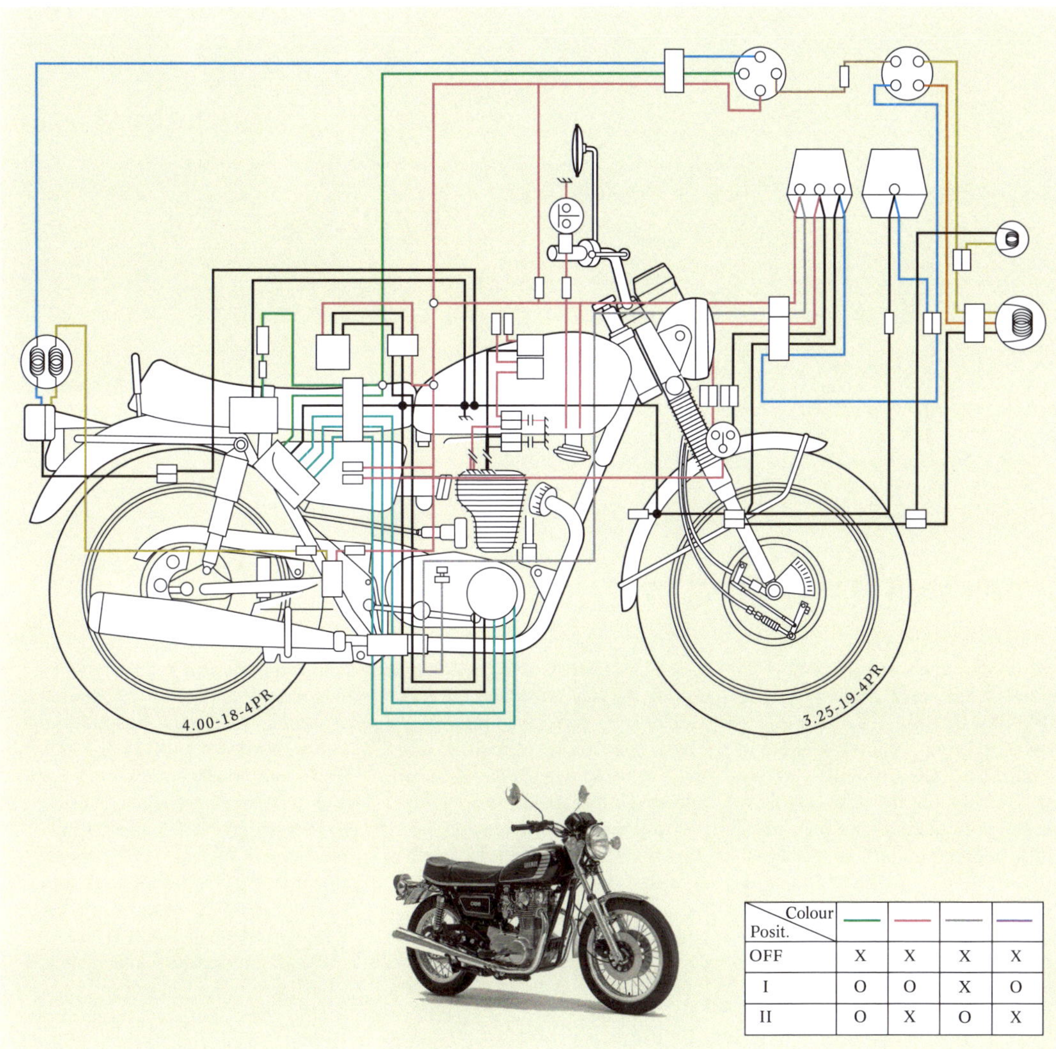

Colour / Posit.				
OFF	X	X	X	X
I	O	O	X	O
II	O	X	O	X

Different visual languages for engineers and designers

Buckminster Fuller's interpretation of trensegrity is a vulnerable example of a principle

3.2 CONTRIVED SIMPLICITY

One of the most intriguing lightness-related phenomena is the impact of one word, namely 'tensegrity'. A contraction of tension and structural integrity, it was coined by Richard Buckminster Fuller. In practice it means that the structure as an integral concept is characterized by a radical division into components that only take on pressure forces and components that exclusively undergo tension. It is not at all special. In fact, it is universal and found everywhere. Look at one of your lower limbs and think of how it works when you walk. It contains bones that exclusively take care of pressure loads and muscles that pull the strings, in other words the tendons connected to your bones. Insects and lobsters function similarly, except they are turned inside out. Even some species of bacteria contain similar organs of movement.

In the field of tensegrity Buckminster Fuller worked with an art student, Kenneth Snelson, who made wondrous sculptures consisting of struts and cables to guide opposite forces. The compression loaded struts hold the tension cable loop open and the loop in turn keeps the struts in place. It was an illustration of pure tensegrity. As a consequence, the public believed and generally still believes that the meaning of tensegrity is something smart and intriguing with struts and cable, or matches and yarn, or pipes and ropes. Many art and architecture teachers have a tensegrity model in their room. Art academies may have one in the yard. Occasionally this model is used in a design for a functional object because it has so much promise, so much in fact that the awareness of the same principle existing in arms and knees and even within composite structures is overlooked. Designed tensegrity objects tend to look somewhat contrived.

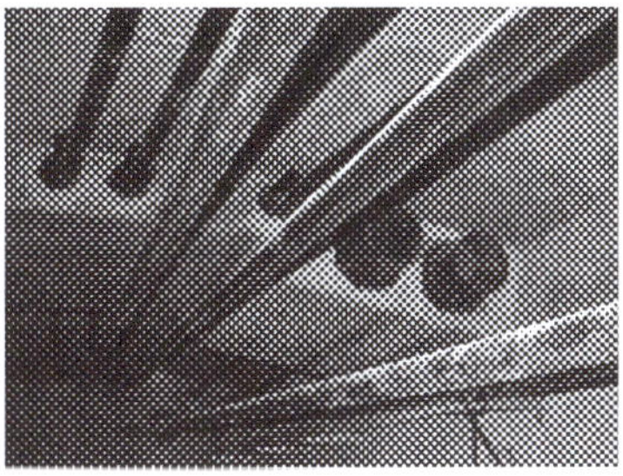

Top: Engineer Eugène Freyssinet in 1940 was the first to design a box girder bridge (top). It is a prestressed redundant tensegrity structure. Bottom: The principle is applied all over the world

omnipresent principle also underlying the function of composites.

Conventions about appearance directly influence the way materials and structures are applied. Here we find very interesting clashes between the mentality of composite engineers and that of designers specializing in textile and fashion. The former focus on the functional potential of textiles (according to their interpretation of the word function) for taking up certain forces, possibly in combination with other materials. The latter professionals consider textiles as personalities that must be allowed their individual behavioural freedom. Stiffening a fabric with a polymer is nothing short of criminal to them.

Over the past few years carbon fibre reinforced polymers have become quite popular, because of the appearance of their surface. And it's true: these structures are applied in very expensive supercars, prestigious yachts and aircraft and now the look is being copied in products for which strength, stiffness and weight don't really matter, such as watches and plant pots.

Carbon has now brought an image of preciousness upon itself. This extends as far as using the name 'black carbon' for cosmetics and the image is copied onto anything from T-shirts to toilet seats. No doubt the prestige gained by 'carbon' has also been a boost for real, non-superficial composite design. Like most superficial tricks to endow products with a 'progressive' reputation the carbon makeover is subject to the vagaries of fashion. We'll get over it ■

Silk arrow-proof clothing

3.3 DIPPED IN CARBON

Fibre reinforced polymers used to be mysterious super-strong 'materials' hidden in dark laboratories under the surveillance of scientific men (no women) in white coats. Then they came out into the open as airplane parts and, much better still, bodies of Formula 1 racing cars and extremely expensive automobiles. The next thing you know is what always happens when images become celebrated: superficiality takes over and the dark glow of black carbon fabric printed on anything stands for high-tech prestige. Even the words Black Carbon on cosmetics for men suggest that they are advanced coating substances.

PRINCIPLES

4. NO MATTER NO FORCE

One reason this chapter starts with fire ants from the tropics is that it hurts when they bite, just so you won't forget. But the really important reason is that as a colonizing army they behave like matter and are very good at illustrating how forces work. They manoeuvre their way along dicey roads and use their little red bodies to create towers, bridges and rafts to survive. Just watching them on the Internet clarifies spectacularly what is going on when structures perform. Designing lightness benefits from wondering what fire ants would do.

Don't be afraid of formulas; they are just 'shorthand' attempts to get to the essence of phenomena through symbols and abbreviations. Formulas are easy. Doing calculations: now that's difficult.

Obviously, lightness is concerned with the seemingly simple issue of weight. Isaac Newton discovered what it does by observing a falling apple that fell straight down (but didn't land on his head as legend would have it). Moreover, he figured out the relationship with gravity, which is the acceleration caused by the Earth's mass attracting the fruit's mass. He did not find out how gravity actually works. Science is still not entirely there yet, but because of Einstein's genius we know that gravity doesn't 'exist' as some kind of autonomous force, but that it emerges from the curvature of spacetime caused by an uneven distribution of mass. Luckily you don't need to understand all this to design lightweight structures.

Fire ants don't have a clue. They probably don't even know that the relationship between force, mass and acceleration can be expressed in a formula. Don't be afraid of formulas; they are just 'shorthand' attempts to get to the essence of phenomena through symbols and abbreviations. Formulas are easy. Doing calculations: now that's difficult. The relationship between force, mass and acceleration is Newton's second law:

$$F = m \cdot a$$

in which F is 'force', = symbolizes 'equals' (as if you didn't know), m is 'mass', the dot is 'times' and a is 'acceleration'. The meaning of the symbols in a formula is traditionally revealed afterwards in a clause that starts with 'in which'.

For a real outcome the quantity of every abbreviation is expressed in units with consistently chosen dimensions. For instance, you can't use kilometres for one quantity in the expression and millimetres for another, or you could end up with elephant-sized ants bungee jumping on Mars. In this formula, force is correctly expressed in newtons, mass in kilograms and acceleration in metres per second squared. Here's a small step towards physical reality: at sea level on Earth the standard acceleration due to gravity amounts to 9.81 metres per second squared, which means that every second a falling body's speed increases by 9.81 metres per second. Again, the sudden mention of this number may be slightly startling to some, but it can be measured precisely, with a chronometer and a tape measure, and some patience. Numbers in formulas like these don't appear out of the blue, like the ones in economics. They can be checked, and these checks are repeatable. To make life easier the gravity number is usually rounded up to 10 and weight is expressed in kilos, with 1 kilo equal to 10 newtons.

Fire ants are subject to this gravitational acceleration. Multiplied by their tiny mass, on average (depending on species and type) they weigh about 1 milligram, which is the force they exert on the ground, or on each other when they play acrobat. When they do climb each other, they keep on moving. In that way they can carry about 750 times their own weight. If they didn't move, they would be crushed. This illustrates that reacting to load is an interactive process. Materials react as well, by deformation and by adapting their properties. The whole fire ant metaphor adds up to minimizing the stress caused by effort. Fire ants build minimum energy structures. The more ants involved, the more energy they need.

Think fire ant.

In order for structures to work they have to deal with forces and minimize the stress these cause. The planet pulls objects down in every particle of matter they consist of. Obstructions may counteract, magnets may pull or push metal areas. Gases or fluids may push considerable surface areas, such as wings. And let's not forget what engines do, often by rotation.

Opposing forces may deform structures by bending, twisting or buckling them.

Right: Crossing a chasm at Mount Everest

4.1 MASSIVE INTERFACES… AND LIGHT ONES

Buildings float on land. Their weight is not distributed equally over the site where they stand and the centre of gravity may shift due to the movement of masses, such as concert audiences or trucks, or because there is an earthquake. Fast movements of ground are often noticeable. A light earthquake feels like a tube train passing, without the actual presence of an underground rail system. Slow movements may have dramatic effects, but they may only be noticed in long time lapses of ten years or so. In many cities the land subsides because of a falling groundwater level, ground settlement, erosion, soft soil, or pests damaging the underground structure.

A foundation serves to even out most of these forces and provide stability. It is an interface between the building and the ground on which it stands. This substrate is supposed to be able to resist pressure forces that can be considerable. Rem Koolhaas's CCTV building in Beijing is a remarkable construction project, since it consists of two leaning towers, both with a kink towards the horizontal and meeting halfway. The whole thing is out of balance and the structure's foundation has to compensate for this conceptual choice of 'otherness'. It is shaped like two 'rafts', one for each tower and each supported by 370 piles. These rafts 'float' on groundwater. Each raft is 7 metres thick and contains 39,000 m3 of concrete. The total substructure, including the rafts, weighs approximately 440,000 tonnes. It's the founding layer underneath this acme of construction machismo.

It may be akin to the feelings people on the Chilean island of Chiloe undergo when they move to a different home in the Minga tradition, a derivative of Mayan culture. The word Minga means requesting help and offering something in return. This is what happens: with friends and family they literally move house. The entire building is pulled by oxen over hills, onto the beach when the trip includes sea transportation, and across fields. A house such as this is characterized by 'structural integrity'. It holds itself together and its lightness renders it invulnerable. It may jump up and down during earthquakes (which are quite frequent in Chile) but it won't collapse.

Above: The Basílica de la Sagrada Família is a large unfinished Roman Catholic minor basilica in Barcelona, Catalonia, designed by Catalan architect Antoni Gaudí (1852–1926). Right: Gaudí sketching the building with upside down candles

4.2 BARCELONA SUSPENSION

Antoni Gaudí's (1852-1926) contribution to the fame of the Catalan capital Barcelona must not be underestimated. The houses and the park he built and particularly the Sagrada Familia, are all part of the city's assets. The works are special because of their somewhat confusing combination of their appearance, which architects tend to consider 'organic', and the intelligent functional (as in engineering) principles behind them.

By suspending loops of string, tying them together and correcting shapes with small wooden balancing weights, Gaudí was able to develop complex 'catenary' structures that served as upside-down models for his masons to build. A catenary – derived from the Latin word 'catena' for chain – is the line defined by a piece of string, or indeed a chain, hanging between two points. Gaudí's method for developing the direction and the basis shape of his structures is nothing short of genius.

There is a glitch, however. When masons translate the ropes into standing and bent columns, they can't help but introduce thickness to be able to deal with compressive stresses. By doing so, parts of the structure will inevitably be subject to bending, which brings about tension. Because of this there will be cracks. Gaudí's buildings are not as perfect as he would have liked them to be, but rest assured, they won't collapse.

4.3 GRASS IN MID ABYSS

They rebuild it every June, the Quechua people that live around the Apurímac River in the Peruvian Andes. The hand-woven 'Q'eswachaka bridge' consists of ropes and braids of ichu grass. It spans 35 metres and connects the banks of the river that flows 18 metres below. Making the bridge, an Incan tradition that dates back at least 500 years, takes three days. About 1000 people are involved and they each know their part in the ritual. It is the only remaining hand-woven grass bridge in existence and significantly is on UNESCO's list of the Intangible Cultural Heritage of Humanity. A suspension bridge like this, with a load at one place, locally turns into a stayed bridge: there the catenary curve (normally shaped like a hanging chain) is straightened.

Moreover, forces are not stationary. They are subject to scenarios and change over time. When they increase and decrease according to a certain cycle, it has a special effect on structures, which may lead to material fatigue. It gets even more complicated when other physical phenomena interfere, such as moisture, electric current or heat. But let's keep it simple for now, or ants will no longer suffice as an example.

When ants form a horizontal suspension bridge between two branches, like a thin living suspension cable, each insect has to stretch to keep in touch with its mates in front and behind and pull to keep the connection in working order. The balance of pulling and stretching is called tension.

If, on the other hand the red biting rascals have to form some kind of vertical ladder or tower to get to a higher level (which they do in the event of an emergency), they can only achieve this by climbing on top of one another. And they have to keep writhing, or the structure will collapse. Since ants don't really understand what they're doing and simply follow their swarm rules, this is a very stressful situation involving a whole bunch of moving ants. This kind of cumulative force is defined as compression.

Unlike fire ants, materials are good in certain tasks and bad in others.

Already it is clear that tension requires only a few ants, just enough to span the gap, whereas compression can take hundreds. The higher the tower, the more ants there will be at the base. Unknowingly they illustrate how well Gustave Eiffel understood how to restrain the forces of gravity in his tower and also in the suspension bridges he designed. We can observe that, to save weight in a structure, it helps if tension gets the largest part of the deal, because fewer ants are needed: this is an example of material reduction.

The next step is more complicated. To cross a gap with a larger group of ants, allowing more of them to make it to the other side and increase the speed, there has to be a thin link from one side to the other with a few layers of extra ants on top, or the tension ants wouldn't be able to manage. Now we get tension in the bottom layer of ants because they have to pull the whole thing together. Their weight, however, no matter how modest, will cause the line to sag so that the ants on top will be gradually compressed. Fire ants won't notice because they are continuously on the move and adapting. The same thing happens in materials: put a bar across a gap and push it down in the middle (or load it with an object) and the stress in the lower part will be tension, whereas compression will rule in the upper layers. In the middle there will be no stress. In mechanics this is called 'the ideal line'.

Tension on one side and compression on the other have a deforming effect, which, of course, is called bending. Our red construction-happy insects don't care one way or the other, because they can adapt. Here, temporarily stepping back from the ant metaphor and turning to structures, we encounter an important notion:

Unlike fire ants, materials are good in certain tasks and bad in others. Materials have properties and must stick by them. Some, like the ones mostly used for building and construction, are better for taking up compression; others, such as the fibres that ropes consist of, behave well under tension. It makes no sense to push a cart using a rope, which is for pulling and for building suspension bridges and suchlike. Metals such as iron and aluminium are used for both, but are not all that light. It may surprise you that concrete is lighter than aluminium. We'll get to that later.

Bending involves both tension and compression and it occurs when the component involved has a certain thickness. Stress needs space. Since materials usually are not good at both, this implies that in structures bending should be avoided altogether, or that it should be dealt with in terms of shape and material composition. The simplest but still a quite sophisticated example is the composite bow, originally used for hunting and warfare by the ancient Egyptians some 1650 years before the common era. It has horn for compression, sinew for tension and wood for everything in between, with all parts carefully glued together.

Rafts are other implements that fire ants can morph into. It is likely to be a vessel with behaviour, because the little creatures it consists of are all either trying to hold on to the others and pulling the whole thing together or checking if there is a way out. They don't do this for fun. Rafting is a way to escape from floods. This implies that the raft is always reaching out for firm ground. If no way to abandon the state of floating vessel presents itself, the raft is likely to be kept as round as is logical under the circumstances. The circle is the shape for agile gravitating matter in exile against a flat surface. It is the shape that water adopts when on the ground, or mercury, or molten wax ■

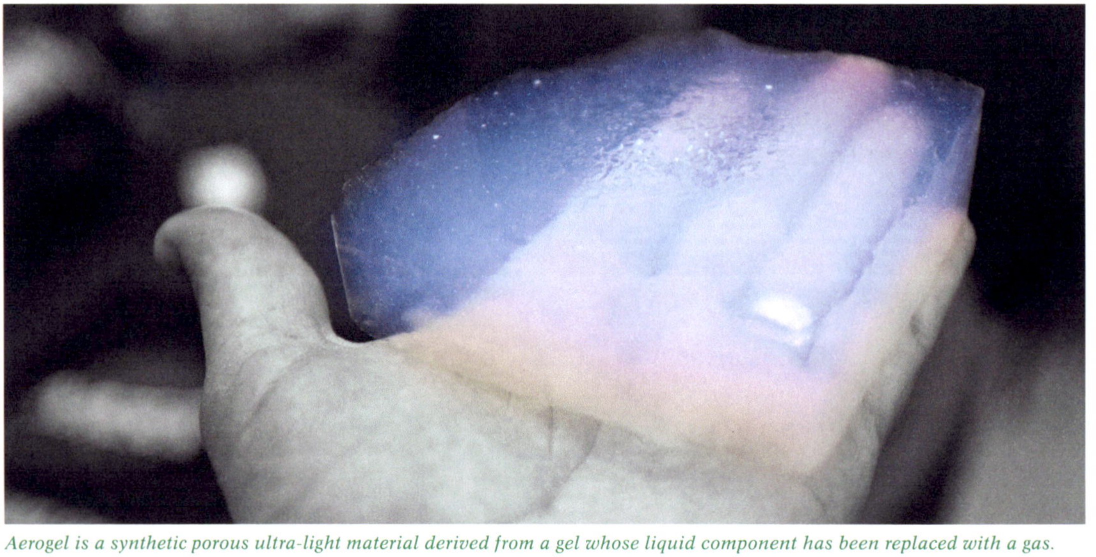

Aerogel is a synthetic porous ultra-light material derived from a gel whose liquid component has been replaced with a gas. Good for insulation but otherwise useless

4.4 SPORTY SPIDERS

Their common name is 'ballooning' spiders. We must have seen them first and then invented kitesurfing. It makes no difference to these creatures. They use neither balloons nor kites. All they need is their own spider silk. This they produce in lengths approximating the size of a web. Along comes a perfect gust of wind and off they fly, sometimes hundreds of kilometres. How it works is not entirely clear. Recent research suggests that electrostatic forces play a part in it. Why a ballooning spider travels that far is unknown. Does it know where it's going? Is it desperate to leave? Or is it just adventurous?

5. THE FAMILY OF LOADS

Loads cause our metaphorical fire ants to react in specific ways. They are the stuff that structures are made of. There are of course different materials, but we'll get to that in the next chapter. First, here is a simple overview of forces and their specific directions in relation to the shape of the material they impose themselves on. It is more complicated in practice, with multiple loads influencing each other and environmental conditions such as heat interfering as well, but these very basic phenomena are a good introduction to the ways in which structures behave.

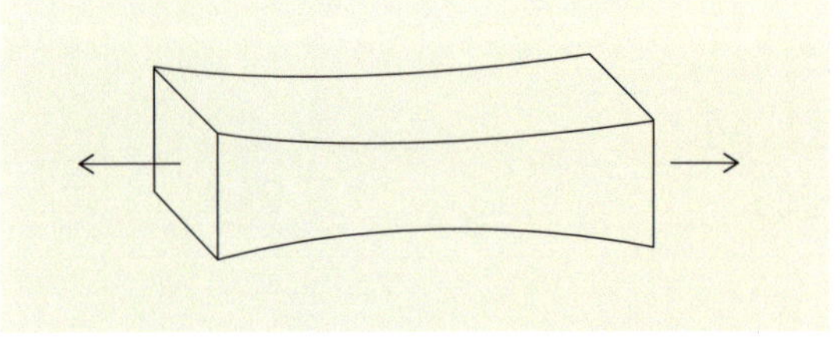

TENSION is the simplest force for demonstrating what happens inside a structure. Pull a bar at both ends and imagine the red ants trying to keep

together. The larger the diameter of the bar, the more ants can help and the less stressful their job. This brings us to the definition of stress, represented by the Greek letter σ (sigma). It is the force per unit of the cross-sectional area perpendicular to the force direction. Suppose the pulling force is 100 newtons and the bar has a 100 mm2 cross-sectional area, the stress is then 100/100 = 1 N per mm2, or 1 MPa (megapascal), which is the standard unit for stress.

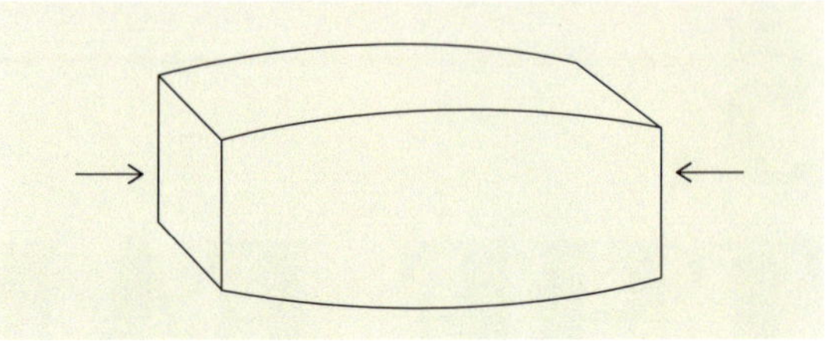

COMPRESSION is very similar, except the industrious little animals now have to try and withstand pressure as best they can. The unit of stress is the same, although materials usually react differently to tension and compression.

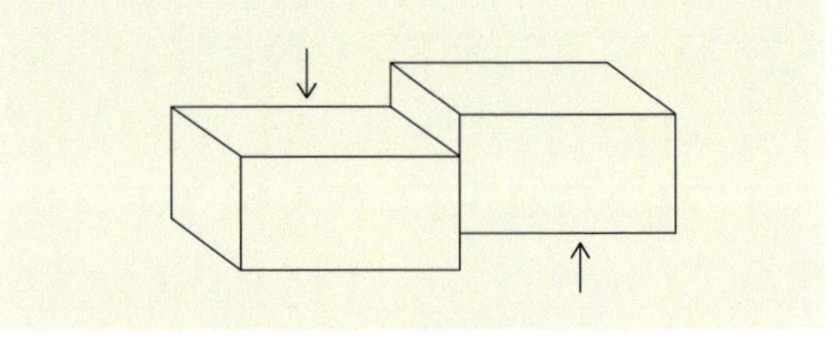

SHEAR force comes from both sides too, but it is nastier because it is sharp and precise. Scissors, by definition, are very good in exerting shear forces. If the bar (from the earlier tension) has to suffer from shear, the ants, now as a group, have to put up with a force that tries to cut it in two. This type of stress is named τ (tau)average, which is the average force per unit area in the force direction. It is averaged, since this kind of stress varies according to the reaction to load.

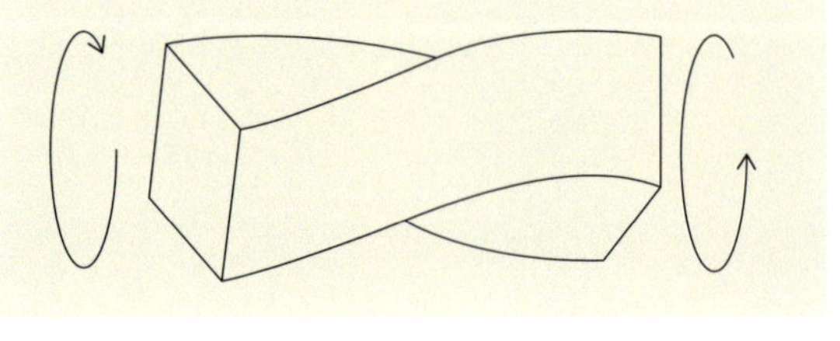

Category	Depiction	Systematic	Formula	Systematic	Formula
1. Tension		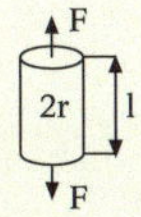	$\frac{E}{\rho}$ $\frac{\sigma_f}{\rho}$ Tie (tensile strut)		
2. Compression (pure)	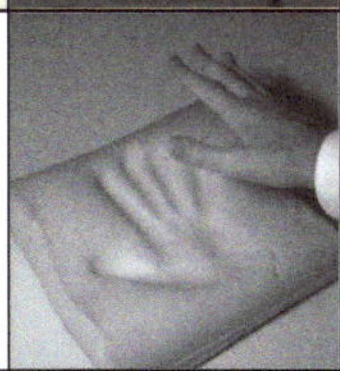	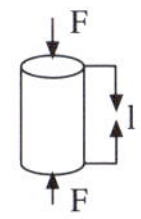	$\frac{E}{\rho}$ $\frac{\sigma_c}{\rho}$ $l < l_{critical}$		
3. Shear					
4. Torsion		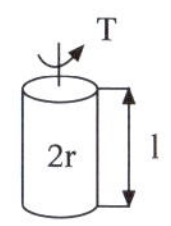	$\frac{G^{1/2}}{\rho}$ $\frac{\sigma_f^{2/3}}{\rho}$ Torsion bar	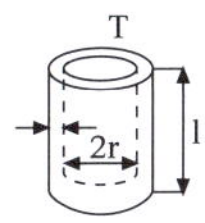	$\frac{E^{1/2}}{\rho}$ $\frac{\sigma_f^{2/3}}{\rho}$ Torsion tube
5. Bending	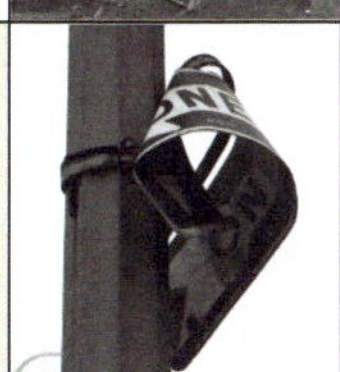	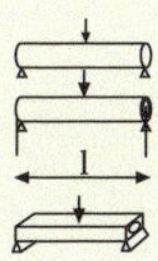	$\frac{E^{1/2}}{\rho}$ $\frac{\sigma_f^{2/3}}{\rho}$ Bending of tubes	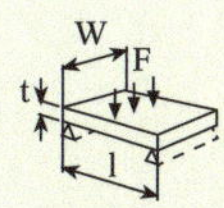	$\frac{E^{2/3}}{\rho}$ $\frac{\sigma_f^{1/2}}{\rho}$ Bending of plate
6. Buckling		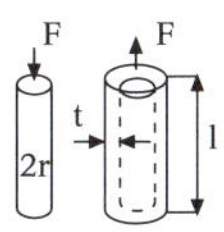	$\frac{E^{1/2}}{\rho}$ Bending of column tube	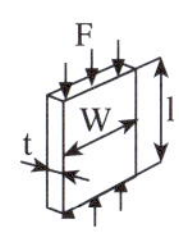	$\frac{E^{1/3}}{\rho}$ Buckling of plate
7. Internal Pressure		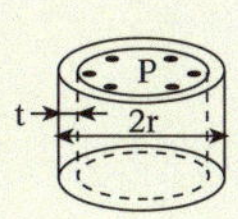	$\frac{E}{\rho}$ $\frac{\sigma_f}{\rho}$ Cylinder pressure		$\frac{E}{(1-v)\rho}$ Sphere pressure

Minimize mass by maximizing specific engineering properties

Typology of loads

5.2 WHAT STRENGTH IS

The word 'strength' begs for refinement because of its bearing on lightweight structures. Recording deformation is the common way to understand what is going on. It quite simply starts with a rod of material that has been prepared to fit into a machine for testing strain. After this specimen has been put in place the device starts to pull it at both ends, steadily increasing the force until it breaks. Both strain, represented by ε (epsilon), and stress σ (sigma; force per unit cross-section surface) are recorded in a graph that shows the relationship between increasing pulling stress and the resulting elongation.

The steel graph has it all. First, the line rises steeply. Here we typically have elastic deformation, elastic meaning that the material returns to its original length when the pulling force is taken away. The steepness of this line, or the ratio between elongation and stress, which we call Y (for Young's modulus), is crucial for material behaviour. No damage has been done. The modulus defines material stiffness. As a material property Young's modulus is used in many elastic deformation formulas related to 'Hooke's law' ($\sigma = \varepsilon$. E), which simply means that deformation is directly proportional to stress according to the constant ratio Y. Like stress, Y is measured in gigapascals. Strain ε has no dimension but is expressed in percentages. Elongation involves contraction according to Poisson's ratio. It depends on the type of material.

But let's turn up the stress in the machine. All of a sudden, there is a strong increase in elongation with only a slight rise in stress until a maximum σ_{max} is reached. Here deformation turns plastic. Elongation is definitive. Turn off the pulling machine and the specimen has been stretched for ever. In addition, it has become stronger. Reset the machine with the strained specimen and the elasticity line will rise higher, because metal crystals have broken down into smaller ones, increasing the number of borderlines between them. Borderlines hamper the progress of cracks.

In any case, after reaching the maximum, the stress collapses until the specimen breaks. Maximum stress: that is what defines strength.

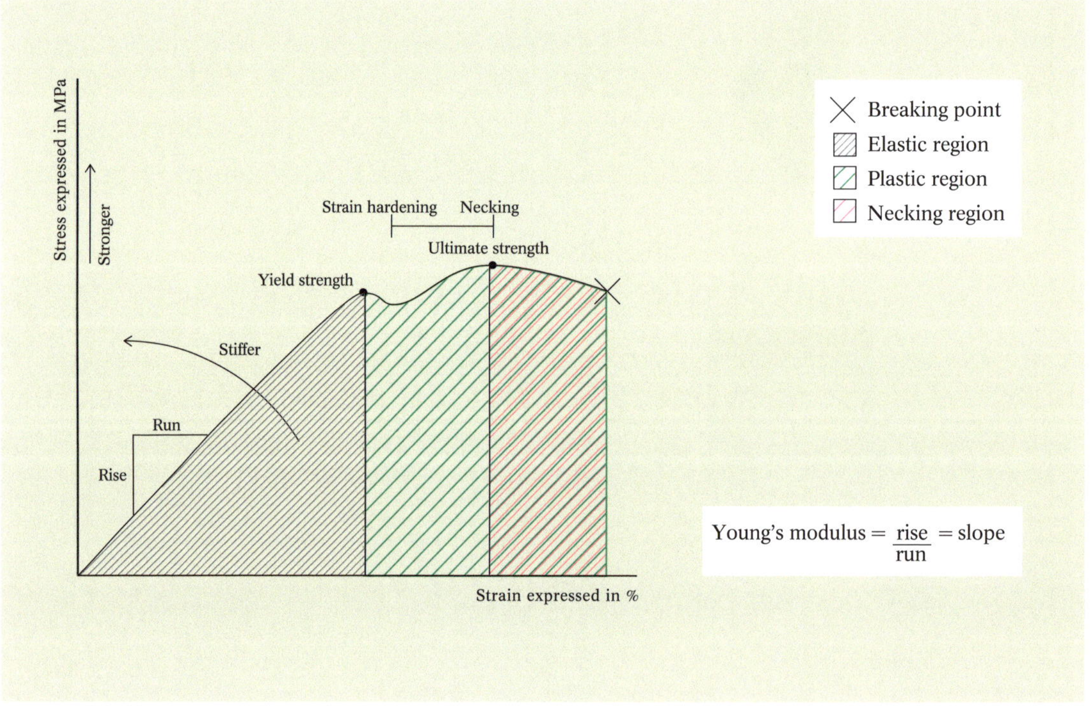

5.3 MECHANICAL COMPARISONS

For a structure, transgressing the maximum stress, or strength, is usually devastating and therefore not very useful as a material property. However, an understanding of strength is useful for production, which often involves plastic deformation to produce certain shapes. This process also depends on temperature, dimensional requirements and – let's not forget – the amount of processing energy, because, for instance, polystyrene is much easier to deform than steel.

Every type of material has its own characteristic curve. Fusible plastics are easily deformable and show little elastic capacity, so you get a long horizontal curve. Rubbery materials are similar, but they're very good at stretching by exerting little force and returning to normal. Ductile materials like steel and aluminium, in fact many metal alloys, show a clear distinction between elastic and plastic deformation. Brittle materials, however, such as ceramics, are not ductile, so they just store energy in a smaller elastic deformation range until they break.

Fibre reinforced polymers are elastic and strong. They can absorb quite a lot of stress deformation, but get torn when the constituent materials start to separate: we call this delamination. The principle of giving in to stress differs considerably from what you saw in previously described homogeneous ductile materials. Nevertheless, it is possible to estimate the 'reduced' Young's modulus for inhomogeneous materials. Suppose the composite consists of glass fibres arranged lengthwise in a polyester matrix, then the steep modulus is reduced because the glass fibre part of the cross-section will suffer from the part occupied by polyester.

The trick now is in the fact that Young's modulus depends on the place in the cross-section. Armed with the assumption that stress is lengthwise and that the fibres and the matrix behave similarly, in the sense that their strain and their respective contraction ratios (as in Poisson) are the same, it is possible to calculate the combined 'reduced' Young's modulus.

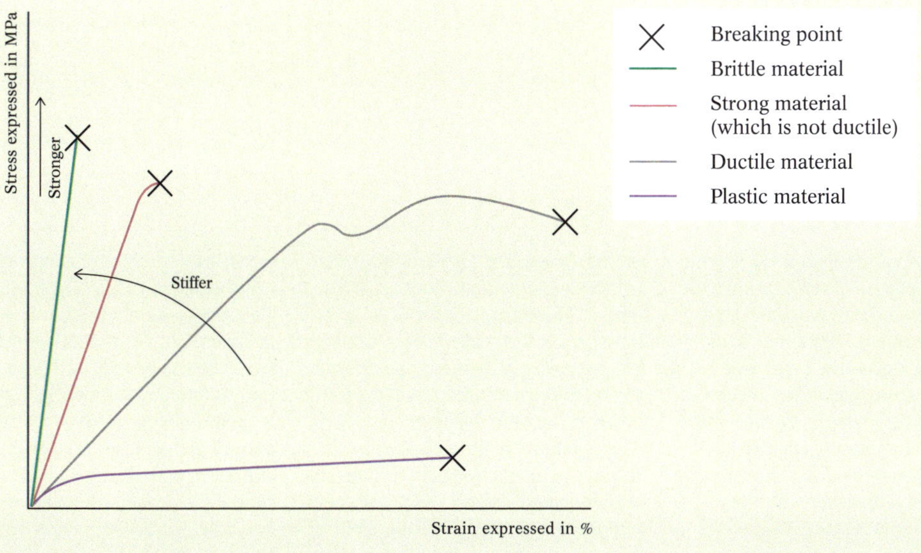

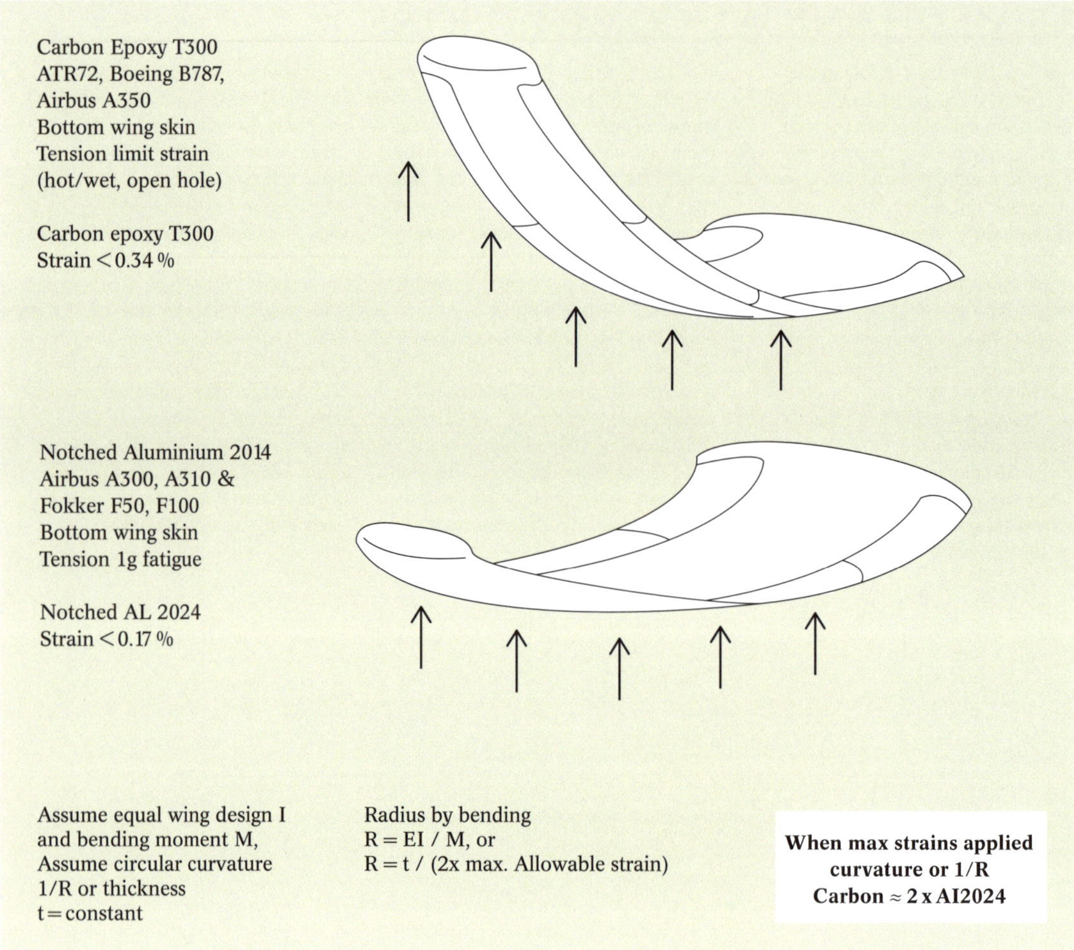

5.4 BENDING CAN BE USEFUL

On the one hand bending should be avoided, because of the combination of compression and tension that gives some materials a hard time. Wood usually breaks on the inner side of the bending curve, since it has trouble withstanding pressure. Stones and concrete can't handle tension at all and therefore break on the outer side.

Bending, however, may also provide energy storage. This has been known for ages, ever since our predecessors learned that you could bend a branch, let it go and knock your enemy off his feet. The bow in archery is a more advanced tool that can hold energy and shoot an arrow with it. Much smarter is the 'recurve' bow, which was invented in Asia some 4000 years ago. Because of its shape the spring can be spanned backwards, bending the bow the other way. So it can be relatively short, and one can shoot it while on horseback. The power is enormous with a reach of several hundred metres. Pole-vaulters build up power in their pole to launch themselves to record-breaking heights.

Both the recurve bow and the vaulting pole have a composite structure, just like the wings of the latest generation of passenger airplanes. This has yielded remarkable consequences. Whereas aluminium wing structures have to be stiff and resistant to fatigue by allowing limited deformation, composite wings can bend about twice as far and store energy enabling them to return to their original shape. Maximum allowable strain defines their functioning and not fatigue. In addition the ability to bend has an energy-saving and smoothening aerodynamic advantage.

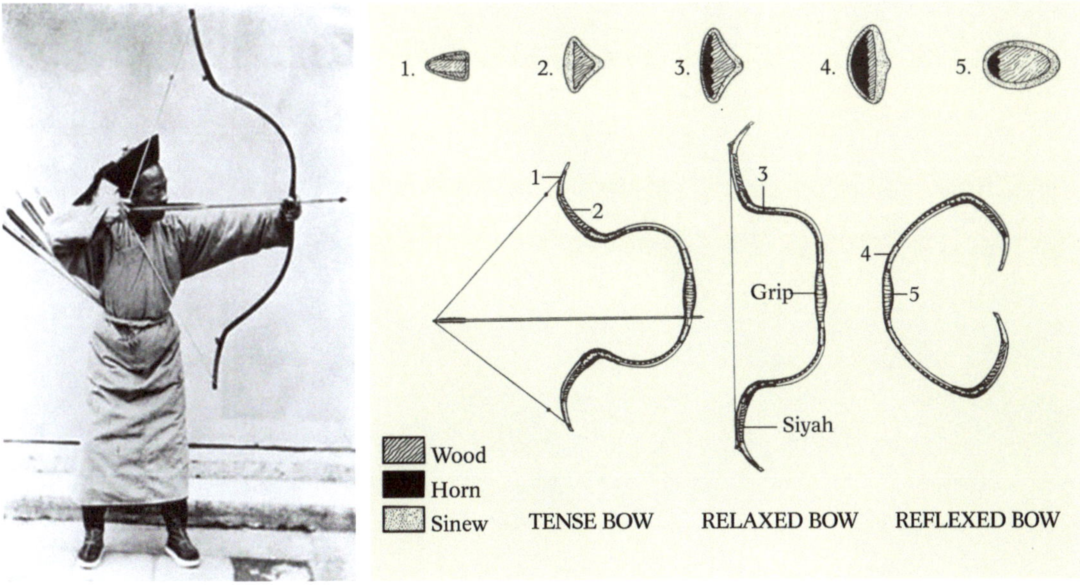

A bow can shoot because it stores energy in deformation

Torsion is more complicated, since forces are exerted in a circular movement around an axis. The distance to the axis is called the 'moment' and shear stress varies accordingly. Inside the bar you get the kind of stress you will find inside a key that doesn't fit well and despite trying won't turn because of that. The amount of stress depends not just on the surface area of the cross-section but also on its shape. The derivative of this ant formation that is supposed to counteract torsion is called the polar moment of inertia J, in which the word inertia somewhat awkwardly expresses cross-sectional resistance to deformation.

Calculating J requires math skills not addressed in this book, but it is defined in metres to the fourth power. In general, the material farthest from the axis contributes most to resistance and is most vulnerable: a key that won't turn (possibly because it doesn't fit) may crack along the edge and not in the middle. Hollow tubes on the other hand have excellent anti-torsion profiles.

Bending is even more difficult to understand since it involves opposing forces and stresses, in which typically a force tries to displace the bar, while this is counteracted. Bend a ruler or a sheet of paper: you know the drill. There are various options for exerting bending forces, such as clamping one end of the bar and trying to move the other, or crossing a ditch using a plank. As in torsion, the geometric characteristics of the bar's cross-section partly define the potential to counteract bending. Grab your ruler again and try to bend it perpendicular to your

Soap bubble measurement device developed by Biezeno and Rademaker

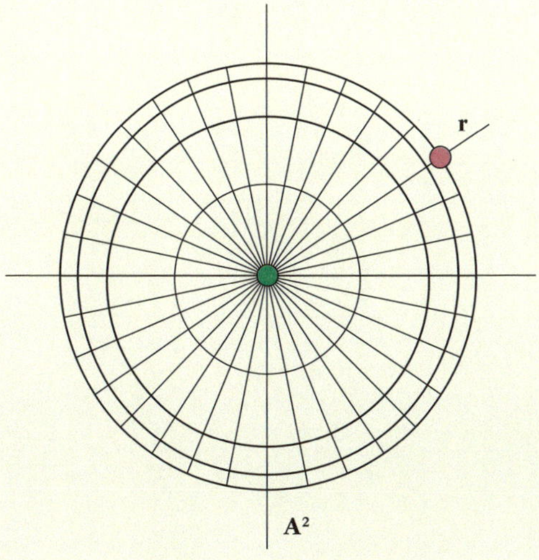

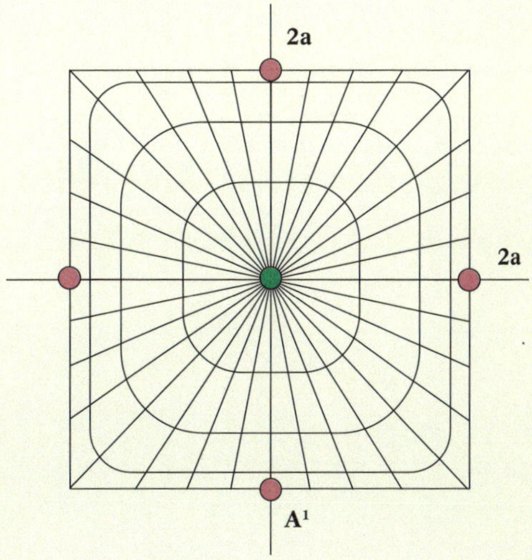

Points or Contour of Maximum Shear
Points of Zero Shear

When **a** equals **0.9 r**, the cross section $\mathbf{A^1}$ equals $\mathbf{A^2}$, when materials are equal, area weight equals the maximum allowable shear stress $\tau_{allowable}$.

Performances of square $\mathbf{A^1}$ & circle $\mathbf{A^2}$ compared:
When torque load **T** is similar
$\tau 2_{max} \cong 0.7 \times \tau 1_{max}$ (shear)

When $\tau_{allowable}$ is guiding
$\tau 2_{max} \cong 1.4 \times \tau 1_{max}$ (torque)

5.5 TORSION, THE SOAP FILM

Tension causes stress in elastic strain to be equally distributed over the cross-section. Bending causes stress to follow a linear gradient. Torsion is something else entirely. Apart from depending on a different material property, shear modulus G instead of Young's modulus E, stress is distributed over the profile cross-section in a non-linear way. This is easy to imagine. Find a wooden slat in the attic or wherever and twist it. You will see that deformation at the edges is far more radical than that closer to the middle.

The gradient is three-dimensional and these days can be calculated with computer modelling software that provides insight in stress distribution according to what is known as the Finite Element Method, or FEM. It can be used for very complex profiles.

In 1903 the mathematician Ludwig Prandtl discovered that the result for simple cases is the same as what you see when a soap film is spanned on a drum with air pressure applied to one side. The shape of the drum, representing the cross-section, determines the shape of the soap bubble. A rectangular cross-section will show a stress increase towards the corners.

But torsion is no match for a cylinder – or even better, a round tube, because that would save weight. At Delft University Biezeno and Rademaker built the Soap Film Analogon, a dedicated and precise soap bubble measuring machine to test Prandtl's theory.

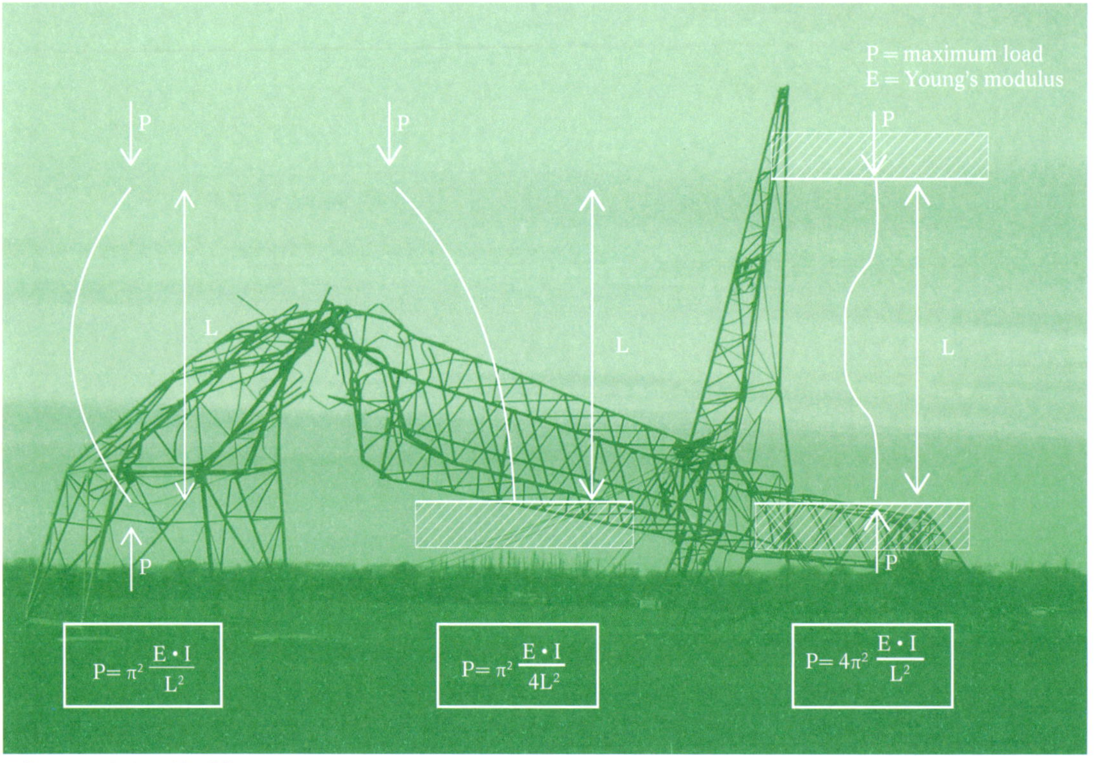

Pylon as a victim of buckling

5.6 FORESEEING BUCKLING

Buckling is likely to happen to slender bodies under pressure. This depends on the material and on the geometric definition of the object being compressed. A material's resistance to deformation is defined by Young's modulus. The geometry of a bar threatened by buckling is defined by its length and cross-section, but also by the way in which a load acts on it. In 1757 the Swiss mathematician Leonhard Euler developed a simple representation of their interrelationship:

$$P_{cr} = \pi^2 . E.I. (K.L)\text{-}2$$

P here is the critical load, E is Young's modulus and I is the planar moment of inertia at the place where the column is at its weakest. Below the line we find L, which is its length and K the factor that reduces that length to the part that counts. If for instance the column is clamped in place, buckling is counteracted. There are ten 'backstage' assumptions behind this formula, one being that the material is homogeneous. They can all be found in the Wikipedia entry on 'Euler's critical load'.

first attempt. You'll notice that it is not just the cross-section's surface that hampers your attempt, which is exactly the same, but also the shape and the amount of mass at the greatest distance from the unstressed heart of bending. This geometric property is named the planar moment of inertia I, which is defined in the same dimensions as the polar but calculated in a slightly different way. The effect of bending is that inside the bar the stresses are opposed in the form of tension and compression. So, the ants on one side of the bar are trying to pull everything together whereas the ones on the other side do the opposite. The best group always wins.

In the described examples of bending and torsion, as in all load cases mentioned so far, the assumption is that the materials are homogeneous. Later on, we'll get into composites, which consist of different materials – spiders and worms, to pick a metaphor – and as a consequence the loads will evoke resistance.

In the case of BUCKLING, work becomes very difficult for fire ants. They form a slender body, which gets compressed from both ends, but there's not enough space to move around and properly react. There may also be some disturbing element at the side exerting some bending force. It could be the wind. In the middle the group gradually becomes more fearful until the poor tiny insects panic and lose their cool. The balance is gone and the body swings out and gives in.

BUCKLING can come from several directions, particularly in sheet material. We call this SURFACE BUCKLING. Well, take a sheet of paper, stretch it between your hands and then move one hand parallel to the other, while keeping the paper firmly stretched. You will see that it becomes wavy and if you're lucky you will feel and hear a distinct buckling effect. Again, the ants don't know what to do to counteract this asymmetrical load. It's not uncommon and may occur in any artefact with a distinct structural skin, such as airplanes and hammocks – oh, and clothes and curtains and newspapers.

So far we have examined forces as phenomena that happen and have a more or less instantaneous effect, as if a couple of minutes are sufficient to understand structural behaviour. Of course, life cycles are more complicated than that. Except for things like robots built to defuse bombs, most of the products we make are supposed to last for a considerable time, centuries even. The Pantheon in Rome, partly consisting of self-repairing concrete, has been around since about 126 CE and is subject to forces exerted by gravity. Because of the aspect of structural sustainability, time has to be included when discussing loads.

The first kind, then, concerns forces that change at regular intervals. A material is under stress, then that force disappears, then it returns and so on. In the case of bending, for instance of a wing or a diving board, it could bend up and then down again, causing tension and compression to alternate. In the long run our industrious red pests are likely to get tired of all this swapping places and give in. Indeed, stresses that take turns cause FATIGUE. The alternating frequency can be quite low. It is not all that difficult to break a thin iron rod by hand just by bending it back and forth for a short while. Frequency can easily extend to a couple of hundred times per second. There are many different load patterns too. That's why prototypes of entire airplane structures are made to undergo varying loads in simulated flights. The result is often failure, which is easily recognizable from the fracture surface: there is always a smooth patterned part caused by the growth of the small crack where fatigue failure began.

CREEP put very simply means slowly giving in to continuous load. It can take months before the fire ants, which seemed to be perfectly capable of doing their job, gradually succumb. It leads to gradual deformation to the extent that functioning is compromised. Creep depends on material and on circumstances. Resistance to creep tends to decrease with heat, particularly (and obviously) when it approaches melting temperature. Plastics are more likely to deform under continuous load than metals, because they have a low melting temperature and particularly because many of them don't have a melting point. They just get softer over a trajectory when the temperature rises and become more brittle when refrigerated ■

Trees are prestressed structures

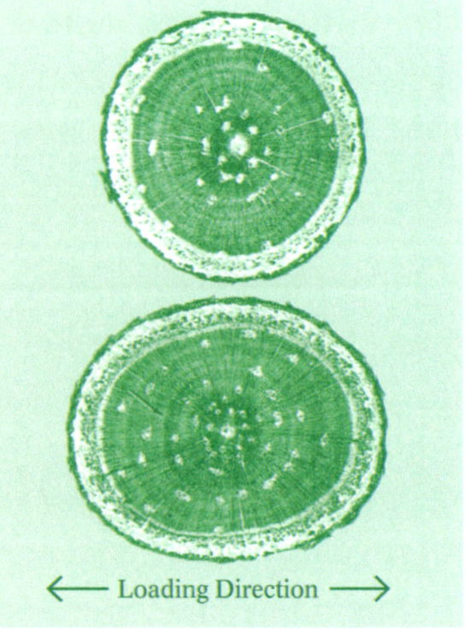

5.7 BUILT-IN ENERGY

In a combination of structural parts, stress can be stored in one material to protect another. As a matter of fact, this happens spontaneously in trees. A trunk has a wooden core with bark around it. The bark is out in the open and because the wind evaporates moisture, it shrinks – except that it can't, because it is attached to the wood underneath. All it can do is develop tension, which pulls the core of the tree trunk together. This is called pre-compression.

Here comes the wind that bends the palmtree that we are using as an example. As a consequence, the bark at the leeward side of the tree will be compressed. Normally that kind of stress is difficult for bark to handle, but it is prestressed under tension, which can compensate for the compression: the tree can deal with a bit of bending.

This kind of compensation can be built into the structure of large sailing ships and yachts. The rigging is spanned under pre-tension over spreaders, which on old ships were called crosstrees. This means that wind bending the mast will put pressure on ropes on the leeward side. As we all know, cables normally have no concept of counteracting compression, but when tension is built-in, they do. The mast stays upright, because in a sense its diameter has been artificially increased with strings of 'bark' under tension.

Prestress is commonly used in concrete, when steel rods are installed under tension, usually with threads and nuts, to keep the concrete under full pressure, even when bent. Prestress is not always well understood. It can happen that a designer bends a pipe in a way that is unstable, feels its power to resist deformation and perceives that as stability. Next they will think this power is useful to support the weight of, say, a human body. It doesn't work like this, since the weight will only put extra bending load on the tube. Here stress increases deformation force instead of compensating for it. Just feeling the force doesn't mean you can exploit it.

5.8 FALLING COMET

Stress and fatigue do not have an immediate impact on structures. It takes time and tragedy to discover them. De Havilland developed the first jet airliner, the DH 106 Comet, which was clearly recognizable by engines slender enough to integrate them into the wings. Its first commercial flight was in 1952. It had a pressurized cabin and square windows.

This fact turned out to be the Comet's Achilles heel, for within a year three Comets crashed. Repeated pressurization tests in a specially made large water tank revealed that after a number of flight mimicking cycles the fuselage tore open full length along a line defined by the lower corners of the windows. Overstressing and metal fatigue turned out to be the cause of the accidents. Improved versions were designed, but the Comet's reputation never recovered. There were several modifications made for military tasks. The last one to leave service, in 2011, was the Hawker Siddeley Nimrod.

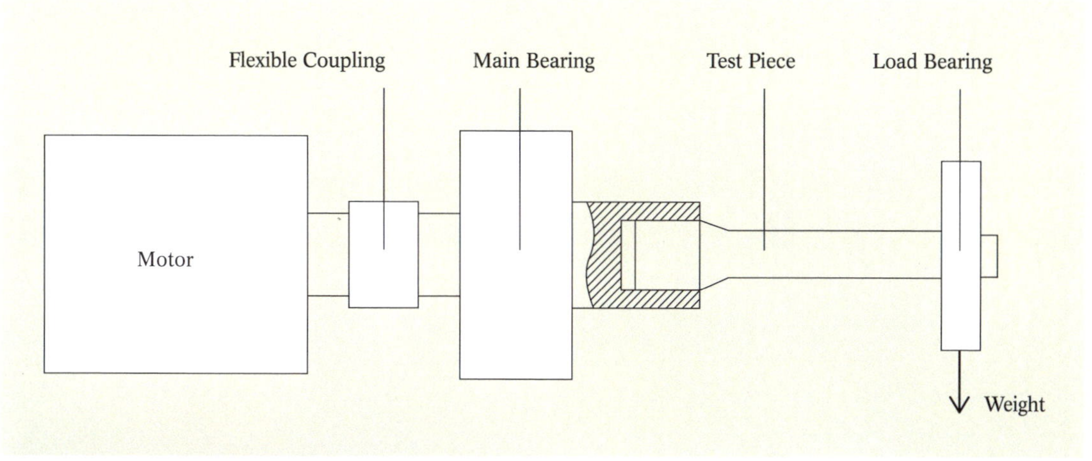

Top: Rotating cantilever bending fatigue test machine.. Bottom: Train axles can break through metal fatigue

5.9 TIRED OF IT

Metal fatigue – it takes a long time to figure it out. It depends on many different factors that have different effects on different metals. Some alloys resist fatigue, as long as the load doesn't exceed a certain limit. Load itself is by no means a simple matter. It can be positive and negative, and occur in varying frequencies with varying amplitudes, at different places and under different environmental conditions. It proceeds in different ways that are very difficult to monitor, which implies that it is not easy to arrive at the right assumptions for defining a reliable structure.

Since fatigue is such a determining factor in metal structures and has been under intensive scrutiny, it provides us with a lot of experience and a set of principles that boil down to proceeding with care and keeping design on the safe side: don't pass the limits of risk and don't allow damage to be fatal. Fail-safe structures, for example, involve multiple points of failure so that what is left can continue to function. Such considerations also apply to other kinds of loads. It depends on the kind that happens to be dominant in a given structure.

6.
THE SHAPE OF STRESS

Honeybees lead the way from the fire ant's social body-building to applying materials. Socially, these insects appear to take slightly more distance from each other than those fiery hexapods from the previous chapter. They work together closely, but don't exploit each other's bodies as parts of living mechanical structures. Foragers even have a certain skill in abstract communication, through pheromones and dance patterns, regarding good places to get nectar. This sweet substance allows them to make honey. Worker bees convert the sugar content of the honey into wax, which they secrete from special glands. They get 1 kilo of wax from about 4 to 6 kilos of honey.

Stress can be applied on purpose to magically evoke hexagonal patterns.

Beehives mainly consist of wax, for bees an expensive commodity considering it takes a visit to an estimated two million flowers to produce half a kilo of honey. Bees therefore had better be efficient with this costly greasy stuff that they use to build arrangements of cells for storage and to incubate their larva. The honeycombs they build (and have been building for at least 34 million years) consist of hexagonal cells. Marcus Terentius Varro (116-27 BCE) concluded, without mathematical proof, that the hexagonal structure was indeed the most efficient option. His notion became known as the Honeycomb Conjecture. It wasn't until 1999 that mathematician Thomas Hales from the University of Michigan proved what had seemed so obvious. For scientists it is almost inconceivable that all bees ever needed all those millions of years ago was the proof of the pudding, which was in the eating of nectar.

Honeycombs, not unlike other wondrous bee products, emerge from many bees building tubular cells that they weld together as a result of which the cells slightly deform to become hexagons, probably because wax between the cells shrinks when it cools down. Hexagons result from evening up material stresses. They simply appear automatically under certain conditions. Hexagonal patterns can be found in some species of turtle and giraffe. When clay soil dries out, the pattern of cracks that will appear on average is hexagonal, not as regular as the ones produced by bees, but still. Basalt columns formed by cooling lava are quite convincingly hexagonal, so much so that they are used to reinforce dikes without anyone noticing that they are not man-made. Nevertheless, stress can be applied on purpose to magically evoke hexagonal patterns.

German researcher Frank Mirtsch invented a principle to produce cans with a honeycomb structured cylinder wall, whereby the 'vault structuring' as it is called, appears just by compressing the tin cylinder, which for support has rubber friction rings inside it. The hexagons just appear out of the blue. No mould defines them. The process can be described as controlled 'buckling', which is succumbing to stress in unstable conditions. Isn't it weird that in unstable conditions

Left: Marcus Terentius Varro. Right: Circles turn into hexagons when pressed together

Basalt walls of the Garni Gorge in Armenia, referred to as the 'Symphony of the Stones'

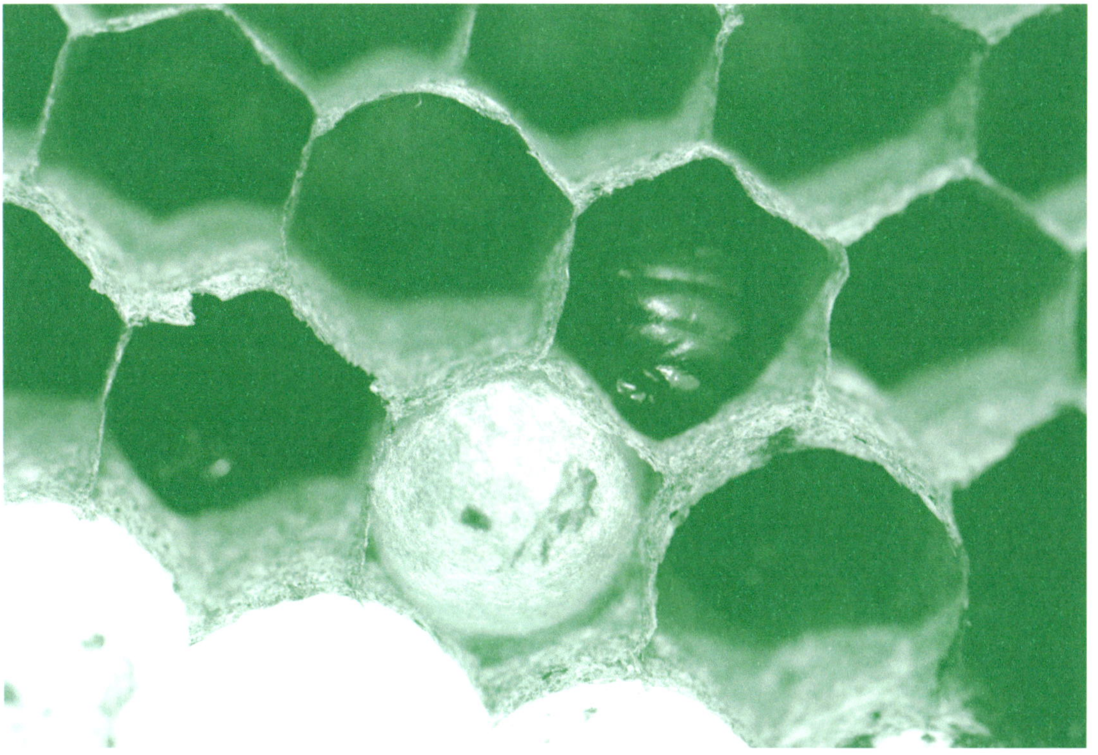

6.1 BEELESS HIVES

Honeycomb structures are common and can be found inside and outside many organisms. Paper wasps produce hives, like bees do, for the same purpose. But the arrangement is different. Every cell is cone shaped and because of this, nests open up like flowers. These cones don't lock edges with neighbouring cones. Because of this they are round and not hexagonal. Wasps are not interested in maths. Like bees, they don't care that the structures they glue together with spittle from wood fibres and plant stems are in fact composites.

predictable forms appear? This way of structuring increases stiffness, because of which cans could be produced from thinner sheet metal.

Several technologies have been derived from this principle for the continuous production of stiff lightweight plates. It has been used to produce washing machine drums that are said to be less damaging to laundry, lighting fixtures, and car parts wherever stiff sheet is required. Vault structuring also caters for special sound and light reflection properties.

Hexagons give expression to equal stress distribution in two dimensions. The step to three dimensions is not all that complicated in principle. Create a cluster of soap bubbles and you're there. There is compression of the air inside the bubbles and there is tension in the skin of soapy water holding the gas together. Replace soapy water and air with some other fluid and gas and you get a different kind of foam. Neighbouring bubbles will share areas of skin, which will be drawn flat. (This is applied in double airplane fuselages, one on top of the other with a flat floor in between, appropriately named a 'double bubble'.) When a bubble is completely surrounded by fellow bubbles, sharing skin with all of them, it will no longer be round. Instead it will be a tetrakaidecahedron, a volume with fourteen flat faces. Here we have foam, or at least one principle to form it.

Anyone can blow foam with spittle. Froghoppers, however, are much better at producing foam by blowing into saliva than humans. These insects put the product to good use too. Their nymphs, known as spittlebugs, construct their own cover of foam and when it dries up or washes away in the rain they simply blow themselves a fresh sleeping bag.

In current technological practice there are many kinds of foam. First, we make a distinction between closed and open celled foams. The latter are known as sponge materials. The closed celled kind is produced as described earlier, by blowing a gas through a liquid substance. Plastics can be turned into foam in this way and so can metals. Closed cell foams may enhance stiffness because the enclosed gas contributes to the structure, which is a kind of composite since it combines the properties of two materials, one of which is a gas. Sponge materials are produced by adding a blowing agent. This starts a chemical reaction that produces a gas that is not 'locked up' inside cells. A sponge structure also renders the original material lighter. Other properties depend on the spongy material, which can vary from metal to polymers. If it is a rubbery plastic, it will be soft. Polyether typically is a soft open celled foam used for bedding.

There are hard and brittle foams as well. Placed between two sheets of dense material they can provide lightness and insulation in thick panels. Polystyrene foam technologically is a hybrid. It has its own production recipe. The main ingredient, polystyrene, consists of long chain molecules clustered into small beads. These

Top: Closed-cell foam is the 3D version of a honeycomb (p112). Bottom: A sponge is not a closed-cell system

need to be expanded to turn into foam. This is effected in two stages. First, they are pre-expanded with steam or hot air in a vessel where they are agitated to keep them from fusing together. With air the result is a high-density foam, the kind used for coffee cups. The expanded closed cell beads are much lighter and will come out on top. After pre-expansion the beads are stored for 24 hours to 'age'. Air diffuses into them, which makes them harder but also more susceptible to further expansion. This happens in the mould, where the beads together assume their final shape, heated inside and out by low-pressure steam. Finally, the mould is cooled, which is not easy because Expanded Polystyrene, or EPS, is a very good insulator. In terms of open and closed cell foam this material is both. It consists of closed beads that are opened up and melted together during processing. Foam beads that can easily escape can be a nuisance. They are difficult to control and flammable to boot.

The creation of something light is not just a matter of choosing a low-density material.

EPS is used to reduce the weight of road foundations. It has the ability to adapt to the unevenness of the ground underneath it, where its surface vulnerability is an asset. The foam is also used for lightweight insulation in building and construction. At a smaller scale, EPS can be easily moulded into shapes for protective packaging. Some years ago, the process began of gradually phasing out the use of plastic foam in packaging applications for electronic equipment: it is difficult to get rid of, because controlling the material flow for recycling is more costly than producing new packaging. If protected against damage, EPS can be used in more durable packaging and other durable applications.

There is yet another kind of foam, though it isn't known as such because it stems from replacing the watery component of a gel with a gas. It is called aerogel and there are many different kinds. The first aerogels were created by Samuel Stephens Kistler in 1931. Aerogels that mainly consist of air are excellent insulators, better even than the gas they contain. They are smoky transparent solids. There is a low-density contest going on among aerogels. In 2013 the champion was aerographene (containing carbon atoms) weighing 160 grams per cubic metre.

Because of their ultra-lightweight reputation many people are inclined to think that aerogels might be applied to create lightweight structures. Unfortunately designing lightness doesn't work like that. The creation of something light is not just a matter of choosing a low-density material. It is much more complicated. Honeycombs and foams have structures. Hexagons and tetrakaidecahedrons serve specific purposes, but there is much more potential. Fortunately, there are more chapters to come ■

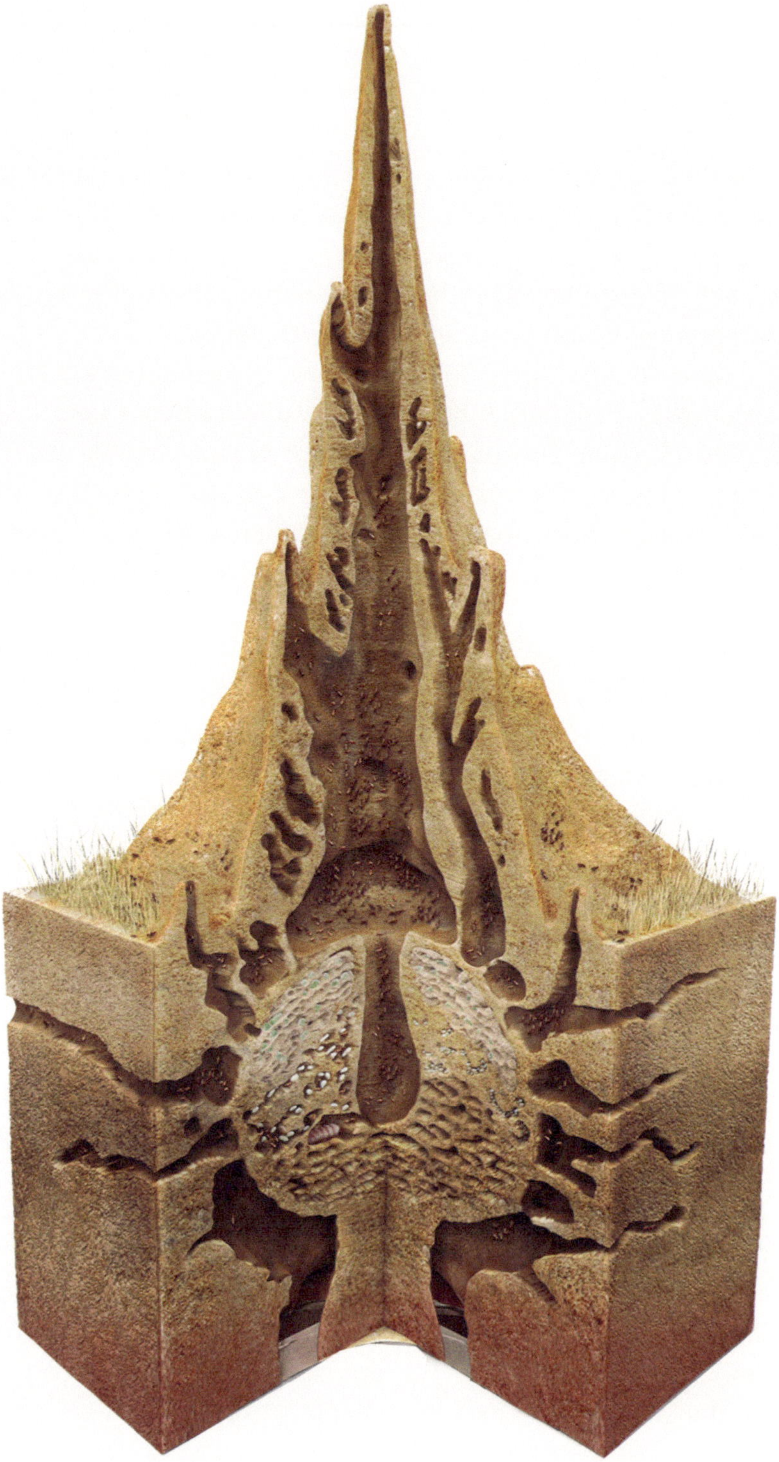

Cutaway through termite mound

6.2 TERMITE CLIMATE SYSTEMS

Termites are similar to fire ants, except that they use earth to build structures. Termite hills are famously ingenious. For example, their internal climate is self-regulating because of the interior structure and the positioning of ventilation holes. For some it is hard to believe that there is no such thing as a termite hill head of engineering. The structure is defined merely by obeying behavioural rules. Humans can self-organize as well, for instance in the way that thousands of men get lunch from their wives through an improbable delivery system. Systems often benefit from lack of systemic awareness.

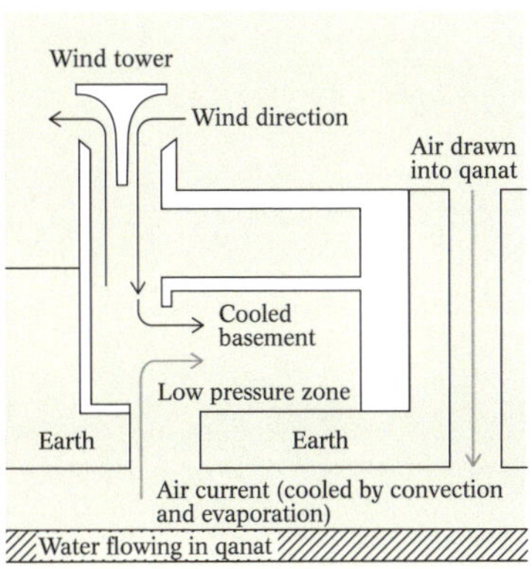

A qanat is an ancient underground climate control system in Persia

6.3 FUNCTIONAL INFLATION

The soap bubble principle sets examples, for anything really. A thin skin with air inside can fulfil all kinds of duties. In the 1950s, Goodyear even built 12 prototypes of an 'inflatoplane' that featured a wing made of fabric with air inside. The zorb ball in which one can stumble on water is everywhere these days and inflatability is an obvious advantage for bridges. Given a strong skin, the potential of air verges on the miraculous. One can exert superhuman forces just by pumping air into a bag. Of course, pneumatic tyres are so familiar that it's easy to overlook that they are bubbles with a twist.

6.4 LIBERATED FOAM CHAIR

When you discover, as a designer, that well over half of all timber produced for the furniture industry is wasted, it makes a lot of sense to experiment with the leftovers. Marjan van Aubel and James Shaw did just that. They mixed wood shavings with a bio-resin and to their surprise the goo began to foam and turned into stiff lightweight airy matter. They decided to find out what would happen if the mixture was slapped against the back and bottom of a mould for a seat above a controlled wooden leg structure. The shape of the resulting piece is partly unpredictable, which livens up the conventions of design. They named it Well Proven Chair.

7. TRIADIC TIES

Ice is one of the lightest materials available, so light in fact that it floats on water. It is in the same density range as most plastics and families of wood. And of course wood comes from trees, which are rather complicated biological structures. Still, there are some disadvantages to ice. Its tensile strength and resistance to bending are feeble, even when compared to low-grade plastics. Its compressive strength is not very impressive either, but increases somewhat with lower temperatures, from 0 C° down to about -20. This implies that making useful load-bearing ice structures requires vast quantities of the stuff.

This hasn't stopped a group of artists from exploiting the renowned Icehotel in the village of Jukkasjärvi in northern Sweden. It attracts 70,000 people all year round and during winter it is extended with a large ice building that features an extraordinary exhibition space and cold but beautiful hotel rooms. Every spring this ice facility melts down, which may be advantageous as an utterly unique hotel experience. However, melting is not generally considered an asset for hotels. Luckily every November the Icehotel is resurrected. Average living conditions for humans on Earth limit the use of frozen water to cooling fish and drinks. Ice dwellings are giving in to climate change.

Over the past twenty years, materials have unjustly been rated spearheads for innovation.

The point here is that lightness of functional objects doesn't just depend on the choice of a material that may be lighter than other materials. Ice weighs very little but has certain practical drawbacks. That is true for all materials. Over the past twenty years, materials have unjustly been rated spearheads for innovation. Policies were all about smart materials, light materials, metamaterials and more, leaving out concept and process. The preferred catchphrase in innovative strategies and policies should have the word structures in it.

The weight per unit volume of concrete, for instance, is lower than the density of aluminium, but with just a little of the latter you can do so much more. Steel is about three times as heavy as aluminium, but more accessible as well as stronger, stiffer and tougher. Carbon and Glass Fibre Reinforced Polymers by comparison can be much stronger per unit weight than steel, but although they are widely known and talked about as 'materials', they are in fact structures that have been designed for a specific purpose. You can go to a hardware store and ask for a certain amount of carbon composite, but unless you want premanufactured plate, or piping, or a profile, you won't get any because it consists of carbon fibres and a polymer that have yet to be combined in some designed structure.

The preferred catchphrase in innovative strategies and policies should have the word structures in it.

Here we arrive at the essence of structural design, which includes defining minimum energy structures. The function of an object, including its weight, always

The Icehotel is a hotel rebuilt each year with snow and ice in the village of Jukkasjärvi, in northern Sweden. After its first opening in 1990, the hotel has been rebuilt each year from December to April. The hotel, including the chairs and beds, is constructed from snow and ice blocks taken from the nearby Torne River. Artists are invited to create different rooms and decorations made by ice. Besides bedrooms, there is a bar, with glasses made of ice and an ice chapel.

7.1 HEAVYWEIGHT ARCHITECTURE

This building designed by Archipelontwerpers pretends to be light by using far more steel than necessary. Aside from the weight aspect, materials need only be used where they contribute to structural quality and function. Let us begin with the top sunscreen made with steel slats: for shadow all you need is a piece of spanned fabric. The steel I-beams used for the ribs of the structure are quite common, which doesn't mean that other quite common alternatives couldn't have saved a considerable amount of material. When span and load are unchanged, we only have to compare moments of inertia and the volume of material they represent by comparing surfaces areas.

The job can be done using relatively little material at a certain distance from the neutral bending line (the horizontal beams) and the neutral buckling line (the columns). For the supporting columns, thin walled tube could easily save about 50 per cent weight but it would look bulkier – something new to get used to. Adjust your mindset and the cold steel beams and columns become inflatables, saving even more material, but that would change the concept and require other ideas for connections.

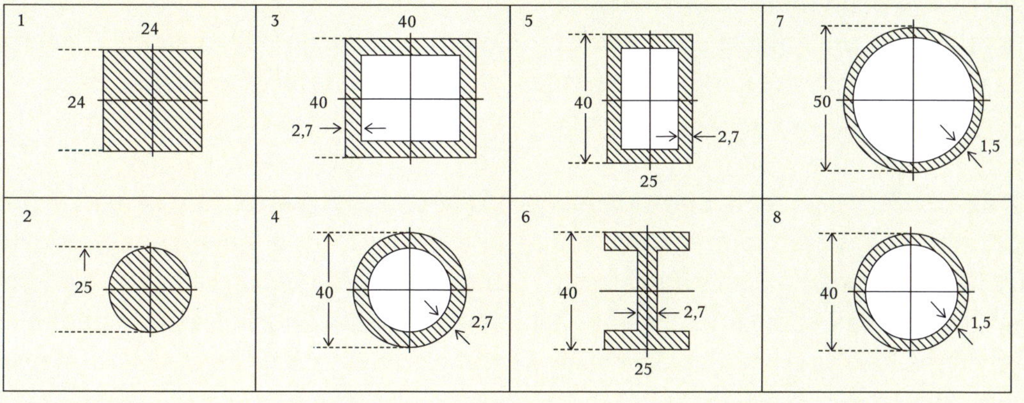

Cross Sections	Relative Weight (%)	Relative Rigidity Buckling & Bending (%)	Relative Bending Strength (%)
1	100	142	150
2	85	100	100
3	70	489	306
4	55	289	180
5	55	347	214
6	40	295	184
7	40	353	175
8	30	180	110

depends on a triad of interdependent characteristics, namely material, process and concept. This is the implication of the fact that material properties never travel alone. Steel for instance has a certain strength, namely the amount of internal stress needed to pull it apart. Steel also has a weight per unit volume known as 'density'. This implies that strength is relative: steel may be strong but it's not very light. Here we run into a combined property called the 'breaking length': take a steel wire and let it down into an extremely deep canyon. Now the lower it reaches, the more stress the wire will feel at the top, due to the weight of the portion hanging down. At a certain point, when the wire has reached about 35 kilometres deep, it will break at the top. The wire has reached the breaking length of steel (see Analemma Tower on page 35).

Material properties never travel alone.

Material properties are always in combination. Plastics, as another example, have a certain elasticity, expressed in Young's module. This defines the elastic deformation that a material can undergo without losing the ability to return to its original state. Of course, it varies with the kind of plastic, but many kinds have properties that depend on temperature and other environmental conditions. If the plastic in your design is supposed to function in the tropics, do make sure it has the right properties for those conditions. Often there are trade-offs. There may be a stronger alternative for a certain material but it may be less resistant to fatigue, or UV radiation, or the corrosive effects of sea water. By choosing a different material the concept is altered. Don't tamper with the concept. There are other considerations too. A material may simply be unavailable, or it may have toxic properties.

By choosing a different material the concept is altered. Don't tamper with the concept.

What you can do with materials depends on the grand total of their properties – and some inventiveness on your part. If you are unsure whether a material will undergo a method of transformation, just give it a try. This is where processes enter the picture. Each material will only allow specific treatments in feasible circumstances to get the desired structural properties. Plaster can be cast to make plates, but these will be brittle. You can make up for this by making them thicker (but heavier) or by protecting them with paper. It is impossible to shape plaster by bending a cast plate. Steel and aluminium by contrast can be calendered into thin plate that allows bending and, depending on thickness, very precise pressing and deep drawing in moulds. These metals can be cast as well, at fairly high temperatures. Many plastics commonly are injection moulded at relatively low temperatures (melted and injected into a mould at high pressure), which enables the most precise mass production of complex parts. It is possible to make extremely thin-walled products by inflating plastics. Injection

7.2 PEDAL POWERED HELICOPTER

Sometimes a challenge is sufficient to make something happen. The American Helicopter Society had the Igor I. Sikorsky award on offer: anyone managing to fly three metres off the ground for one minute under their own power would receive $ 250,000. Aerovelo, a small company founded by Canadians Todd Reichert and Cameron Robertson, took it up with their Atlas and in mid 2013 Reichert stayed airborne for 64 seconds, slightly above the required height.

Covering a total area of a staggering 1,282 square metres, Atlas has four rotors with a pedal defined human energy transformer in the middle. Nevertheless, it weighs only 55 kilograms.

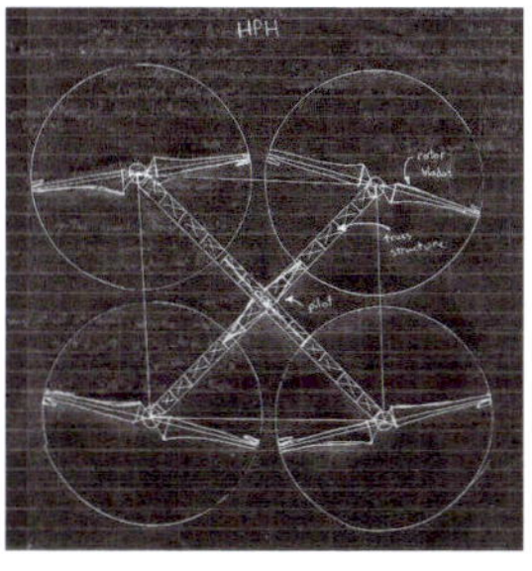

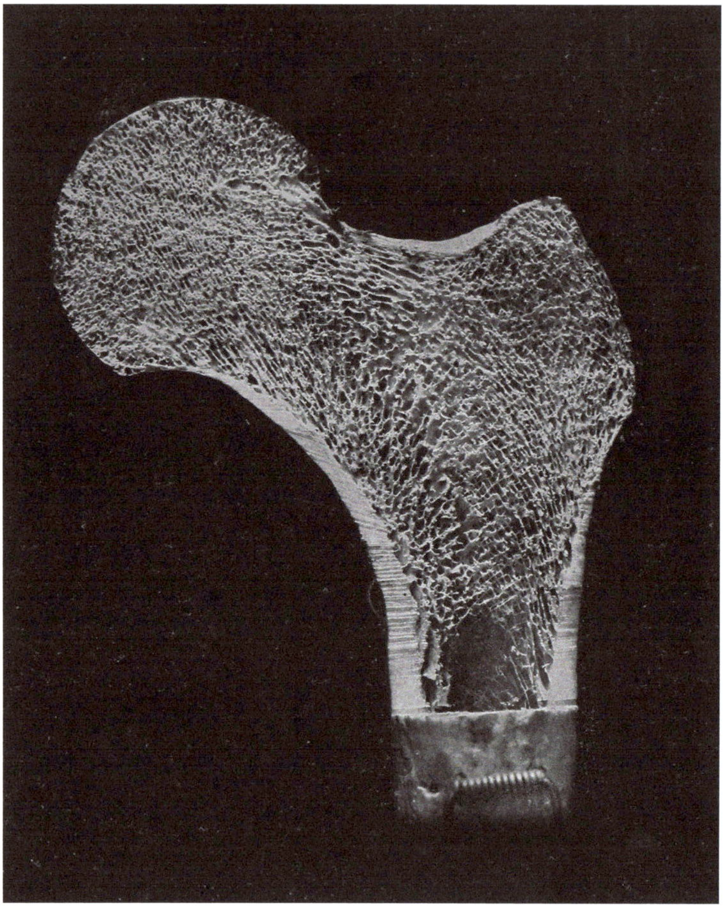

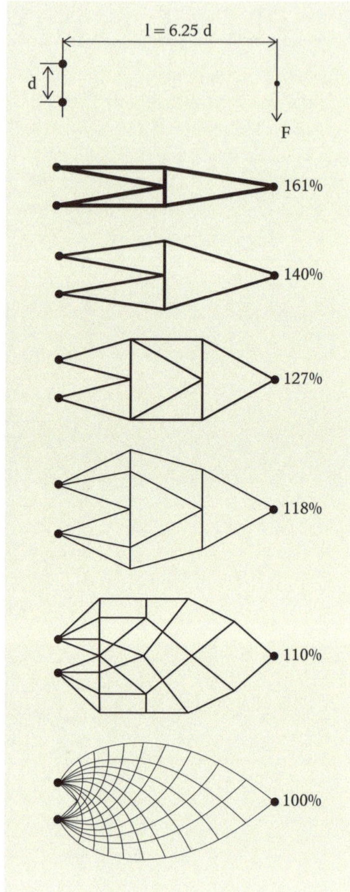

7.3 MICHELL STRUCTURES

This kind of reasoning extends into two- and three-dimensional structures. Load a simple truss extending from two points and you may need a particular strut thickness to withstand a certain bending force. Add some well-chosen supporting struts and their thickness can become smaller, thereby reducing the weight of the structure that can withstand the same force. This can be repeated a number of times until a so-called Michell structure emerges. It is similar to what you find in bone, which is naturally organized into an optimum stress distributing structure.

moulding can be achieved with some metal alloys too, but the moulds need to meet much stiffer requirements in terms of wear and heat resistance. Batch size is an important determining factor for process choice. The price of tooling generally rises with the number of products. In some markets (yachts, supercars, conspicuous accessories), costs are not that much of an issue, but then those aren't meant to be mass-produced. In air travel the number of airplanes is quite modest in comparison with the number of passengers that fly in them. Providing travel is a mass market. Selling airplanes is not.

Concept is the third contributor to the triad. For engineers, it is an expression of the cluster of rules and demands that define function during the entire life cycle, whereas for designers, architects and those carrying responsibility it is an expression of appearance or identity.

Strange things may occur that can illustrate professional preoccupations with the meaning and importance of concepts. Once upon a time there was an architect who was commissioned to adapt an existing building to the demands of new users. The architect envisaged adding a large concrete canopy over the entrance. In structural terms it is never a good idea to add something heavy that protrudes, as it may harm the building. The engineer in charge advised against it. So the architect had to find a lightweight alternative. The choice fell on a Styrofoam canopy covered with a thick water-based resin. It took a dozen tests before the architect was convinced by the concrete-like appearance of the coated Styrofoam.

Particularly in lightweight design the triad of material, process and concept demonstrates the intimate entanglement between these three. Change one and the other two follow suit. Take the Van Brienenoordbrug in Rotterdam. This began life in the mid '60s as a single steel highway bridge. Twenty years later, it no longer had sufficient capacity. So it was decided to add a twin version that was built elsewhere and brought in by ship. The twin part was opened in 1990. Between the first and the second version, stronger kinds of steel had appeared on the market. The second bridge therefore had a thinner, lighter and stronger deck, or so it was believed. Seven years after the opening, cracks appeared and corrosion threatened the reliability of the new bridge's moving part. This had to be replaced. Two common errors had been made.

The first is that material stiffness is constant, no matter which ingredients you add to the alloy, and no matter what kind of treatments you apply to it. So, when you make steel stronger this will not add anything to stiffness or resistance against bending. In fact, strength, or resistance to fatal strain, as said earlier, is almost always far too extreme to be useful as a design parameter.

The second error is – here it comes – that by choosing a different type of steel the concept changes. The stronger steel starts cracking because it is more susceptible to fatigue. Therefore, the bridge changes from a structure for which sufficient stiffness is the dominant requirement into a structure that has to be able to withstand fatigue, in this case the continuously changing loads caused by trucks and cars crossing the bridge.

> *An awareness of assumptions is crucial. It is important to understand their origin, particularly for lightweight design. Beware of the obvious.*

The influence of the concept on material and process in designing lightness is not as trivial as it seems, for it emerges from the desired solution. A concept often begins as something vague. It grows in an iterative trial and error process of assumptions, considerations, judgements and tests, all of which include materials and processes.

An awareness of assumptions is crucial. It is important to understand their origin, particularly for lightweight design. Beware of the obvious. Often choices are implicit because they are so familiar that one doesn't notice that there may be more favourable alternatives. In current aluminium passenger aircraft fuselages, for instance, the distance between the frames, the parts that define the shape of the fuselage's cross-section, is usually 500 millimetres, or 20 inches, which is convenient since that used to be the standard length of rulers on a drawing board. Widening the gauge and compensating for the loss of support by applying slightly thicker plating for the skin can in many cases save weight. Such tacit assumptions can be found in every trade. They may concern measurements and proportions, but also choice of materials, processes, use and even tradition. The least convincing argument in assessing a concept is 'We've always done it this way'.

Lightness imposes precision on the concept because within our triad the desired situation for which the concept offers solace usually fuels the mindset for innovation and an occasional breakthrough. In practice it may occur that a newly discovered material, or the investment in a costly tool that cries out for recoup, is the main incentive for something new. This may work, but our triad more often than not carries the burden of trying to find just the right problem for the solution at hand.

Concepts allow for a plethora of approaches. It may concern something technical, such as a way to mount batteries in existing cars to electrify them. Responding to fashion trends and identity desires is an important stimulus for concept development. Fashion is not necessarily limited to clothes. Architectural styling, electrical tool design, furniture and kitchen culture are subject to principles of fashion. As a matter of fact, anything is prone to fashion, even political issues, but not everything is designable. In general concepts are strongly related to context. They depend on place, time and circumstances of 'touchdown'. Camera drones have become immensely successful now, because systems for telecommunication, digital cybernetics, sensing, activation and navigation have become light enough to

7.4 HYPERLOOPING

Insanely efficient fast public transportation concepts have been around for a while. Currently Elon Musk is cleverly promoting the Hyperloop, promising speeds in the region of 1200 km/h, or travelling from Amsterdam to Paris in about 25 minutes. He organizes competitions for the best design of a system consisting of vacuum (no drag) tubes to connect cities over medium range distances with frictionless transportation pods. He presented his version of the principle in 2012, although one of the first predecessors dates back to 1864, when the Crystal Palace pneumatic railway ran for a few months. Air pressure came from a steam driven fan 6.7 metres in diameter that stood next to the tunnel. The carriage had bristles all around it to close the gap with the surrounding tunnel, sort of. It travelled 550 metres in 50 seconds. The experimental setup has vanished completely. People do say that the original location is now haunted.

The first Hyperloop competition, in a 1-mile testing tube in Hawthorne CA, next to the SpaceX facility, took place in January 2017. The student group from TU Delft got the highest overall score. Of course, the development of such a system doesn't happen overnight. It is currently the subject of an open source design project. Worldwide some nine organizations are involved and technologically the design project is enormously attractive because of the dream it follows of clean and fast transportation.

Hyperloop practice, however, is not just a matter of technological development, which is complicated because of the accuracy needed for high speed and the vulnerability of a tube system. A serious drawback is that one needs to low-speed travel to and from high-speed Hyperloop stations. The main caveats are in energy provision, economic feasibility, political support, or in short, social acceptance. Even if an experimental demonstration system provides proof that it works, there is a lot of convincing to be done before it's accepted as a viable alternative system, for instance when compared to conventional high-speed trains. Technical concepts need a welcoming community to succeed.

7.5 THIN-WALLED KEGS

We can be brief on the subject of beer vessels for transportation: first ceramics, then wood, glass and metal, and now plastic. However, the last part of the evolution, from metal to plastic, deserves more attention. About 25 years ago, the whole system of transporting beer to the catering industry was organized around metal vessels. These were brought in and once empty they were collected to be cleaned and refilled at breweries that transported them back to the clients, and so on and so forth. These common vessels were heavy and noisy to boot.

In Delft a small company looked for a lightweight alternative. It developed a vessel with a plastic keg protected against expansion by fibres wound around it. In a sense it was a composite with separated components. At first these kegs could be refilled, but by making them disposable there were better opportunities. They saved a considerable sum in transportation costs. Still, major breweries continued to prefer the system that was familiar to them.

The keg developers didn't stop there, however. They developed a better alternative that consisted of a PET (Polyethylene terephthalate) outer sphere with a bag inside. The beer (or wine) was put into the bag. By applying gas pressure in between the vessel and the bag, the fluid, beer or wine, was squeezed out through the tap into drinking requisites. The spheres needed a cardboard box for handling and familiarity, but commercial success was on the way. Currently Keykeg is a fast-growing multinational, based in the north of the Netherlands.

Their keg's outer shell is produced by heating and inflating pre-injection moulded bottles. This is where the weight advantage comes in: the wall can be much thinner than metal would allow. Inside is a thin bag for the fluid. The outer containers are almost 100 per cent recycled, the bags slightly less so, since they have contained the drink. Interestingly, because Keykeg recycles its own products it is now considered a recycling company, which brings with it an additional layer of discouraging requirements. Keykeg containers are feasible for small breweries because of their ease of use. Although breweries are still reluctant, their clients want these lightweight vessels.

The wound predecessors of the keg were intended to be disposable, whereas the current kegs are recyclable

provide affordable equipment for professionals as well as gadget lovers.

The greater the quantity of a given product, the more important that responsibilities are clearly articulated.

The concept of a product imposes a slew of demands and requirements regarding materials and the processes that accompany them. The number of requirements and the angles from which they are perceived is on the increase. The concept no longer merely defines convenience and identity but also cultivation of value in time, during the product's life cycle and whatever happens next. Future is part of the concept. The product may be repaired, refurbished or recycled, or it may be discarded, in which case it has to be harmless. The production of waste should be prevented or kept to a minimum. This entails a general principle of sustainability: the greater the quantity of a given product to be manufactured, the more important it is that responsibilities relating to the existence of the products and the material flow they constitute are clearly articulated and allocated. Allowing material flows to escape our attention and not get proper treatment isn't as affordable as we used to think, let alone the amount of energy it takes to pointlessly move stuff around and scrap or dump it. Doesn't the case of the Icehotel set a great example again? It is rebuilt every season and there is no effort involved in producing and recycling the building material ■

Constructed of 'high-grade steel', the second section of the Van Brienenoord bridge soon fell victim to corrosion

7.6 DOMINANCE? NEVER HEARD OF IT!

In August 2018, the Morandi Bridge in Genoa collapsed. There was not one straightforward cause – let's say the structure was ambiguous. There were four stays per section, and they consisted of steel cables surrounded by insufficiently prestressed concrete. This cracked and started leaking, exposing the cables to corrosion.

'What exactly is happening here?' is a question we tend to overlook. A degree of calculated risk avoidance can help prevent accidents. However, part of the danger can also be avoided by not allowing routine to take over engineering procedures and instead profoundly analysing applied structural principles, especially when the impact of failure is large.

Replacing one material with another is a simple way to illustrate that this may drastically change a concept and alter the way a structure should be understood and tested. Take a simple plank over a ditch. It will bend when you walk on it. Now replace the plank with a fabric attached to the banks. It won't bend. Pure tension has now become the dominant factor.

Something similar happens with composite aircraft wings taking over from aluminium ones (see page 318). The fatigue that would be harmful to an aluminium wing underreaches the strain that the composite wing can handle. Here maximum strain is dominant. Fatigue, traditionally the culprit to beware of, is irrelevant in well designed composite wings.

Metal became very popular for airplanes in the 1920s because, among other advantages, it was believed to be non-flammable. The US Airmail Services invested in eight small Junkers-Larson JL-6 aircraft, four of which nevertheless fell prey to flames. The fact that fuel burns easily and can fatally melt metal structures was entirely overlooked. This time meltability proved to be dominant.

The opposite can occur too. A small firm in Delft was developing a fibre reinforced plastic LPG tank for cars. It had to pass one final test in which a full tank was thrown into a fire. A steel tank would have exploded. The plastic one melted and the gas just burned, without an explosion. Here the ability to submit to heat was dominant.

Left: Morandi Bridge in Genoa after a section collapsed. Right: Rescue workers among the rubble

7.7 HAND-MADE COMPOSITE

Designer Tjeerd Veenhoven has a studio in Groningen where he collects things that may come in useful some day. At some point he realized that he had loads of bicycle parts and that there might be enough to build several new bicycles, except for frames. So he decided to improvise and build a bicycle of his own. For this he believed he could use contemporary materials and turn them into something rather old-fashioned looking.

His working procedure was very straightforward. He made a wooden jig to position the saddle, steering column, wheels, etc. Next he connected the parts with a bundle of carbon fibres, initially 'dry' to check lengths and arrangements and then for keeps after guiding the bundle through a small container filled with epoxy resin. After this was done, all that was left was to wait until the resin had set and there it was: an old-fashioned looking carbon fibre reinforced polymer bike. Material costs: 10 or 20 euros. Frame building time: 3 hours. This is very cheap, although this beautiful frame will probably behave less predictably than if it were an expensive machine-produced one.

Typical example of design

7.8 DESIGNING RECIPES

Even designers, of all breeds, harbour misconceptions about the creative process. This may well be because designing involves a bit of everything, which means that it is not just one thing, such as getting 'the right idea'. There are those who think that you design something first, by thinking a lot and scribbling and making sketches. Next, they say, you decide on materials, colours, structure and form, until you've finished 'the design'. The final step in their book is to execute the 'concept'. This usually contains setbacks. The cause of these is simple enough: executing the concept is not 'preparing the recipe' but should be part of the design process. You need models for all relevant aspects and then you need to test them, as realistically as possible, to find out what your brain has been up to.

On the other side of the designer spectrum you'll find the systematic ones. For them, problem-solving is a structured procedure in which a fixed line-up of well-considered problems is solved. This approach is certainly useful in the background, for communication within a project between participants and clients. Nevertheless, this is not what actually happens.

Designing involves going seemingly haphazard through the triad of material, process and concept over and over again, alone and cooperating with others, trying things out and making mistakes, going bottom up developing new combinations of materials and technologies, as well as top down, wondering what the precise requirements are from various contextual points of view. Designing requires a concentrated and simultaneously open mindset.

Being a complicated process, it often leads to several different possible outcomes, the concepts, which can be compared and elaborated to finally arrive at something that can be called the design. Even that may need time to mature. There are bound to be teething troubles and during the result's life cycle unexpected problems and windfalls may turn up that need to be addressed. In short: designing is fascinating.

7.9 CLASSIC LESSONS LEARNED

- Avoid discontinuities, whether geometrical, mechanical or thermal.
- Take extreme care with structural details. Places where loads occur determine the strength and durability.
- Minimize the number of joints.
- Understand the significance of trajectories and stress/strain distributions. They will give clear and proper guidelines for good structural design, preventing extensive strength analysis of the wrong concept.
- Striving for optimal fully stressed structures increases the danger of all kinds of buckling and pin loaded holes failing simultaneously.

Poor structural design will always remain poor, no matter the effort made in structural analysis and optimization.

The functional value of structures is also determined by continuous use in whatever form. Include considerations of disassembly, functional alteration and recycling.

AZ football stadium collapsed due to structural design faults

COMPOSITION OF MOVEMENTS

8.
SPEEDING UP

8.1 AIR MILE VALUE
8.2 COMBINE AND SEPARATE
8.3 MAX PAYLOAD
8.4 WEIGHT ON WHEELS
8.5 LESS WEIGHT IS LESS ENERGY
8.6 URINATE BEFORE BOARDING
8.7 SPEED PERCEPTION
8.8 SPECIFIC DRAG
8.9 QUEUING FOR SPEED
8.10 SO MANY CONTAINERS
8.11 A WASTE ODYSSEY
8.12 NO PACKAGING
8.13 MEDICINE BY DRONE

There are many people like Mr. Whodunnit. He believes that when he's driving and his car almost runs out of petrol, it helps to race to the next filling station as fast as he can, because he may get there just before his tank is completely empty. He takes the consequences of velocity for granted and at the same time speed defines him, and all of us. It is one of the main stimulants behind technological development and energy abuse. Speed defines us as impatient, hyperactive, respectable and smart, and longing for the sensation of movement by just pushing or turning something small, maybe even an intangible symbol on a screen.

Ideally, we would like it to be even simpler. Devices should be able to understand our every intention and react accordingly. Currently even the *Star Trek* catchphrase 'Beam me up, Scotty' to initiate quantum weird transfer, has become too much hassle. Wireless transmission of people would be unparalleled in terms of speed, but the business of taking one's place in a scanning machine and then waiting for an officer to give the key command is not what people would want.

> *Placed together, people-moving schemes are not a perfect match, to put it mildly.*

The desire for quick and easy transportation has led to the evolution of a number of different transportation systems, for goods as well as for people. Placed together, these people-moving schemes are not a perfect match, to put it mildly. If we limit our observation of speed to people commuting and travelling, the gaps between systems could be the consequence of the evolution of different means of transportation, all trying to be the fittest and provide the perfect future, like tortoises and teals on the Galápagos Islands. An overall coherent system never happened. All we got – most of the time – was peaceful coexistence.

What we do have now is trajectories that connect a collection of designed or evolved transfer areas where travellers switch from one kind of transportation to another. Sometimes the difference between the two is minute, for instance when neoliberal ideology dictates that there has to be competition between different travel providers to maximize profit instead of the number of people transported. This spells trouble when they operate on one and the same railway track. In Japan, high-speed trains have their own tracks, thereby preventing conflicts. In a more radical example, there are several places in Russia where train carriages have to be put on alternative bogies because of a difference in gauge. This may happen in the middle of the night, when cars with sleeping passengers on board are hoisted up and mounted on different sets of wheels.

This is the physical consequence of different gauge standards for the same mode of transportation for different regions. It can be a cultural issue too. Amsterdam had trams. Then, in the early 1970s, it gained a metro system, immediately

Train car hoisted onto a different wheel set to accommodate the difference in gauge

initiating feuds about different standards because of different conventions. The Hague is now connected with Rotterdam via light rail – light in name only, since a complete train weighs about 500 kilograms of vehicle per passenger at full 100 passenger capacity. Regrettably, carriages from one of the two cities have a larger step height, because of which platforms in between the two have to be extra-long to facilitate both kinds of trains.

What drivers feel and think adds up to a demonstrable decrease in safety, clean air and traffic manageability.

When systems are truly different it becomes hard to dovetail them. Google Maps currently allows users to choose a route for a combination of different modes of transport – theoretically, that is. For instance, the algorithm will let you travel from home to a train station by car, which will take 19 minutes, ignoring the time you need to find a parking space and walk to the platform, which may take 20 minutes, if you're lucky. Next the train will bring you to a station in a different city where you can rent a bicycle, except that they may have run out of bikes. It's a great idea, despite its practical imperfections. No doubt the guidance system will improve in time. For now though, inclusion of the fastest transportation mode, air travel, still depends too much on planning, reservation arrangements and maximum payload to make it part of a well-functioning guidance app. To say one can fly

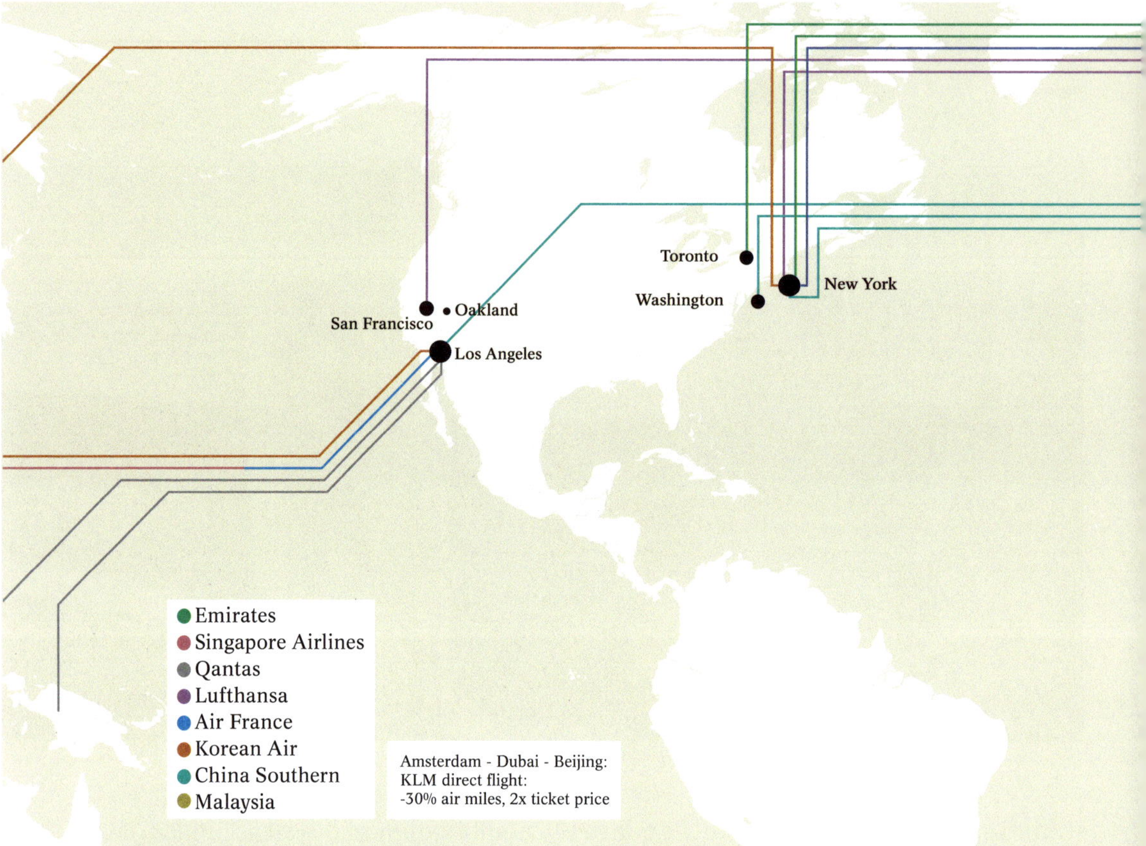

8.1 AIR MILE VALUE

The meaning of value as an economic term is unclear, for it is determined by feelings, which are abstract, and expressed in amounts of money, which unjustifiably suggests precision. In fact, there are two descriptions. The first is a sense of 'oughtness', pointing in the direction of right or wrong, morality if you like. The second is a sense of potential, or what you expect to get out of something, good, bad or in between. Value can be cultivated or kept in good order. 'Adding value' merely represents a snapshot in the cultivation scenario. Value is also negotiable, to come to an agreement, which can be a deal, but also a rule.

High-speed magic has allowed air carriers, airports and governments to tamper with the value of flying for a long time. As a consequence, energy consumption is much higher than it should be. The effort being put into making aircraft more efficient is partly undone by the way the market is made to work.

To start with, flights used to be mainly organized via central hubs, the home of a carrier, for instance Amsterdam Schiphol for KLM. The disadvantage is that such flights tend to include a costly detour. Developments toward smaller planes indicate that there is now a shift to direct, 'point-to-point' transit, thereby saving fuel. There are exceptions. Carriers in the Middle East seek to replace oil as a source of income with tourists and therefore subsidize the exploitation of Airbus A380s to bring in consumers.

An extra complication is that long haul flights take off with more fuel at the cost of the payload share. In general flying is over-subsidized because of its reputation as an economy enhancer, which is defined by assumptions about value. These tend to exclude capital that, historically, has no monetary expression. As a consequence, competition is stiff and based on full capacity flights with hardly any profit. It would be wiser to relate pricing to the potential of speed – more specifically, travel time reduction – compared with other transportation modes. Slow low-energy train trips without subsidy are far too expensive by comparison, even although they directly connect city centres.

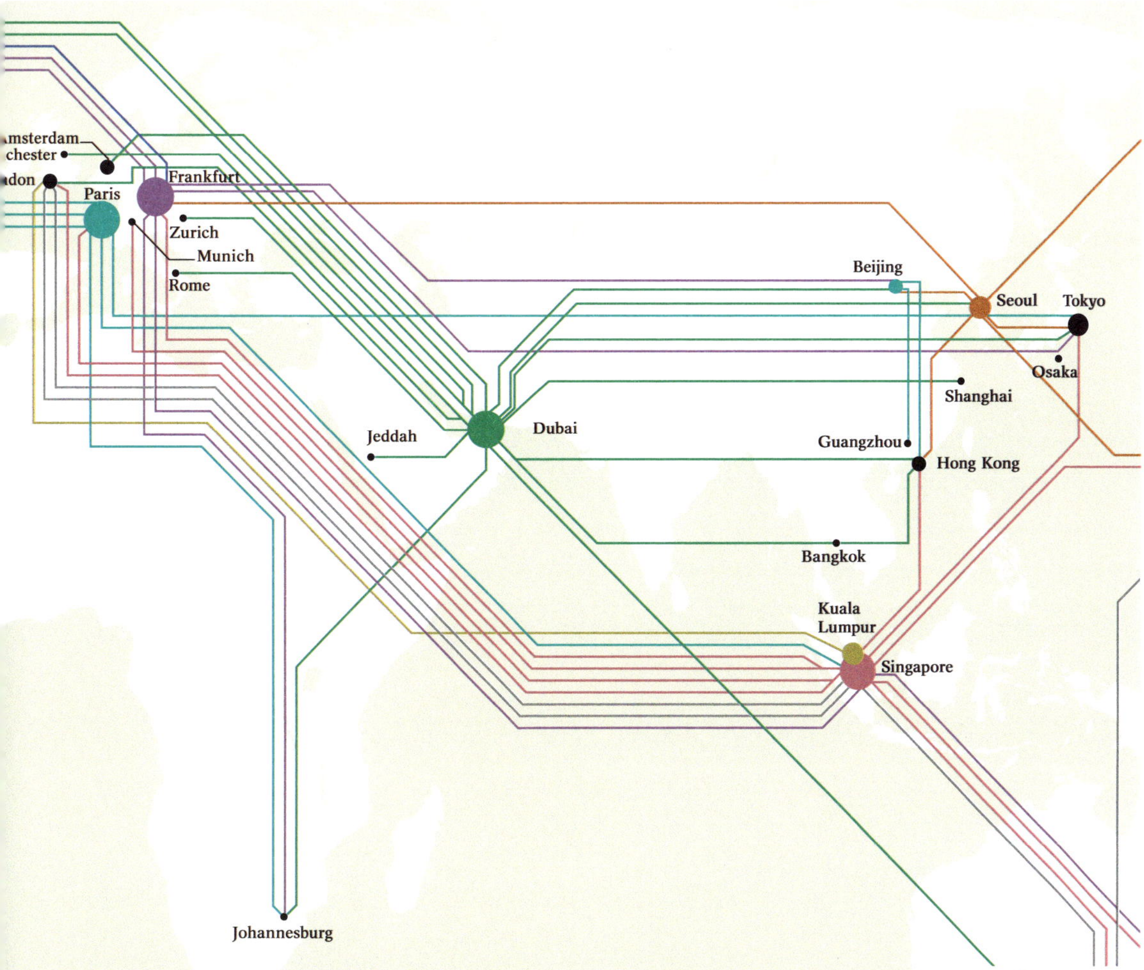

A380 Aircraft Delivered and Ordered

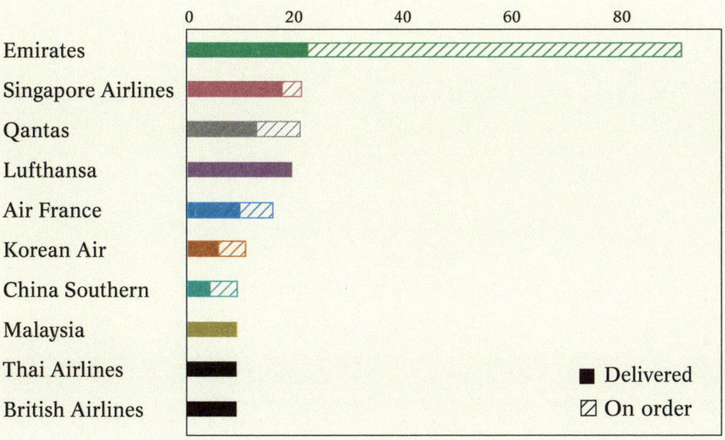

Aircraft Weight or Mass Fractions

Weight or mass fractions [%]	Single aisle		Long range	
Payload		**24**		**18**
Fuel		**18**		**37**
Systems, crew, etc.	18		12	
Power	11	**29**	10	**22**
Structure		**29**		**23**
Total		**100**		**100**

8.2 COMBINE AND SEPARATE

An organization needs clarity and tradition. If an organization is cut up into parts, there is a serious risk of losing cohesion and damaging imperceptible but crucial communication habits. A similar risk occurs when an organization is confronted with a different strategy. Both happened in the Netherlands to the national railways, when a political decision based on naïve neoliberal ideals led to an organizational split-up literally between the train exploiters and the track facilitators, to open up competition between different train companies that within a few years would be allowed to enter the Dutch market.

In Japan the tradition is smarter. Each bullet train company has its own track, also where trains run by different companies stop at the same station. The precision of the services is admirable and can be measured in terms of seconds.

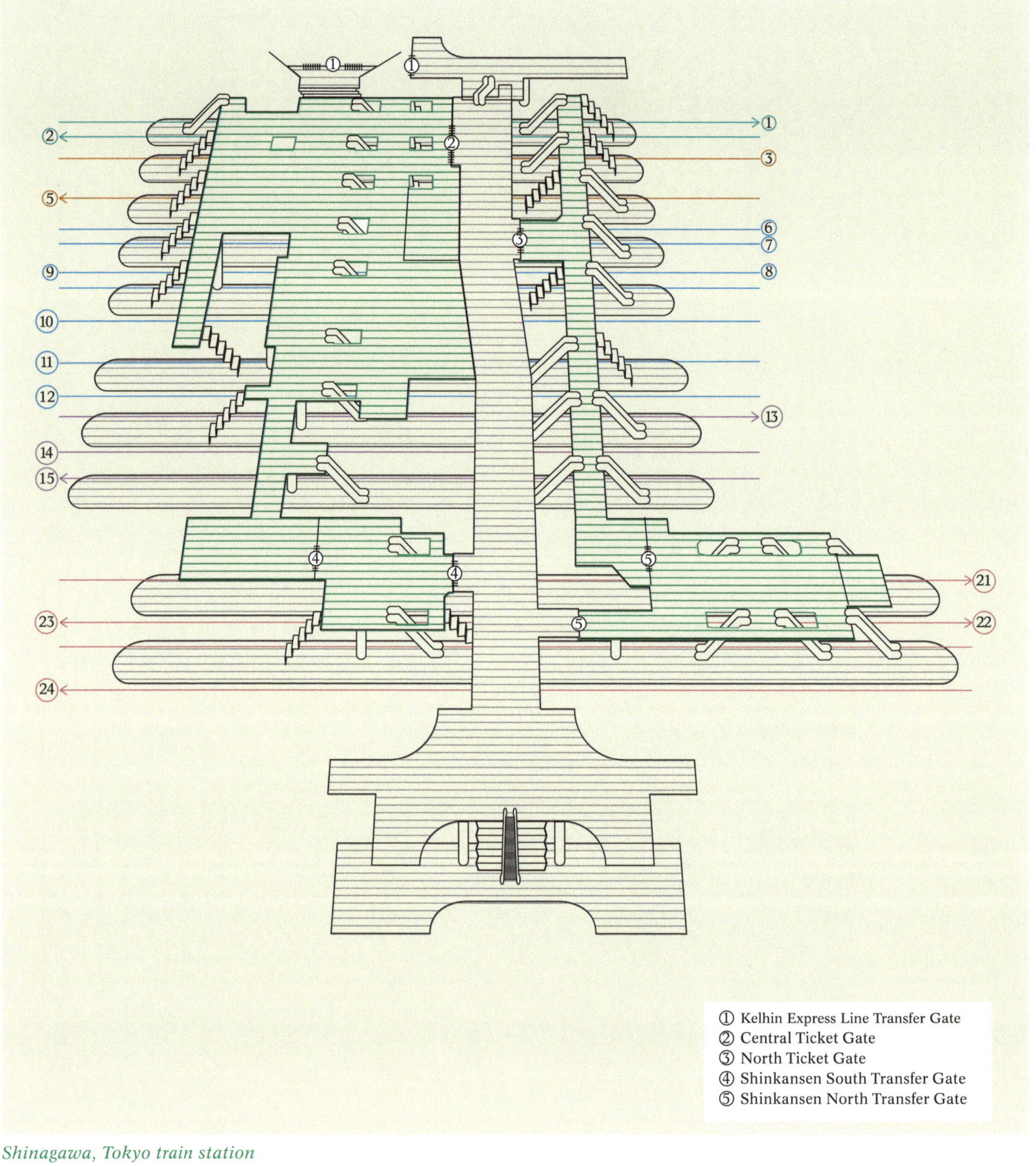

Shinagawa, Tokyo train station

anywhere and one can fly at any time is about as good as it gets.

Nevertheless, access to more or less regular transportation has been unleashed, with the most complex transfer areas, the urban ones, getting jammed with traffic, people, energy and pollution. Governments are struggling to control smog and smooth traffic flows, but they're lagging behind the increase in the number of vehicles, which of course is directly linked to the outdated ideal of quantity related economic growth. Combating traffic jams is a political issue defined by the delusional choice between freedom of speed and a definition of efficient flow. When the Dutch Minister Melanie Schultz was told that the car speed increase from 120 km/h to 130 km/h on motorways she had initiated in 2012 would only save one and a half minutes' travelling time, she replied: 'That's not the point. This is about the driver's perception.' Evidently what drivers feel and think adds up to a demonstrable decrease in safety, clean air and traffic manageability. Traffic jams all over the world are approaching gridlock because of it. In general, car drivers like to believe that the solution is adding more and more road surface. Yet traffic jams occur where there are differences in speed and directions. Moreover, motorways connect city centres, where slowness rules. Many cities in the UK have official Park and Ride zones, where you can leave your car to proceed to the centre by public transport, which works quite well. Combined with this principle it would be possible to decrease the number of exits, because that is where speed differences occur. A similar principle could work for freight, which could be transferred to small electric vans, as these would be less likely to clutter the streets.

Lowering the speed limit is not a bad idea either, because slow moving cars take up less space than hurrying ones.

This principle is hard for many of us to imagine. Of course, all these schemes are in conflict with the way drivers perceive freedom, which is imprinted on their memories by advertisements showing cars with a seductive 'design' solitarily moving around in remote places, such as the Sea of Tranquillity on the Moon.

Believe it or not, small lightweight vehicles have puzzling effects as well. Bicycles in Amsterdam are so prevalent, under the backsides of inexperienced tourists and habitual Amsterdam bike riders alike, that it has become a convenient urban asset as well as a risky one. In other cities cheap bike rental schemes are filling the streets with unused bicycles and electric scooters. In some Chinese cities you may find complete landscapes of unused bikes. For many cities in India on the other hand, riding bicycles in public areas is scarcely a viable option. Traffic during rush hours is so busy that there is not enough space. The idea of bicycle lanes has been suggested, but these would occupy space desperately sought by buses, trucks, cars, rickshaws, motorbikes and mopeds and in some cities, elephants, camels and cows. It looks like the thriving Indian bicycle culture of yesteryear has simply disappeared to make way for smog, noise and wheels. Systems for the transportation of goods are much better tuned to each other. Occasionally something goes wrong, when a tanker spills oil, polluting coasts, or a container ship loses a few, spoiling beaches with toys and sneakers and quickly turning them from products we ordered into junk we need to clear up. Not that the containers ever complain. We scarcely notice when filling stations, shops, markets, supermarkets, building and construction sites, factories and warehouses get their supplies. Trucks may be the one exception. They have a strong presence in traffic, because of the relative size of the container they carry. But put that steel box on a container ship and suddenly it has all but vanished, not least because of its relative size: one large ship can convey some 20,000 containers and the number of these huge carriers, with a capacity of almost 50,000 cars, or a staggering 386 million pairs of shoes, is on the increase.

Slow moving cars take up less space than hurrying ones.

So far, we've discussed journeys that are straightforward and almost uneventful. They describe the trajectory from the starting point to a certain destination. A person travels from A to B and back, or maybe they continue to the next place. Routes for goods are not that clean-cut, once they've reached the target location. Let's take a Pokémon toy as an example. It was produced in the Far East. In most instances thousands of them will find their way to the right place on the right shelf in the right warehouse, or hanging from the right hook in the right shop, or indeed delivered at the right front door. Logistic arrangements are perfect. Even so, they are improving all the time. Delivery speed is a major weapon in online ordering systems. The Emperor of the Logistic Universe has this recurrent dream about customers getting their wishes fulfilled even before they knew they had them. Consumption speed pushes at the limits of the human household system.

Logistics of the leftovers of food, Pokémons, microwaves and whatever other item of consumption should be well designed and executed.

Then there is the other side of consumption, which is what happens afterwards. The transportation system for used Pokémons, and whatever comes in their wake, is supremely primitive compared to delivery systems. It starts with product packaging, which has a complicated array of functions. It protects against damage, tries to hamper petty theft and screams identity and branding: Buy me! The remnants of cardboard and plastic lose all value the minute they are torn away from their contents. Quick and easy turns into quick and dirty. Scraps of material are not going to end up at exactly the right place. Waste has no precision.

The arrangements aren't much better for the toy. Okay, a few of the thousands will

Systems for transportation of goods to their destination are quite well tuned to each other. Logistic arrangements for used goods on the other hand, are supremely primitive.

Bicycle landscape in China

become sought after, because they will have become vintage. Most of the products, however, after all the effort that went into designing, producing and delivering them, will be treated just as clumsily as their packaging, only not so fast.

Waste has no precision.

There is a great challenge in gaining control over the flow of leftovers. Partly it is about continuation of use, something packaging could be designed for, and partly it is a matter of 'reverse logistics'. This term has been in use for some time already, mainly with reference to the return of products with a systemic malfunction. Its meaning can be extended to products returned for refurbishing or recycling, generally when the procedure involves a change of user (not necessarily the owner).

As far as lightness is concerned, the most relevant issue is packaging. The first and most challenging question in any product development story is: do we need it? The second is: can we do with less material and volume? At the next level, products are packed together and we arrive at the quantity per packaging unit, which could be a box, a pallet or a tank. The top level in most cases is the container, which needs to be as full as possible, expressed in the utilization rate that in its turn multiplies to the utilization rate of trucks, trains and ships. The pressure to reduce prices is now so great that utilization needs to be maximized in volume or weight to keep transportation affordable.

This holds true for people as well. For air carriers, every empty chair jeopardizes profitability. Of course, transportation of people also leaves behind a trail of waste, bits of stuff with no particular place to go but into the bin, if they make it that far. People spread waste. In air travel, weight is important and the amount of waste is meticulously recorded. According to a report by the International Air Transport Association (IATA) the total amount in 2017 was 5.7 million tonnes, including toilet waste, but most of it paper, cardboard and plastic. On average a passenger produces 1.4 kilograms of waste per flight. Knowing that a weight reduction of 100 kilograms in just one plane saves approximately 19,000 litres of fuel per annum, it must be worthwhile looking for ways to get rid of what is unnecessary and superfluous.

On average a passenger produces 1.4 kilograms of waste per flight.

And what happened to Mr. Whodunnit? He just about made it to the filling station. Now he has a full tank and an empty bladder. He also ate a bar of chocolate, because he felt he deserved it, and threw the metallic foil wrapper neatly into the bin ■

8.3 MAX PAYLOAD

'Resigned to quantity' paraphrases the expression 'resigned to mediocrity'. There is a general tendency of market developments to surrender to average quality and style. At the same time, current economic assumptions are forcing trade towards mere quantity. The consequence is proverbial: the cheapest is always the dearest in the end.

This is not a matter of conscious choice, but rather of intuitive behaviour. Besides sales tricks like 'TODAY ONLY!', at consumer level sales are pushed by offering more for less, for example 'TWO FOR THE PRICE OF ONE'. This stimulates demand, because of which the manufacturers have to produce more, which they can only do by investing in equipment for mass production, which in turn forces them to push more sales to be able to afford it. And so on. As a result, we make more than we need, leading to both cultural and corporal obesity with a plethora of objects and food.

Something similar is happening in transportation. Mass travel has become so cheap that carriers only make some kind of profit when all seats are occupied. That's why services that used to be included have now turned into extras that one pays for. The price of transportation also forces companies to fill up containers and ships to the max, transporting more cheap freight made in sub-standard conditions for sub-standard wages.

If 100 per cent utilization is the rule, the result is the suffocation and reduction of effectivity. It requires buffering capacity for overflow, which implies wasting goods and rendering travel ever more inconvenient. Responsible economics should not allow this. In all probability there is a balanced optimum utilization rate, in which space can be full, but never crammed.

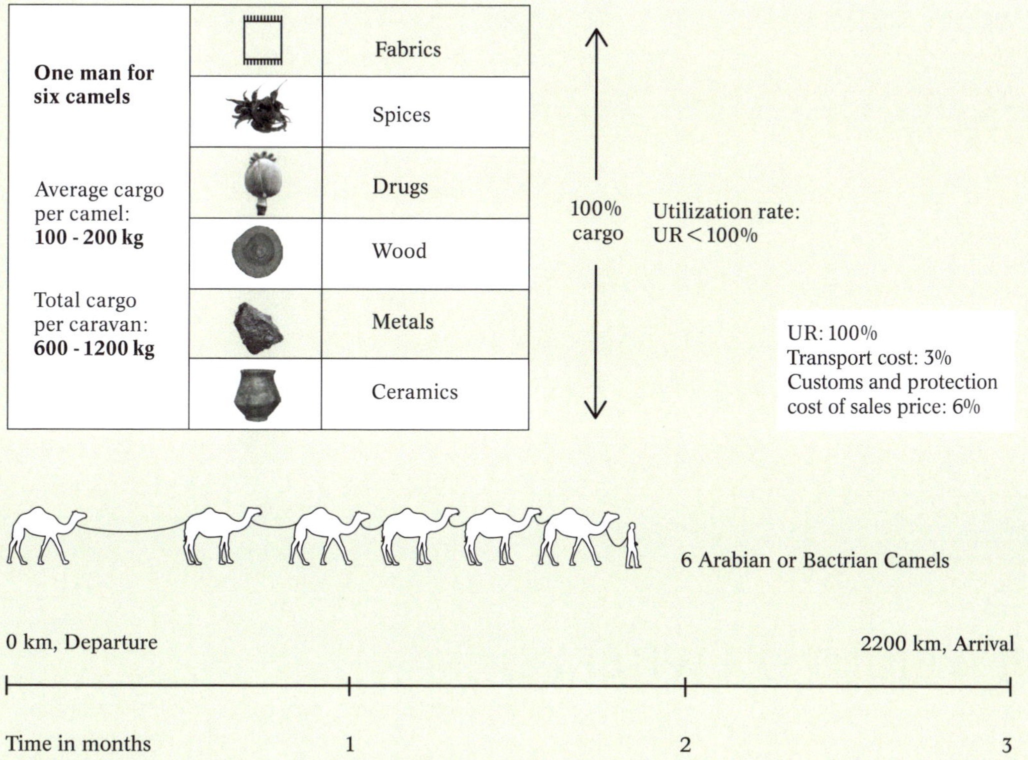

Ships of the Desert
1000 caravanserais subsidized. Giving protection, free storage, food, drinks, entertainment, tax free trade.
After the digging of the Suez Canal the Silk Road was no longer the most efficient land route.

	**Small Barges**	**0.3**
	**Buses**	**2.5**
	**E-Buses**	**3.5**
	**Cars** ●●●	**3.0**
	●●	**12**
	**BMWi3**	**3.5**
	●●	**14**
	**E-Cars**	**6.0**
	●●	**24**
	**Tractor + Trailer**	**2.0**

	**Supersonic Aircraft**	**12.0**
	**High Speed Train**	**10.0**
	**Subsonic Aircraft**	**4.0**
	Ballistic Orbit	**23**
	Global Orbit	**66**
	Lunar Orbit	**500** ●

● System Empty Weight = Structure + Systems + Fuel

● Mainly fuel

●● One occupant only

●●● Standard SUVs, S-CLASS, 8 (25 ●●), specifics almost those of crafts in ballistic orbit

Transport efficiency depends on empty weight per unit load. Cars usually only carry the driver; hence the double bullet

8.4 WEIGHT ON WHEELS

Here we have something that isn't apparent to everyone. A normal car easily weighs twelve times as much as its driver. It mainly conveys itself. If it were intelligent it might even be too smug to care about carrying a little human inside. Humanity owns a gigantic supply of steel and plastic moving back and forth over the roads of the world.

It's not all that complicated to list various kinds of vehicles by the amount of 'empty weight' required to transport 1 kilogram of payload. Let's assume that all vehicles in the list are fully loaded except for cars, which only have a driver. The results are quite revealing. The weight needed to take people into space is doubtful. The rationale behind manned space travel has been superseded by what can be achieved with microtechnology. The list is continually changing due to new developments.

Road Transport 1 & 2 Energy reduction or Production increase	Vehicle Type	Lifetime energy savings per 100kg weight reduction [litres]	Lifetime Performance [million km]	ref. IFEU 2004 [GJ]
	**Cars** **Gasoline** **Diesel**	 **700** **600**	 0.2 0.2	 23 21
	**Trucks** **Articulated 1 & 2**	**718**	1.2 12yr	26
	**Trains** **Subway/Urban** **Intercity** **High-speed**	 **1800** **1050** **1320**	 3.0 8.0 15	 60 35 44
	**Ferries** **High-speed**	 **42,000**	 20	 1400
	**Aircraft** **Short-distance** **Long-distance**	 **450,000** **600,000**	 30 30	 15,000 20,000

1GJ = 30lt Kerosine

1 TankWell/CPT 2014
- 1400 kg lighter, increased lifetime production or energy saving of -11,000 lt fuel

2 Coldfeather 1994
- 2800 kg lighter, increased lifetime production or energy saving of -22,000 lt fuel

$Tare + Net < Gross_{max}$

For aircraft:

$OEW_{ac} + W_{pay\ load+fuel} < MTOW$

Energy consumption per unit load

8.5 LESS WEIGHT IS LESS ENERGY

With a few not unreasonable assumptions and a little effort, it is possible to estimate and compare the amount of energy saved by removing 100 kilograms of weight from different types of vehicles. One glance is enough to understand that mass reduction in aircraft pays, and could be translated into passengers and space inside the cabin. This would actually work if aircraft fuel weren't subsidized. On the face of it, the effect of weight reduction in cars would seem a much more modest affair. However, given the fact that there are almost 1.5 billion cars and that they are too big and too heavy (and that they are driven needlessly fast), the reduction that could be achieved is beyond imagining.

8.6 URINATE BEFORE BOARDING

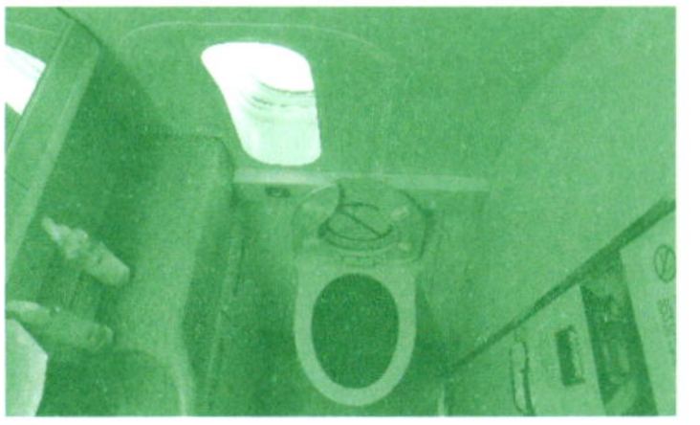

In October 2009, All Nippon Airlines (ANA) tested the idea of asking passengers to go to the bathroom before boarding. It would save an estimated 100 kilograms per flight, reducing the amount of fuel in a year by 19,000 litres, as noted elsewhere in *Designing Lightness.* According to an ANA spokeswoman, CO_2 emissions would be reduced by 4.2 tonnes a month. The test was discontinued. It has become less uncommon though, particularly among price fighters, to charge extra for luggage. In the Pacific region, airlines, beginning with Samoa Air in 2013, have started charging customers according to body weight.

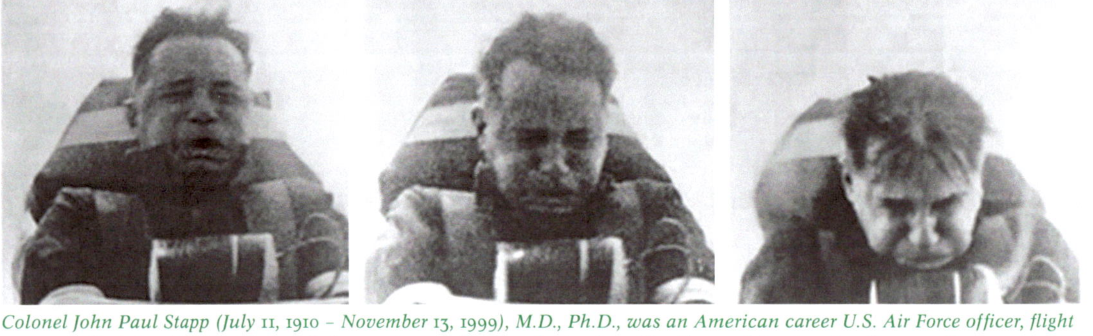

Colonel John Paul Stapp (July 11, 1910 – November 13, 1999), M.D., Ph.D., was an American career U.S. Air Force officer, flight surgeon, physician, biophysicist, and pioneer in studying the effects of acceleration and deceleration forces on humans

8.7 SPEED PERCEPTION

Speed is an imaginary friend. This friend is invisible and nobody talks to it directly, but everybody longs for it when it's away. Even a small amount of it is welcome and it doesn't have to be real, as you would expect of a presence so intangible. But you can see speed too. Movies and many games are about speed. It is even the title of a film. Speed on the other hand cannot be felt. What you feel is speed change, or acceleration. Some love that change and take rollercoaster rides, or they take hyperbolic flights to experience the absence of acceleration.

Speed is good at influencing behaviour. We do silly things like driving fast even though, in the back of our minds, we know it doesn't really make a difference in arrival time. It also makes us take shortcuts to evade traffic jams, despite the risk of the journey taking longer. But at least we're moving.

This principle was set in motion at Houston Airport. To shrink the waiting time (or rather the perception of waiting time) at the baggage reclaim area, they increased the length of the walk passengers had to take to get there by relocating the arrivals entrance. At least they are moving, which disguises the fact that they're really waiting with a twist.

In Plopsaland, a theme park in Belgium, a group video game was installed in 2014 in the waiting space of an attraction. The games were simple, and children could operate them by banging hands-on buttons on the top of wooden fence pickets.

Apparently, it is possible to distract our brains from the aggravation of a lack of movement. It would be interesting to investigate how an illusion of speed can replace the desire for the real energy-devouring thing.

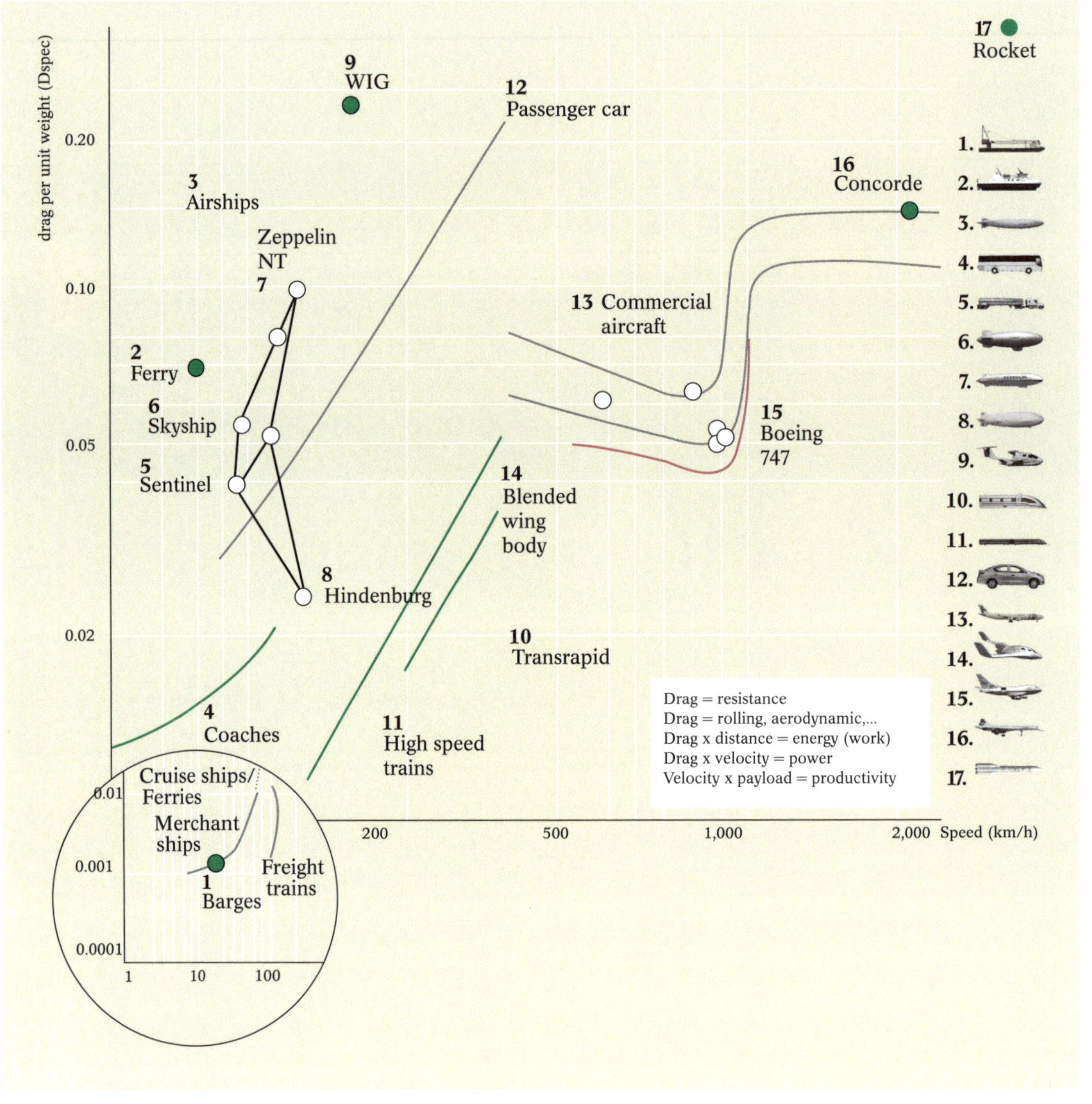

8.8 SPECIFIC DRAG

Drag is what you feel when cycling upwind, pushing a car or pulling a boat. There is resistance from air, wheels and water, depending on the speed. The faster the speed, the greater the effort required. The towing barge used to be an efficient mode of public transportation. It wasn't very fast by today's standards, but one horse could pull many times its own weight, because a boat's *specific drag* is very low at walking speed.

Let's look at the diagram von Kármán and Gabrielli developed in 1950. It shows transportation efficiency as the relationship between speed and specific drag. The former is familiar, specific drag less so. However, it is quite important in two ways. Firstly, it demonstrates the importance of being specific. As a structural property, drag is meaningless without weight, just as weight is meaningless without considering volume. The diagram shows that in almost every case, or transportation system, the drag per unit weight increases with speed. This means that it takes more effort, energy, fuel or emission to keep the system going at an increasing speed. Travel time is valuable. The longer the distance,

Transport systems air, road, rail, maritime	Speed 'range' [km/hr]	Operations 'range'	Price of speed [---] (net+tare)	Productivity by speed of net mass
Aircraft	800	inter-continental		high
Fast ferries	70	regional		medium
Cars if no traffic jams	130	regional	**5kgf to move 100kg**	low
Small airships If no wind	80	continental		low
High speed trains	200	continental		high
Cars, trucks and buses	<100	regional	**2kgf to move 100kg**	medium
Tall airships	80	inter-continental		low
Intercity trains	120	regional	**1kgf to move 100kg**	high
Barges	20			high by net mass
Merchant ships	40	regional	**1kgf to move > 100kg < 1000kg**	
Super tankers	40	continental		
Freight trains	100	inter-continental		

[---]

Tractive force per unit gross weight (net+tare)

Constant force to overcome drag per unit moving weight

the greater the desired speed.

Secondly, the graph is very good for comparing the efficiency of different kinds of transport. Coaches and barges are doing quite well. Commercial jet aircraft have a considerable specific drag that diminishes with speed, the reason being that at cruise speeds they fly higher, where the air is less dense.

The worst case in terms of specific drag is the Russian Ekranoplan or WIG plane. WIG is short for wing-in-ground-effect. When air is caught in between a fast low-flying object and the earth's surface, it gets denser, like a cushion, and provides extra lifting force. Nevertheless, specific drag is very high, even at relatively low speeds. The thing devours energy. Zeppelins reappear with regular intervals as the green solution to flying, with the argument that it requires no energy for them to rise up. Usually it is overlooked that 'up' is not the point. You want to go 'somewhere'. And for that purpose, a zeppelin is inefficient. Drag per unit weight is sky-high, even at a low speed.

Conclusion: lightweight (loaded) vehicles and low speeds save energy.

8.9 QUEUING FOR SPEED

Speed is a desirable quality. As a matter of fact, people are prepared to sacrifice time and relaxation to travel at high velocity, up to the point that waiting becomes highly inconvenient. Looked at this way, speed turns from an effective quality into a possibly hugely entertaining but otherwise pointless and energy-guzzling experience. We might define a simple rule of thumb for the rationale behind high-speed travel: velocity increase thwarts benefit.

There used to be a supersonic passenger airplane called the Concorde. It was developed as a cooperative prestigious project, supported by France and the UK. The development costs were extremely high, exploitation was expensive, and it produced so much noise and pollution that Concordes weren't allowed at all airports. A total of 16 were built and used. Taking off from Paris in 2000, a Concorde crashed, heralding the end of a quarter of a century of supersonic travel.

Commercial flights were mainly limited to Paris and London with connections to New York, Washington and Mexico City. This implied that it saved very little time, if any, if you wanted to fly from, say, Madrid in Spain to Lima in Peru, which brings us back to our paradox. High-speed connections tend to be exclusive and unfeasible due to high initial investments. What you end up with is the conspicuously rich and famous being subsidized to travel fast.

New ultrafast paradox airplanes are still being developed and may follow a similar path. The same is true of the Hyperloop. Affordable high-speed travel is a lovely promise, but feasibility depends on mass transportation, which is far more complicated than a pod on a 5 km test track. Freight transportation has its own utopias. There's an idea floating around of a 2.5-kilometre-long zeppelin for transporting non-liquefied hydrogen and goods, blown forth around the globe by the meteorological jet stream. Here we have the same exclusiveness: freight needing to be transported to a transfer area. Question: if the jet stream drives this giant, then why does it need to be shaped like a zeppelin?

8.10 SO MANY CONTAINERS

It would not be entirely true to fact, but you could argue that the shipping container has led to the invention of globalization. It all began with US entrepreneur Malcolm McLean. In the mid 1930s he started a truck company, which grew and prospered. He was bothered by two things: 1) he'd noticed how long it took to load and unload ships and 2) it was expensive to own a truck company after weight restrictions and levying fees on trucks were introduced.

McLean didn't take this lightly. He had already been thinking about standard sized units for transportation on trucks and ships very early on. He considered shipping as transportation between harbours, where trucks would take over the freight for shorter distances without having to cross state borders and paying fees.

And this is exactly what he did in 1955. Together with engineer Keith Tantlinger he designed and patented the predecessor of what is today's familiar shipping container. It all developed very quickly after that, because McLean could offer very low rates, compared to what clients were accustomed to, for transporting various kinds of goods in steel boxes. The final push for containers happened during the Vietnam War, when standard lengths of 20 ft and 40 ft were agreed upon. The industry standard for cargo volume now is the TEU or Twenty-foot Equivalent Unit. The amount of labour involved in freight transport has been drastically cut back and costs have decreased to far below the established 6 per cent share per product. The 'disruptive' change only took a little over ten years.

These days most containers are made in China. Currently the standard new container price amounts to $3,000. Liquid containers are about $36,000. New ones are exported complete with contents. How long they last mainly depends on the effects of rough ocean life. Lease companies write them off in 10-12 years. But they can last 30 years for lighter tasks. When turned into dwellings – specialized companies do this – they may even last 50 years. The system is quite robust. The steel they are made from is forgiving. The next step may be light foldable or product dedicated composite containers (cooled or heated, e.g. CPT/Tankwell containers). Replacing quantity of things with quality of life might reduce the total mass of freight.

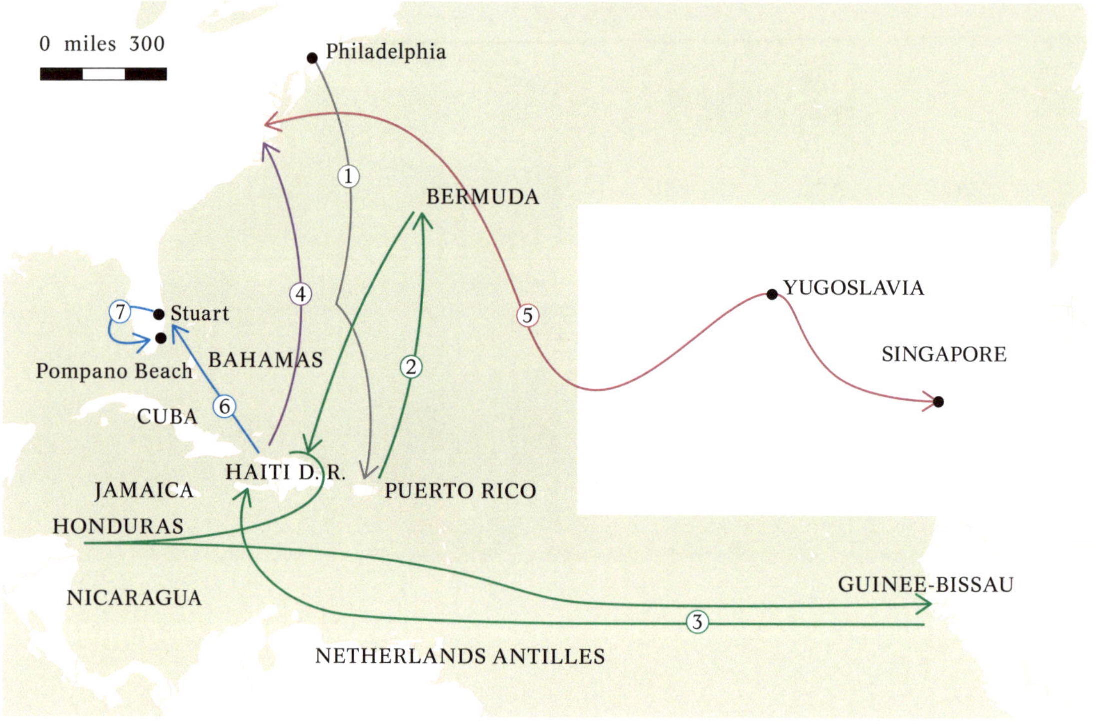

8.11 A WASTE ODYSSEY

The next travelogue took place in the 1980s. At that time, it heralded an important contemporary issue and now it illustrates the urgency of long-term planning of material projects. The story is simple and tragic:

1984 Philadelphia could no longer get rid of its trash. Landfills in neighbouring states refused to accept the ash from its two incinerators. The city decided to load its ash on board the cargo ship *Khian Sea*, nearly 14,000 tonnes of it.

1986 The ship left for the Bahamas to dump the ash there but wasn't allowed in. It then tried Bermuda, Puerto Rico, the Dominican Republic and the Netherlands Antilles, all to no avail.

1987 The *Khian Sea* dumped close to 4,000 tonnes on the coast of Haiti, claiming it was fertilizer. Then, changing its name several times, it moved on to Cape Verde, Guinea-Bissau and Senegal: no permission. And on it went, to Borneo, Indonesia, the Philippines, Sri Lanka: nothing. Sometimes the ship was chased away at gunpoint.

1988 The remaining ash was secretly dumped in the sea.

1993 Two executives of the *Khian Sea's* shipping company were sent to prison.

1996 The US Government ordered that the ash dumped in Haiti had to be picked up.

2000 The barge *Santa Lucia* collected it and brought it to Florida, where nobody wanted it.

2002 The ash was tested to be non-hazardous. A train brought it to a landfill in Franklin County, a couple of miles from the place it had left 16 years earlier.

Since then, Philadelphia has found new landfills, despite the lack of space. Disposal costs doubled between 2000 and 2014. Recently China stopped accepting waste and costs have soared, burning currently being more feasible than recycling. This leaves the question of which is preferable. Burning waste produces energy and emissions; recycling waste produces low value raw material and uses energy that needs to be generated. Garbage tends to outstay its welcome.

8.12 NO PACKAGING

Lightness shines at its brightest when there is no product, simply nothing and maybe even slightly less than nothing. The weight of food, and of spices in particular, is reduced by a simple preservation method called drying. Eosta, the international Dutch producer of organic fruits and vegetables, achieved a reduction to zero packaging and got awarded for it in 2018.

There is a rule in Europe that states that organic vegetables in supermarkets need to be easily distinguishable from the common kind. Traders achieve this by packaging organic vegetables in plastic, which is cheaper than wrapping the common ones, because 'organic' is a smaller market. This is silly, particularly since consumers of organic food detest the idea of plastic packaging. Eosta came up with the laser tattoo: information is printed directly onto the peel with a laser that removes pigment with no damage done. And no plastic required. It doesn't work for all kinds of vegetable foods yet, but it introduces a system change that could apply to almost anything.

8.13 MEDICINE BY DRONE

Drones can be inexpensive precision weapons, but they can also help save lives. In Rwanda and Ghana, efficient fixed wing drone services have started to deliver life-saving medicine to remote areas, which is much quicker and cheaper than relying on the development of road infrastructure and improving the ambulance network. Drones developed by the Californian robot company Zipline can each carry 1.8 kilograms of load. The system works with a small number of hubs, each of which hosts about 30 drones. There are 600 flights per day in Ghana alone. The flying delivery service parachutes its load above the destination, one of several thousand health centres. Millions of people now have better access to medicine.

Rotary wing drones are such popular toys in affluent countries that young entrepreneurs like to buy one first and later on decide what kind of service they'll be offering: inspection, insect control in greenhouses, etc. Buy first, invent a problem later.

9.
THE MOTIVE OF INVENTION

9.1 THE LIMPING PHARAOH
9.2 WHAT IS INNOVATION ANYWAY?
9.3 BUILD WHAT YOU CAN
9.4 ANTENNA ARCHITECTURE
9.5 FROM THE KEEL UPWARDS
9.6 THEN AND NOW
9.7 TURN DOWN THE HEAT

A long time ago in Egypt it may have begun like this: they had built a chariot for the pharaoh. It had wooden wheels that all fell apart after a few rides. Then there was this butcher from Memphis (not Tennessee) who was accustomed to selling sinew to the army's archers to make their strings. He suggested that perhaps this strong material could be wound around the wheels. He said: 'You first have to soak it in water, for it will shrink when it dries and then pull the parts of the wheel together.' The butcher, some warriors and the chariot maker experimented, and it worked! They could even remove some of the wood to save weight and make life easier for the horses.

Much later, at the beginning of the twentieth century, the Belgian chemist Leo Hendrik Baekeland developed a material from the chemical reaction between resorcinol and formaldehyde, together with a way to suppress foaming with the help of fillers and pressure. This became Bakelite, heralding the beginning of large-scale polymer product manufacturing and opening up the potential of fibre-reinforced polymers. Fillers such as wood flour were used from early on.

The principle of reinforcing materials with fibrous ingredients was already known and had been for thousands of years, maybe even before the ancient Egyptians. Glass fibres were known as well, but it took the accidental discovery, by the inventor Games Slayter, that these could be produced by blowing a jet of air into a stream of molten glass, a method he patented in 1933. This became glass wool, an excellent insulator. The next step was to use it as a reinforcement for polymers. DuPont developed the first resin that could be combined with glass wool. Then Cyanamid developed a resin (a forerunner of our polyester resins) that could replace the gas in the wool to form a strong material.

Bakelite radio

9.1 THE LIMPING PHARAOH

You may remember the chariot with the laminated composite wheels that was found in Tutankhamun's tomb. Well, he probably never drove it across a battlefield or even just took it for a spin. It is now known that King Tut was a very sick man. He had malaria and a bone disorder, which may have been caused by his parents being brother and sister. And he had a limp. In his tomb they also found 130 sticks and staves, which could mean that he was believed to need them for convenience in the afterlife. However, other pharaohs also had these items in their tombs. They found 250 of them in the tomb of Djehutynakht at Deir el-Bersha. Most pharaohs were depicted with them as regalia. Some of them may have been gifts from other kings. There may have been more disabled pharaohs. Some things we will never know for sure.

9.2 WHAT IS INNOVATION ANYWAY?

Not long ago the name Kardashian popped up. This happens to be Armenian for stone carver. Coincidentally, archaeologists found a piece of rock in Armenia with a carving on it showing a schematic drawing of an oxcart. Look at the picture and compare it with a modern trailer. You'll notice that there is very little difference. Steel beams, axles and rubber-tyred steel rims have taken the place of wooden parts and oxen have evolved into an engine, but the principle is exactly the same. The first oxcart was innovative. Everything that changed after that was merely optimizing the principle.

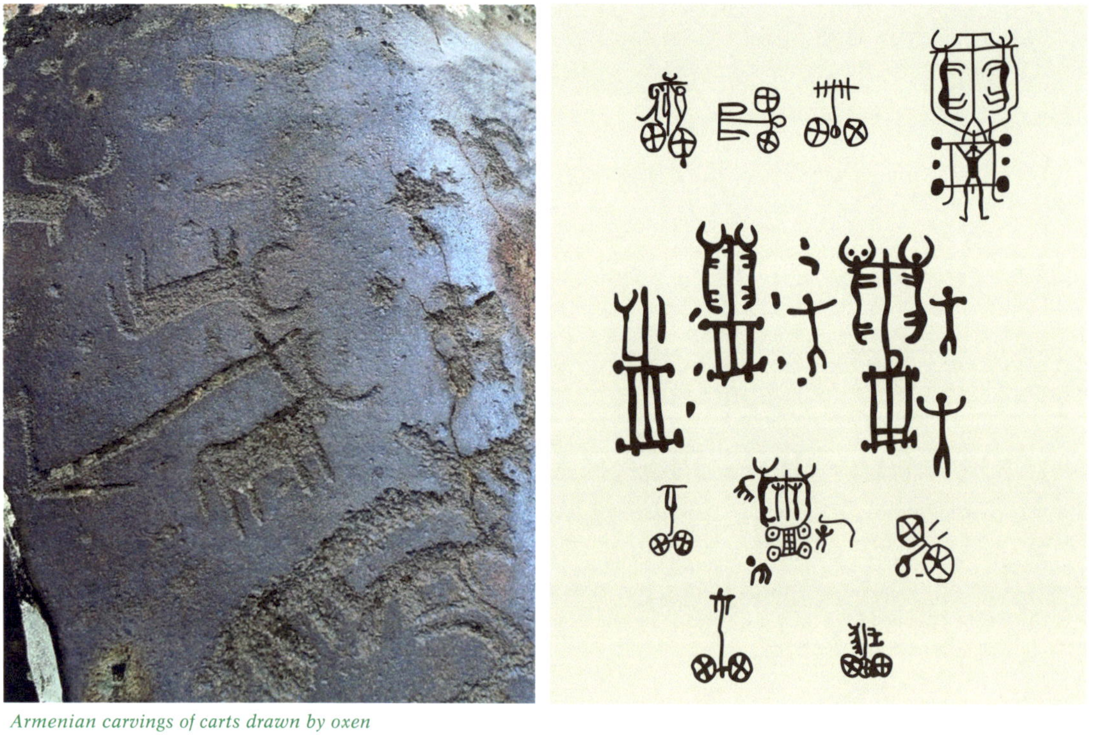

Armenian carvings of carts drawn by oxen

This was somewhat erroneously called 'fibreglass', because of the unnamed combination with a synthetic resin.

In a state of woolliness, glass fibres are not ideal for doing what glass is extremely good at, which is taking up tension forces. For true reinforcement you need it in the form of long fibres and strands that allow for correct alignment within a resin matrix. The process of extruding glass was introduced in 1938 by the then newly combined Owens Corning. Extrusion means that heated glass is pressed through a mould with tiny holes in it.

> *From very early on the development of tooling, transport and dwelling coincided with a change in mentality and the desire for a good life.*

Phenolic resin reinforced with glass fibres is the progenitor of the range of 'composites' existing today. Similar to the word 'fibreglass' being a household name for a particular combination of glass and resin, 'composites' are considered materials that consist of fibres and polymers, a restriction of the original meaning of composite, namely a structure of two or more materials with synergistically cooperating properties. In most cases these properties are stiffness and strength per unit weight. They were originally called composites to suggest they were different from plastics, which because of unpredictable failure in those days had a dubious reputation. They still do, but now for different reasons.

Fibre reinforced polymers owe their quality to the designed combination of strong fibres that deal with tension and polymers that handle pressure. This is exactly the radical split that characterizes tensegrity structures. In composites the components that take care of opposing-force business are very close together, in what seems to be a single material. This makes it hard to recognize as a tensegrity structure, at least for those who know this from the works of Buckminster Fuller. After all, he came up with the term as a contraction of tension and integrity.

The manufacture of precise structures like these from materials especially made for this purpose, marks the transition from crudely mixing materials, making components and connecting them, to going one step further and designing and making the structures at the scale of material composition. This is the episode round about 1940, as depicted in Ashby's 'materials in time' diagram, when the use of metals reached its peak and synthetic plastics and composites began their march, thanks to a growing understanding of the interaction between materials, processes, rules and demands for application.

It's not that difficult to speculate about what happened when humans started to make their mark. From very early on – think Kardashian times – the development of tooling, transport and dwelling coincided with a change in mentality and the desire for a good life, but nobody knew what that would imply. They didn't aim for little glass talking devices with moving pictures, clocks, a sense of direction and telepathy, or for large boxes with wheels and windows that could move all by themselves. It must have been a straightforward process of intuitive trial and error, all the time looking for meaning and convenience: can this rock do the job? Or would that lump of wood be better? Would that bone fit through my nose? Their ideas emerged from a combination of pragmatism and prestige. Is there a river to cross? Find something that stays afloat and hold onto it.

The next early step is that two things can be combined to produce one even better thing. It must have been the awareness that a straight piece of wood could become a very fierce weapon if only its point were a sharp stone that set someone to start experimenting with straw and tendons and sticky stuff to connect the two. Learning to work stone must have been part of that exploration: sharpening it, drilling holes in it. There must have been a gradual wave of realizations that resulted in many different tools, depending on the circumstances for using them. You won't hollow out a tree to make a canoe if there's no forest. Nobody bothers to invent a wheel if there's no flat surface for carts to ride on. Mayan children did have toys with tiny wheels, but adult Mayans had no use for carts.

Humans are not unique in working together.

Cooperation is rooted in those times. Humans are not unique in working together. Think of fire ants, or killer whales catching a prey. An even distribution of tasks can be found in other animals. Still, humans are the only species where individuals can learn very specific tasks and consequently produce complicated things together. One individual has learned to handle wood and another can work goatskin. The emergence of social rituals is even more characteristic. Cats and horses have habits. Humans develop group habits with a speculative rationale behind them.

Even then pragmatism comes first. The construction of mighty pyramids was a consequence of the kind of stone the Egyptians could quarry and work in that region. For religious reasons they had to build high, but all they had was limestone, consisting of sediments of dead chalky organisms. It wasn't very strong so they could only make large blocks and stack them up to build huge geometrical hills, providing very little space inside.

It must have been one big party when humans discovered the power and potential of fire. It certainly had far-reaching consequences. Humans consume energy to rigorously render themselves omnipotent and omnipresent. This mastery of the art of unleashing energy by controlling fire and then transmitting it to future generations signalled the beginning of acquiring knowledge about physics, of understanding heat, melting and pressure. Chemistry became a field of interest too, with the discovery of the ritual of mixing and

Building a pyre is ritual cooperation and fun

The secret of fire is the most dangerous discovery humans ever made

experimenting. Probably the most important fire-dependent inventions were grilling and cooking. Inedible things became digestible, nourishing and tasty. In relation to the later discovery of agriculture, it even laid the foundation for a degree of health degradation and obesity from not moving around enough and consuming too many carbs. Humans gained weight.

> *It must have been one big party when humans discovered the power and potential of fire.*

Fire also proved an important means for changing the properties of materials. Loam and clay could be turned into a stone-like substance. 'Terra cotta' (fired earth) could be shaped by hand into pots, building up a worm of clay in a spiral, not unlike what a 3D printer can do now but less accurate. Of course, stone and flint were familiar before firing was discovered, and people found ways to work them from very early on. Sometimes these were combined with straw or other dried grass stems as wattle and daub when constructing walls to make them less prone to cracking.

Fire is indispensable for freeing metals from ore. Copper and tin were the easiest to find, because of which casting bronze became the first metal-making recipe. Mining iron was more difficult but iron proved to offer many more methods for influencing properties. Through forging it could be made harder and more ductile. The art of working steel became very advanced and provided many a brave knight with a beautiful steel harness adorned with patterns in silver and gold. Those last-named metals are as ancient a discovery as copper but were mainly used for their beauty and enduring value. They weren't suitable for mechanical tools, silver being particularly vulnerable.

The taming of energy to exert force through engines marked the beginning of mechanically driven transportation and mass production in the eighteenth century. It also launched the vision of an economy defined by machines and tough labour-driven mass production, with an emphasis on affordability that was believed to lead to convenience and maybe even paradise. It became a dream that was never supposed to be fulfilled, because humans have no limiter on satisfaction. We have a continuous urge to find ever more convenient and sophisticated alternatives. There is always room for improvement, stimulating us to push on with designing and inventing. 'Designing Lightness' is part of that story.

Steam engines needed mechanisms to drive wheels, cogwheels and belts. Machines needed to know what to do next. As early as 1801, Jacquard invented a loom with punch card control that was destroyed by weavers who saw it as a threat to their livelihood. But this didn't stop its progress, illustrating the classic paradox of convenient production at the cost of social well-being. The era around 1900 saw a peak in mechanical inventiveness, influencing the production speed and consumption of entirely new products. Many

9.3 BUILD WHAT YOU CAN

'Store radioactive waste in very deep salt mines, seal them and you're home free for at least 10,000 years, provided no mistakes are made.' Geologists have a very practical long-term view. Geologist Iain Stewart made a series of BBC documentaries about the influence of earth structures and formation on human activities entitled *Journeys from the Centre of the Earth*. One episode was about architecture.

After an explanation of the principle behind building pyramids, he continues with the desire to build taller and more open structures. In Karnak, the Egyptians built a very tall temple consisting of columns with a roof on top. They had to resort to sandstone, which is somewhat more compact than limestone. It is also a layered material, so it is not equally useful in all directions. The word for this is 'anisotropic'. Sandstone is in fact a laminate, which implies that buckling will easily destroy columns when the layers are used in the direction of gravity, perpendicular to the ground surface. You can reach a much greater height when you stack layered stones horizontally, but the columns you construct have to be very bulky or they would simply collapse.

The stones they used to make roof supports on top of the columns couldn't be too long or they would break because of bending. So all those thick pillars stood close together, which according to Stewart makes the temple look a little bit like a storeroom for columns.

The Greeks had to resort to marble, which began life as sandstone before it was crushed, mixed and heated over millions of years in the midst of a collision between the European and African continental plates. The stone became a very strong mix. Since marble is so much stronger than sandstone, columns can be placed further apart, providing a much more open space inside, as in the Parthenon in Athens. So in the beginning, it was the quality of the stone that defined the architectural grids.

9.4 ANTENNA ARCHITECTURE

Style lags behind technology. Long range radio used to require large devices with huge antennas, so much so that an entire architecture of radio telecommunication made its appearance. In 1922, a Russian architect designed a remarkable constructivist tower, a stack of hyperboloid steel trusses, in the centre of Moscow. The Netherlands gained a more down-to-earth version, albeit in Art Deco style, in an expanse of national parkland. This former radio transmitter for communicating with what was then the Dutch East Indies is surrounded by service buildings and staff housing in what is now the new village of Kootwijk. A special railway line was built for supplying the building materials. These days anyone can contact anyone anywhere. Earthbound antennas have virtually disappeared.

Left: Moscow Tower. Right: Kootwijk communication centre

of the things we use today are rooted in those years. One of the best new products ever was the bicycle, a machine that had the human rider for an engine. Telecommunication made its debut too, as an important part of the human desire to be omnipresent. Early radios were bulky boxes with incomprehensible lamps, switches and strange rotating knobs. They required many metres of antennas. Transmitters were huge as well and led to monumental telecommunication architecture. With hindsight, radio yearned for miniaturization, which is always an obvious target for optimization. At the end of the day technology is supposed to deliver the magic, invisibly.

The taming of energy to exert force through engines marked the beginning of mechanically driven transportation and mass production in the eighteenth century.

Of course, the development of new materials was part of the process that became known as the Industrial Revolution. Most people are inclined to think that plastics didn't exist before Baekeland created his compound. They did, but they were not man-made. For this it is important to know that there are two families of plastics, the *thermosets* and the *thermoplastics*. Thermosets are resins resulting from a chemical reaction. They are relatively brittle and cannot melt, because the large molecules they consist of are chemically bonded. Thermoplastic materials on the other hand consist of very long molecules that have some freedom of movement. They become soft when heat is applied. Horn is such a material and so is tortoiseshell. They have been heated, reshaped and imprinted with symbols for centuries. Bakelite was a first in the sense that a material of this kind had never been formed spontaneously.

The very first man-made thermoplastic originated from an early environmental issue. In 1863, elephants became endangered and could no longer provide enough ivory for billiard balls, since the number of people playing pool and snooker was on the increase. This called for an alternative to ivory, for which a New York manufacturer offered a reward of $10,000. The outcome was celluloid, whose production was dangerous in the beginning, based as it is on highly flammable cellulose-nitrate, which is also used to make fuses. Nevertheless, success was inevitable, because it was ideal for making film – you know, the original carrier of the moving images you watch in cinemas.

The miraculous changes in the first half of the twentieth century in Western culture were nothing short of addictive. The drive for new solutions received an additional boost during the Second World War. There was always a rush because of the prevailing arms race, one of the requirements being convenience, particularly in production, because speed was required to replace and improve weapons. Some of the projects of those years are extraordinary. For example, the Americans produced steel Liberty ships for freight transportation at 17 wharves with uncanny speed. The builder was Henry J. Kaiser. On average they produced one every 42 days, but a record was set at 4 days 15 ½ hours! There were 2,751 ships in all, the largest number ever produced from one design. These figures recall the production of galley ships in the Venetian Arsenal between the twelfth and fifteenth centuries. The English produced efficient fighter airplanes, but also invented a machine to crack the German Enigma code (think Alan Turing) and a more refined electronic installation, Max Newman's Colossus, which enabled the Allied Forces to deceive the Germans into thinking that an invasion was due in Calais. The German company of Blohm & Voss, on the other hand, experimented with extraordinary fighter aircraft configurations. And of course there were the Horten brothers, Reimar and Walter. They dreamt of developing a tailless flying wing airplane and already before the Second World War they had developed a range of glider prototypes. They experimented with combinations of resins, paper and fabrics. The early twin engine driven Horten HV was remarkable because its outer skin was made of a resin called Trolitax, a forerunner of epoxy produced by Dynamit Nobel AG, combined with layers of cotton textile. The structure proved too brittle, however, so the brothers returned to conventional structures of steel pipe and wood. During the war, the Horten design was developed into a fast and efficient jet bomber to meet the challenge set by Hermann Göring: 1000 km reach, 1000 km/h speed and 1000 kilograms of bombs on board. Their glued wooden Horten H229 – wood by that time was unconventional for bombers – came very close. The prototype crashed after two test flights. Luckily the war ended too soon for it to be developed further and have an effect on the outcome. Horten has survived as a brand. The new company recently developed the full composite Horten HX-2 blended wing two-seater. Getting rid of the separate fuselage is in line with the story of simplification behind technological development. Ask the ancient Egyptians ■

9.5 FROM THE KEEL UPWARDS

Evolution of technology may involve a partial return to earlier principles. The classic Inuit kayak is made of sealskin stretched over a bone frame. Seals and whales were all the Inuit had. The skin is prestressed through drying and the structure is an integrated whole. The inside cannot be accessed once the body is complete. A 'modern' ship made from wood, steel or aluminium is built from the inside out. First the keel is laid and the frame and girders are built. Next the outside of the hull is clad with planks or plates that have to be bent. In the case of wood, tar is used as a sealant, whereas metals are welded. A modern vacuum injected resin yacht is built from the outside in. The hull's skin is produced first and then the frames are mounted inside it. Wooden ships built in previous centuries used the same principle: hull first, reinforcements later.

9.6 THEN AND NOW

When we compare the way we looked at the things we purchased and used when they first appeared with the way we look at them now, we are learning about ourselves. It shows us what it is we're after. Paradise is unfolding. Developments in technology serve to make an awareness of that technology disappear. All we are left with are magic tricks that we can now see through, as an inspiration for new and improved magic.

9.7 TURN DOWN THE HEAT

You only have to glance at your smartphone to understand that lightness and composites are not just about forces. It weighs almost nothing, can do virtually anything and would be considered a 'miracle stone' as recently as one lifetime ago. Something similar has happened to heat regulation. In Yemen the ancient city of Shibam was rebuilt in the sixteenth century. Its ten-storey buildings consist of loam covered with plaster. As structures they are vulnerable, but the walls are very good at levelling off temperature differences inside by absorbing moisture during the night and allowing it to evaporate during the day. Passive air conditioning is a surprisingly modern built-in feature of these small skyscrapers.

The idea of passive interior climate control finds expression in different ways, such as the wind tower, which catches the warm wind, guides the air over a water basin and consequently lets it 'drop down' into the living spaces below.

These days we have a better understanding of what is actually happening, which has led to the development of 'nano-encapsulated phase change materials'. Don't look away; it isn't complicated. Ice turning into water is a phase change and so is water turning into ice. The former process absorbs energy and the latter releases it. Water is a phase change material, a PCM, and not a bad one either.

Now one of the best PCMs in the room temperature range is paraffin. It can absorb far more energy per unit weight and volume than stone or concrete and it is transparent. The only disadvantage of using such a substance to control the climate in a building is that it is either liquid or solid (paraffin wax), but still has to be accessible to energy at all times and from all sides without moving around. As it happens, tiny globules of paraffin can be encapsulated inside a translucent polymer skin and turned into a so-called 'nanocomposite'. These tiny heat catchers are packed together and locked inside glazing that has been designed so that it reflects the midday sun, whereas low incoming light will melt the paraffin wax and absorb the heat, for it to be emitted again when it turns dark.

10. COMPOSITES IN THE MAKING

Do you remember Henry J. Kaiser? From the previous chapter? As the builder of Liberty ships? Well, he also worked with celebrity billionaire Howard Hughes, played by Leonardo DiCaprio in *The Aviator,* to develop a giant seaplane for use during the war, to transport 750 fully equipped troops or two Sherman tanks. Ships and planes were the avant-garde of technological development. There was a catch: Hughes was not allowed to use aluminium, as this was needed for ongoing airplane production. Despite the fact that construction was too late, Hughes went ahead and in 1947 finished building the H-4 Hercules, a giant eight-engine plane with, until recently, the largest wingspan ever: 97.5 metres.

The structure was built using the 'Duramold' process: birch plies, impregnated with phenolic resin (similar to the compound that translates into Bakelite), were laminated in a mould heated to 138 degrees Celsius. Hughes's wooden plane was mocked with the nickname 'Spruce Goose', a name Hughes disliked intensely. Wood, unjustifiably considered outdated in relation to progress, is simply lighter than aluminium and stronger when combined with a resin. This material couple is definitely a composite. Duramold had been used to produce radomes, aerodynamically smooth covers that protect nose radar without blocking the waves.

The German Schnellbomber Dornier Do 217 had a rather primitive radar antenna on its nose, which caused additional drag. It was the Mosquito's slower rival. As it happened, in that same era aviation manufacturer de Havilland, mentioned earlier as builder of the ill-fated Comet passenger carrier, also built a much smaller wood and resin airplane. The Mosquito was one

The wooden De Havilland Mosquito combat aircraft

The Mosquito by de Havilland was a successful bomber. It was made of wood and its radar antenna was covered to reduce drag.

of the most successful combat aircraft ever, although some looked down on it because of the wood. Now, it is not certain if the following historical detail has any significant bearing, but the man who started the airplane building company was Geoffrey de Havilland and his cousin is the Tokyo-born American movie star Olivia de Havilland, known from *Gone with the Wind*, among many other movies. She dated Howard Hughes for a while.

And then there was Norman de Bruyne, born of a Dutch father and an English mother in Puente Arenas, southern Chile (just for an added touch of globalism). He was educated as a physicist and became one of the key figures at the cradle of today's composite expansion, in particular because he grew to be an expert on glues.

He founded Aero Research Ltd and together with de Havilland developed an adhesive, the first synthetic glue, for use with wood structures consisting in part of balsa, a very light, soft and vulnerable wood. Balsa comes from a fast-growing deciduous tree and is therefore considered a hardwood, despite is softness. As part of a structure it can act as a kind of foam. Veneer, balsa and adhesive determined the Mosquito's structural design.

The next step was to develop another glue to bond balsa wood with metal. It was given the name REDUX, a contraction of REsearch at DUXford, these days the brand name for a range of polymer-based adhesives.

Gordon Aerolite marked the following new step in airplane construction. Gordon was the surname of Malcolm, one of de Bruyne's students. His family was into linen in Belfast and the new laminate consisted of flax roving and paper soaked in phenolic resin. Flax fibres were, in fact, second choice. De Bruyne had approached an American manufacturer of glass fibres, to be woven into a new kind of silk and combined with the phenolic adhesive. They refused to combine their material with moulded plastics, however, because they had no faith in the outcome: a historically missed opportunity, since glass fibre reinforced polymers, formerly branded as 'Fiberglass', are now all over the place, in anything from sports equipment to outdoor toys and bridges.

The new laminate was not a material in itself but rather a bonding component. Glue could now be a thin flexible sheet rather than just sticky stuff in a jar. Working with glue film, which could be cut to size and consequently heated as layers between the parts to be attached to each other, was much more convenient than handling messy goo with a brush. The production of plywood with adhesive lamination became highly successful.

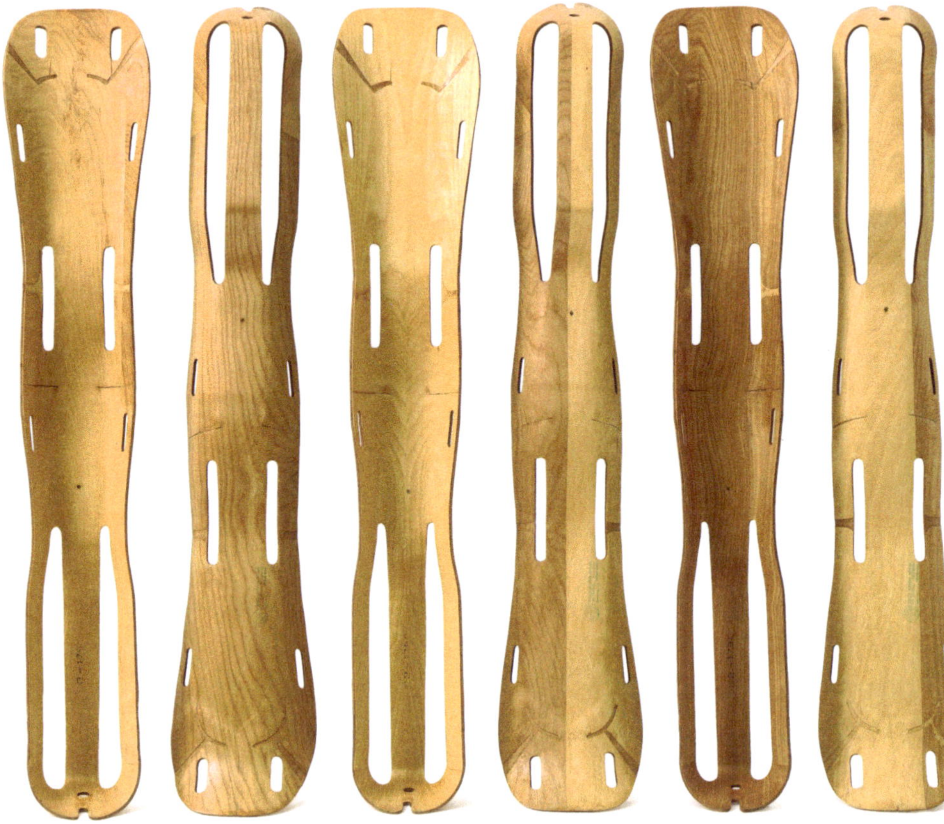

Eames human leg splints

10.1 THE EAMESES' KAZAM! PROCESS

Charles and Ray Eames together belong among the all-time top designers. Many of their furniture designs, such as the famous lounge chair from 1956, are still being produced and sold more than 60 years on. They began by experimenting with moulded wood in their 'Kazam! machine'. Layers of wood and glue draped in a plaster mould with a wooden support were put under pressure with a membrane that the designers inflated with a bicycle pump. The mould was heated from the inside to shape the plywood and make it stick and Kazam! Out came their first seat.

The first products they made along very similar lines were plywood leg splints and litters in the early 1940s for the US Armed Forces in the field. The metal ones hadn't worked well and had even harmed the wounded. During experiments to advance the process Charles's own leg painfully served as a model, inflicted with bruises and burns. Wood moulding was developed into a successful mass production technology.

New larger versions of the 'Kazam' machine were later used to produce airplane parts, such as stabilizers for the Vultee BT-15. Wood served to bypass the consequences of the wartime aluminium shortage. It required a lot of electricity to mould the wood for a large airplane nose dome, so the work was done during off-peak hours.

De Bruyne's Redux 775, first produced in powder form and then as a film, later became an important adhesive for aluminium. Logically, de Havilland was the first to try this system for the Comet, the plane that ran into structural problems despite the use of glue. The Dutch airplane factory Fokker also started to glue wing and fuselage structures together from very early on in its F27 Friendship. They were forced to, because no machines were available that could mill aluminium sheets to create stiffeners and ribs, which used to be the common though destructive way to produce skin with stiffeners. Gluing was the poor man's alternative. They discovered that glued structures were lighter and protected better against fatigue. An asset of a thin layer of resin between layers of aluminium is that it will block the progression of cracks, which was a great discovery for aluminium construction because of that metal's sensitivity to fatigue.

Bonding metal airplane parts together also has important advantages over riveting. An adhesive distributes the forces. For riveting you need to drill holes in metal parts, effectively damaging them. Rivets in holes will cause stress concentrations and increase the risk of fatigue damage. There is tension in the riveted plates and bearing and shear stress in the rivets, possibly requiring extra plate thickness and weight. Both Howard Hughes's wooden structure and Fokker's gluing clearly show that scarcity stimulates creativity.

Generally speaking, those who advocate riveting are inclined to distrust adhesives, which is understandable since their bonding mechanism is invisible. Often, they are convinced of the use of glue when they see that in a failing bonded structure the damage doesn't coincide with the bonding lines. Not all that long ago it became possible to investigate the material principle of adhesive attachment through magnification. An aluminium surface needs pre-treatment before applying adhesive. First it is cleaned with an acid and then anodized, which gives the aluminium a very thin oxide skin that can now be observed with a Scanning Electron Microscope. Fokker Aerostructures' chemists discovered that the oxide layer contains nanoscale holes, almost like a honeycomb made by microscopic bees, that the adhesive resin will cling to. Fokker unknowingly became a pioneer of nanotechnology.

Both Howard Hughes's wooden structure and Fokker's gluing clearly show that scarcity stimulates creativity.

While the stage was being set for the production of thermosetting plastics and composites, work on the now ubiquitous thermoplastics was proceeding in other corners of chemistry. Polyethylene (PE), an omnipresent plastic familiar from shopping bags, drinking straws and zillions of other small things, was hit upon by accident in the nineteenth century, as were polyvinyl chloride (PVC) and polystyrene (PS), but it was only in the 1930s that it became possible to reproduce it under controlled conditions. The discovery and development of polymethyl methacrylate (PMMA), better known as Perspex or plexiglass, followed a similar path. Polypropylene (PP) was patented in 1951. Polycarbonate (PC) began its journey in 1928 at DuPont, a company that was very active in the development of thermoplastics. PC is a very ductile material and often used to replace glass. Another kind of glass replacement is polyethylene terephthalate (PET), which was patented in 1973 for use in bottles. Polyamide (PA), known from the mass production of nylon stockings since 1939, and Polyurethane (PUR) both exist in different forms, including a rubbery version of PUR.

Acrylonitrile butadiene styrene (ABS) is one of the tougher thermoplastics. Like PUR, the BS part of its molecules can be processed to become one of the synthetic rubbers. These are thermoplastics with partly connected molecules. Latex rubber tapped from the bark of certain species of Brazilian trees has been around for quite a long time, since 1600 BCE in fact. Natives of the Amazon region used it to play with. It wasn't until 1839 that Charles Goodyear patented vulcanization, a process that would render it durable. Rubber is, in a sense, one of the earlier plastics.

Shortly after Goodyear's invention it was taken into use for tyres. Two inventors had the idea of pumping air into a rubber sleeve to create a more resilient product. William Thomson from Scotland was the first, in 1845, but he let the patent run out. Nobody noticed. After the second inventor, fellow Scotsman John Boyd Dunlop, 'reinvented' the pneumatic tyre for bicycles in 1888, the principle really took off. It was all a matter of correct timing. The pneumatic tyre is probably one of the most produced composite structures ever, given the billions of cars and bicycles whizzing around. Tyres have been evolving ever since in terms of profiles and fibre reinforcement. New developments in structural technology, propulsion and IT combined with the need to come to grips with the value and flow of gargantuan quantities of tyres are beginning to produce suggestions for alternatives ■

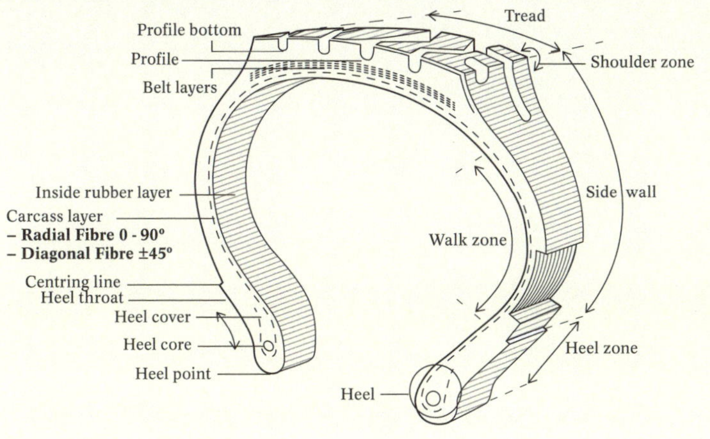

10.2 NON-INFLATABLE CAR TYRES

Whatever the quality of the road surface, tyres can handle it. The market for car tyres is immense, so success in conquering a large share of it by offering a convincing alternative could be very profitable. There may be opportunities, since tyres are extremely complex yet vulnerable products. There have been attempts by various companies to provide airless tyres and now Michelin has produced the 'Uptis'. This tyre system looks promising and altogether new, with a resilient spiralling see-through structure replacing the conventional air compartment. There are online videos that show exactly what happens when this airless tyre hits a bump.

The new tyre won't get punctured and the amount of material has been reduced so as to be less of a burden on the environment. As for rolling resistance – an important factor for energy consumption – its impact on the new tyre is not clear yet, but prototypes are being tested. Michelin claims that the 'Uptis' has been 3D printed, but that doesn't really mean anything if the material and the overall concept are still unclear. There is a rule of thumb that says that a new product has to be about ten times better and cheaper than the most common alternative. We'll just have to wait and see.

10.3 CARRIERS OF PROGRESS

The emergence of one thing requires the availability of another. Cars would have got nowhere without inflatable tyres that made them less dependent on paved roads. These were almost entirely absent and had not evolved since Roman times so inflatable road softeners made up for it. On the other hand the success of rubber tyres turned the Hevea brasiliensis tree into a desirable industrial resource. These were grown all over the world and became a bone of contention. Entire countries, such as Vietnam, were turned into rubber production systems.

Rubber was also part of a totally different development in infrastructure. Together with Bakelite, it was used to create a new line of electrical insulation that enabled electricity to be employed on a massive scale.

The rubber tyre has been crucial for road transportation

The fishing rod was the first product made with CFRP

10.4 COMPOSITE COLONIZATION

Actually, there is another term that has great relevance for the gradual introduction of composite structures: cold feet. This is not difficult to explain. When you are used to the traditional knowledge of wood and ceramics, and the mathematical predictability of metals calculated using Hooke's law, an understanding and feeling for the structural idiosyncrasies of different composites is not an obvious next step. Yes, they are strong and light but not infallible, and foreseeing when and how things can go wrong is different. They don't dent and they tear or delaminate rather than break. When they contain an arranged fibre structure, they may behave more like very stubborn textiles than aluminium, with which they are often compared. Since their recyclability is currently in doubt compared with that of other structures, this becomes a convenient excuse to avoid composites. Most importantly, they are considered expensive, because buyers are inclined to compare prices per kilogram when they should be comparing performances, and better performances should be more expensive.

Nevertheless, it is becoming clear that composite structures have important advantages – being light, stiff, strong, elastic, maintenance free, adaptable, etc. – and they are developing quickly, taking advantage of the opportunities of mass production. Thinking in terms of composites is becoming embedded in design as a useful and affordable alternative. It is interesting to observe how this colonization takes place. Usually the process begins with painstaking laboratory tests. The next step is to cosmetically and harmlessly apply the composite in question in a small hatch, or whatever, and from then on it is gradually taken more seriously. It took about 60 years for composites to 'touch down' in the world of aircraft as some insignificant panel and from there steadily grow and conquer the entire airframe. Something similar is happening with cars, trucks and buses. Building and construction are lagging behind. Cladding panels are in the clear now, but supporting structures currently are way too far out of the traditional building and construction box. In fact builders act like guilds from a bygone age, protecting their trade and knowledge. In bridge building, however, a new kind of guild is on the rise, one based on the modular composite bridge. It helps that technology is constantly being refined. The choice of fibres and polymers is likely to increase. Indeed, the current interest in recyclable thermoplastic composites and organic and renewable materials may go some way towards making up for the lack of attention paid to energy saving.

COMPOSITE
DESIGN

11. PRODUCTION WITH POLYMERS

Generally speaking, synthetic plastic arrived on the scene between the mid 1930s and mid 1950s, the maximum metal part of Ashby's diagram. From then onwards, driven by the economic urge to mass produce and to fulfil the desire for convenience, the mainstream technologies to put them into use were developed and still continue to evolve. Apart from newly emerging bioplastics they all derive from oil and it is generally wiser to put oil to good use than to burn it. Nevertheless, an overview of all manufacturing technologies needn't be complicated. In principle it can be summarized as a combination of materials, material substance, recipes, different kinds of moulds and of course reinforcement.

To keep things simple from the start, it is wise to limit the discussion to thermoplastic polymers and thermosets, the latter including latex rubber. In practice there are hundreds, if not thousands, of different kinds of polymers all with their own specific properties. None of them is suitable for all applications. For example, ABS is a sturdy engineering plastic and not the stuff that foil is made of. PE, to pick a very good plastic for foil, would be useless for a toaster case. Bioplastics and biodegradables have scarcely been mentioned yet. They exist as both thermosets and thermoplastics and can be processed in similar ways. The main difference is in their origin (bioplastics) and in what happens later on in their life cycle (biological degradation).

Thermoset polymers include latex rubber.

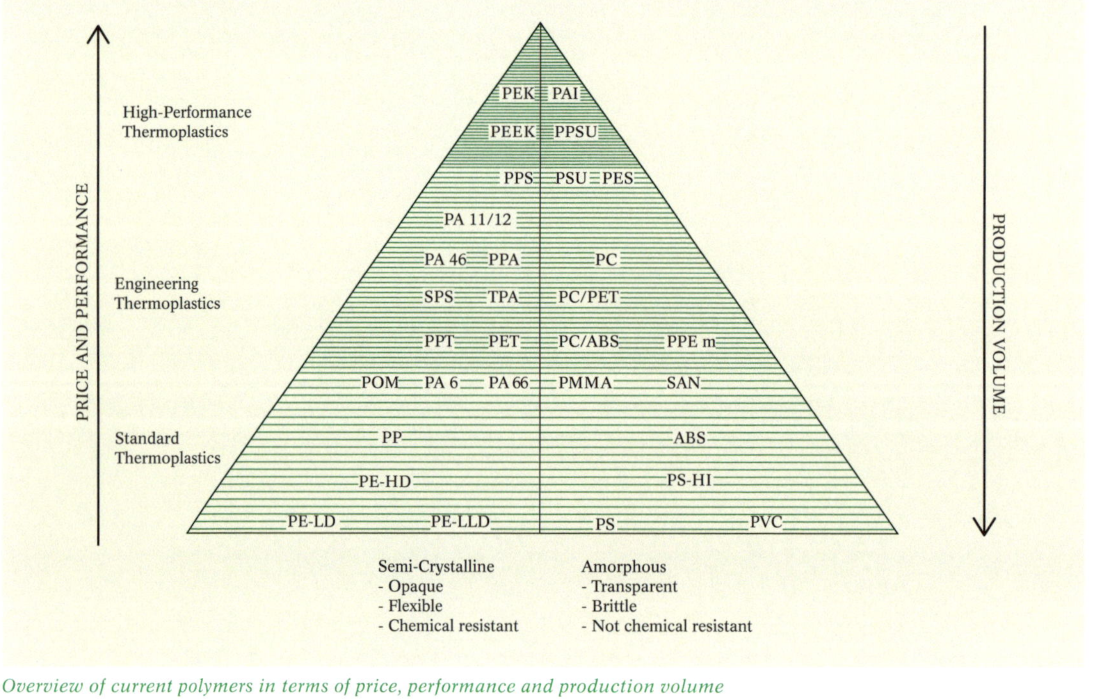

Overview of current polymers in terms of price, performance and production volume

An overview simply is a combination of materials, material substance, recipes, different kinds of moulds and of course reinforcement.

So, we have two types of material. At the onset of a product manufacturing process these come in different forms. Thermosets can be acquired as liquids (often two-components), powders or prepared sheets. Thermoplastics are used in liquid form in niche markets (dentures), but mostly their transformation into a product starts with a GRANULATE made by chopping up thin rods, which is then heated to turn it into a viscous fluid.

This doesn't flow easily and is a bit like peanut butter or molten glass, depending on the temperature and chemical composition. Most thermoplastics, like glass, are amorphous. This means that they're not entirely solid and that they have no distinct melting point. It is a more gradual transition to the product, which is an advantage for many forming processes. At room temperature they are glass-like and when heated they gradually become rubbery and eventually melt. An advantage of melting is that thermoplastics can be welded, although not all equally well. Some types of melted thermoplastics may require considerable heat and pressure to form, most notably high-grade engineering plastics such as polyetherimide (PEI), polyphenylene sulphide (PPS), polyamide-imide (PAI) and polytetrafluoroethylene (PTFE), better known as Teflon.

The semi-crystalline polymers PP, PA, PET, PPS and PEEK have a defined melting point that is generally lower than the processing temperature of the amorphous thermoplastics. Their 'glass transition temperature', an important design threshold, is generally lower as well. Nevertheless, their chemical resistance (to acids and other aggressive substances) surpasses that of their amorphous cousins.

Thermosets can be liquid, powders or prepared sheets.

The equipment and moulds to form products have to meet special requirements to withstand heat and forces.

Both families of plastics come in SEMI-FINISHED FORMS such as sheets, rods and pipes. Thermosets are not easily extruded: continuously forming the cross-sectional profile of a rod or pipe from a fluid pouring out of a bottle is tricky, if not impossible.

Reinforcement helps, but we're not there just yet. Semi-finished can also mean a complicated injection moulded preform. We haven't arrived there yet either. Be patient.

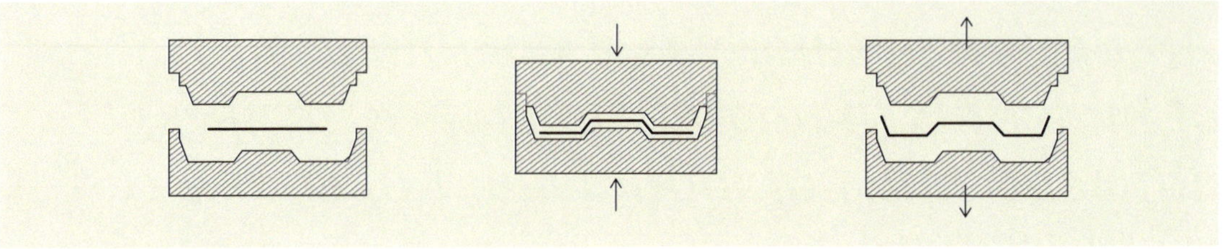

The next level is about making 3D objects. Most hands-on work with thermoplastics consists of THERMOFORMING, literally heating a plastic sheet and then giving it a form. This process doesn't have to be very complicated. For some applications a hole of a particular shape in a sheet of, say, plywood is enough to define the outcome. The form is determined – not very precisely – by clamping the warm sheet of plastic material to the plywood with the hole and then creating a difference in air pressure to stretch the plastic and make it bubble through the hole, as if it were a 'skin' of soap. When the curved shape has reached the acquired height, cool it. This is how they make polycarbonate skylights.

In a more exact procedure, the heated plastic is sucked or pressed (depending on your perspective in physics) over a mould. Fairly large objects enter the world this way, such as ski cases and panels for vehicles. They always have this clamping edge that needs to be removed afterwards or made inconspicuous. The advantage of this type of thermoforming is that the mould can be relatively cheap and so batch sizes can be modest. They don't have to be, though. Moulds can be made of steel and form dozens of products in one go of less than a second. Many packaging cups and disposables are made this way by the millions every day.

'VACUUM FORMING' is a field in which biodegradable plastics are gradually replacing the conventional ones.

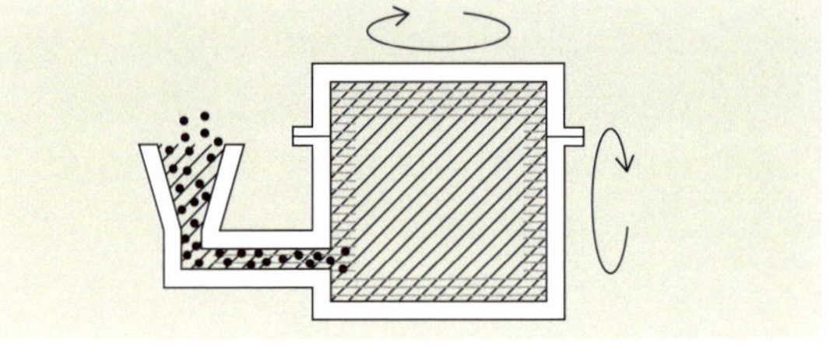

Another hands-on technology that has no large-scale counterpart is ROTATIONAL MOULDING (also called rotomoulding). The mould is a welded steel plate structure suspended in a biaxial rotating machine. There is an opening with a lid for sprinkling in the granulate, usually from a simple plastic such as PE. Processing consists of rotating the mould while heating it, possibly with a simple hand torch. The plastic granules will melt in patches against the heated wall of the mould and solidify as rotation continues. Eventually the whole inside of the mould will be covered with a layer of polymer, which will insulate leftovers inside and prevent them from melting sticking to the mould. What you get in the end is a hollow product with a crude inner side.

In the previous case, thermoplastic material melts inside the mould.

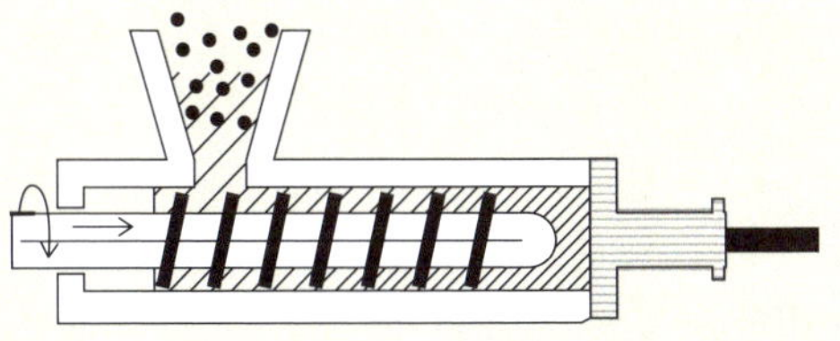

Extrusion begins with melting the plastic and then pushing it through a hole that defines the shape of the product's cross-section. It is a continuous process that squeezes out cross-sectional profiles, like whipped cream out of a pastry bag. The outcome can be a simple round rod, but also a hollow shape that may be quite complex, such as an insulating window frame element. Straightforward sheet is produced in this way too.

Once you have an extruder producing a warm soft plastic pipe it's not that difficult to integrate a following step in the process, namely blow extrusion. All you need is some additional air. Blow it into the tube and it will inflate. It can become metres wide, with the thinnest of walls, as little as a fraction of a millimetre. What you get is foil, with a quality that depends on extrusion speed, material composition and pressure.

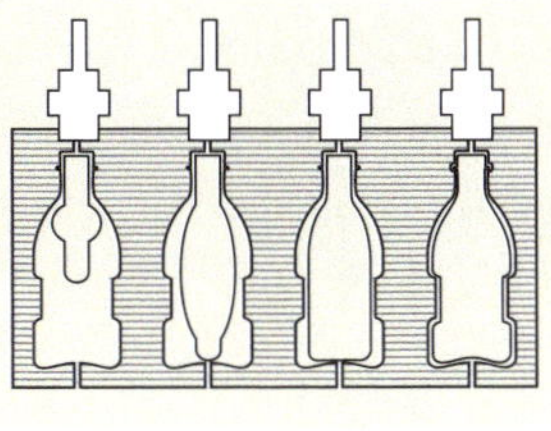

Blow moulding is another option. This involves placing a freshly extruded tube inside a mould into which air is blown until the material covers the entire inside of the mould. It is a simple trick to produce rather crude but tough hollow products. Many a soap bottle and jerry can has been made this way. It is similar to vacuum forming, the difference being that blow moulding allows you to make complete shapes, without a clamping edge.

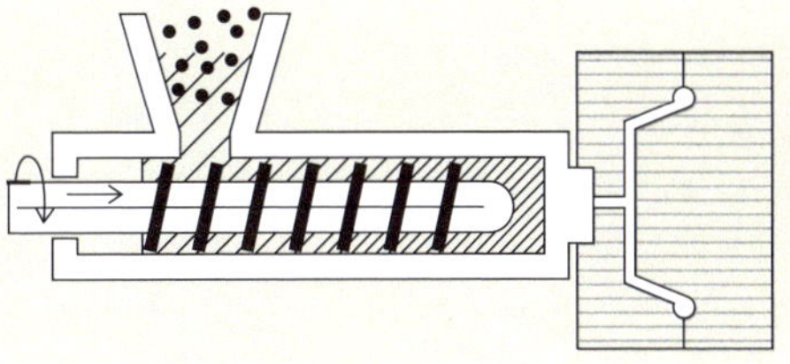

By far the most popular thermoplastic technology is injection moulding. It is extremely precise and can handle the most complex detail. The pressure needed to fill a complete mould is considerable. Moulds with moving parts to free a product after it has set may be mechanically complicated as well as expensive. Recouping such investments may require a large batch size. Injection moulding is a typical mass production technology. It is virtually impossible to find a home interior, no matter how poor, that hasn't got at least one injection moulded object in it. It may be a stool, or a part of a fan, or a pan. The spirit of injection moulding is everywhere.

A moulding principle not requiring a physical mould has become very popular over the past 15 or so years. Here the mould is defined in a computer program that controls the hardware to build your product layer by layer: this is called additive manufacturing. The publicly familiar version of 3D PRINTING starts with a filament or wire that is heated or comes out of an extruder. A robot then drapes the material in the desired position.

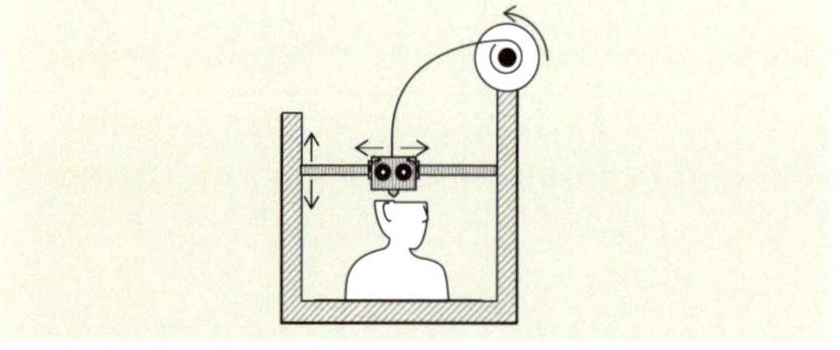

Currently 3D printing is too much of a buzzword. Some think it can solve any problem, from every consumer printing and recycling all they need, to colonizing Mars. However, not all materials can be printed, as the heat involved can affect them negatively. Moreover, it requires machines that need to be kept in good shape. Printing is not very fast either, which can be inconvenient. Here is an example, just for the sake of demonstration: In China they printed ten little concrete houses in a day, just walls and a roof. At its peak Ford produced 9,000 to 10,000 Model T's a day! These were complete and could be driven off the conveyer belt. Slowness is the inconvenient bottleneck of 3D printing, even if you can download your printable commodity software from the Internet.

The strength of 3D printing, on the other hand, lies in its versatility, complexity and refinement. It is very suitable for personalization, from shoe parts to prosthetics and implants. It can be used to build moulds and also test and adapt them. Complex tiny manoeuvrable surgical devices are now being developed that benefit from the fact that devices less than a couple of millimetres big can be made in one go. Assembling countless small parts and then cursing when you miss one is a thing of the past.

A final important remark about 3D printing, and in fact about all making processes, is that it is not complete in itself. More often than not, there are procedures before and after the work at hand. For instance, three colours might be combined before printing begins. Or a hollow object could emerge from the printer to then be heated and inflated, or milled to the right surface quality, or even have surplus parts removed that were just there for the sake of balance.

A final important remark about 3D printing, and in fact about all making processes, is that it is not complete in itself.

This is a bridge towards thermosets. 3D printing is only one facet of automated additive manufacturing. The idea, like most ideas, dates back to the beginning of the twentieth century. But it was only in the 1990s that about ten 3D-making automation principles made a play for the market. In those days it was mainly considered a way for companies to make models very quickly and save development costs. It wasn't called rapid prototyping for nothing. Its main asset was speed in materializing small numbers of objects. The machines to do it were still very expensive.

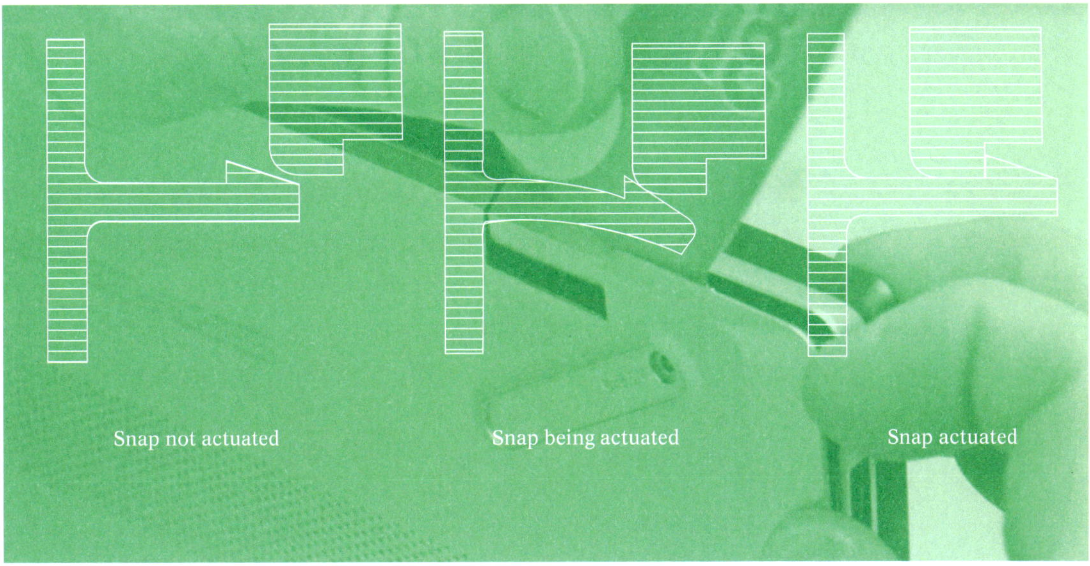

11.1 SNAP!

It's not as if this is a brand new principle. According to archaeological findings, snap-fit as an assembly method has been around for thousands of years. It uses metal parts and can be found all over the world. Who hasn't heard of press studs or the small phosphor bronze springs used to hold parts together?

Thermoplastics have added extra opportunities, because injection moulding enables you to integrate small grip elements into the structure of lids and casings that can bend just enough to open up and clasp a specially designed edge to form a tight connection. They are used to close battery compartments and entire casings of all kinds of devices, from laptops to vacuum cleaners, coffee machines and lighting fixtures. Snap connections are very convenient for closing things. To open them up is a different story altogether. You're not really supposed to even try. Snap extensions are vulnerable. On the whole, the design is reasonably accommodating when accessing battery compartments, but some simply cannot be opened, not even by the Arabian woodcutter Ali Baba. Indeed, the interior of electrical products tends to be a no-go area. The integrated plastic protuberances are inclined to break as proof that you unlawfully tried to open up some such product and stimulate you to get a new one. This opens up a whole field of evolution in repairability.

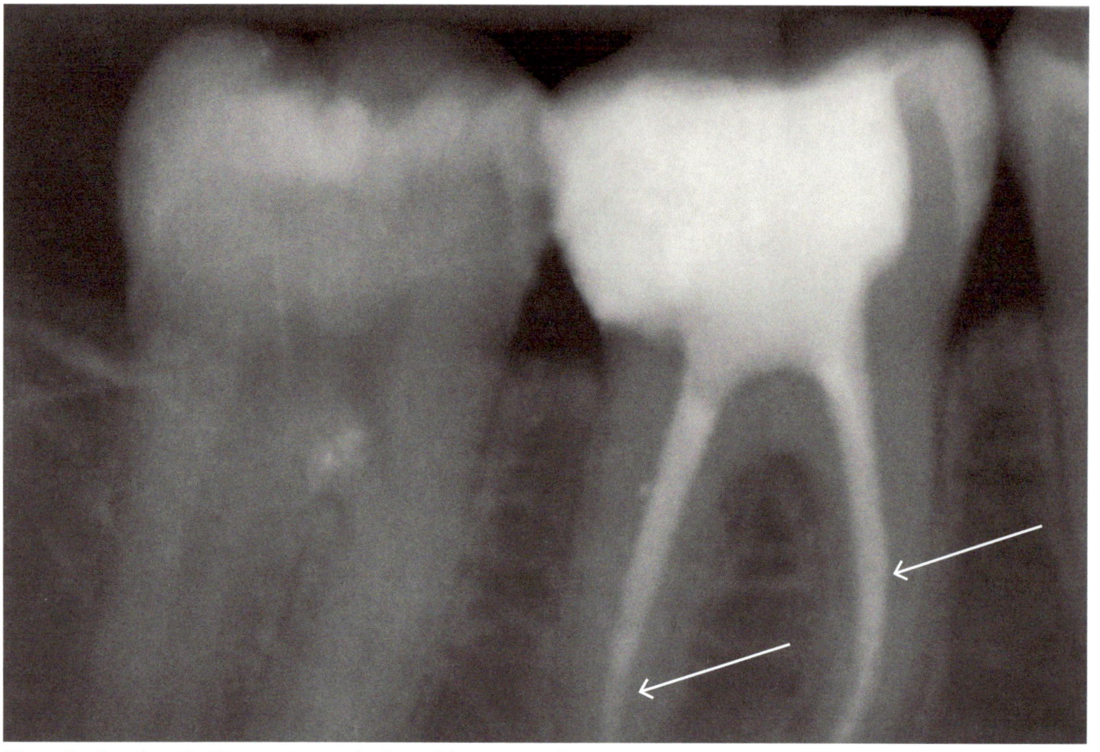

The early plant-based polymer gutta percha is used for root canal treatment

11.2 THE BIO-FACTOR

The first plastics came straight from animals and plants – horn, rubber and gutta-percha, which dentists cram into root canals but is also used to fill golf balls. Oil took over as the most important plastic making resource. This proved to have unfavourable side effects, such as unhealthy processing and its unwillingness to disappear. Oil is a substance that consists of geologically processed dead organic matter, mainly plankton, so it is not such an illogical idea to try to develop plastics from renewable fresh plant life that can rot away when we're done with them.

So now there is an abundance of activity to develop plastics with a 'bio' prefix. A slew of 'bioplastics' have arrived that can be divided into two main groups. We have bio-based plastics, which are made from plant matter, and biodegradable plastics, which can be decomposed by living organisms. Their prefix is about all they have in common. Bio-based plastics are not necessarily biodegradable, whereas biodegradable plastics can be petroleum-based. To complicate things just a bit further: bio-based can be an environmental disadvantage if the plants used serve a competing purpose, such as nourishment. Similarly, decomposition may be poisonous because of crop treatment before harvesting. In addition, the speed of breakdown can be disappointing and if decomposition is supposed to happen in rivers or the sea it may prove a source of pollution.

This implies that a 'bio-factor' material deserves the same investigative attention as any other. Life Cycle Assessment can provide a bigger picture to figure out the environmental impact of bio-production and/or decomposition. But there is more. Biodegradability in particular is not just a matter of material composition. Much more importantly, it is about having control of material flows and taking responsibility for them. One of the main setbacks is that flows often consist of mutually contaminating substances. One more thing: procedures for Life Cycle Assessment don't mention this explicitly, but there is an option to reduce environmental impact with lightness, possibly all the way to zero.

11.3 MAKING EXCEPTIONS

From the onset, the potential of 3D printing has been demonstrated by copying things and by making things that can't be made in any other way, such as producing complicated working mechanisms in one go. It's also very fast when you want to test an idea, or cheaply produce small parts for a piece of furniture before it's decided to mass produce it.

It is useful for mass customizable production too. Nike has introduced 'Flyprint', a 3D-printed easily amendable 'textile'. It is not really woven though. Its plastic fibres are not intertwined but placed on top of each other, so it really is a kind of cross-ply laminate.

Anyway, it seems 3D printing is eminently suitable for making exceptional or singular objects. South African artist, engineer and entrepreneur Jonty Hurwitz sought to bring together artists and scientists to visualize the blur emerging between myth and science. In 2014, together they began to develop extremely small sculptures. Computer models were made by scanning hand sculpted 3D shapes. The resulting scanning algorithms were adapted to tiny processing, with less than 1 µm thin scaffolding elements added to keep the object in balance.

Building the sculptures was similar to stereolithography but, let us say, on a slightly smaller scale, with 'two-photon lithography'. The collision of two photons from two narrow low-frequency light beams provides the energy to cure one 3D pixel. We're talking nano now. Pixels were cured one by one and layer by layer.

The sculpture required a Scanning Electron Microscope to be mediated to the human eye. The most inspiring sculpture was *Psyche Revived by Cupid's Kiss*, after an original by the eighteenth-century artist Antonio Canova. It was about 100 µm long. Rather appropriately (with hindsight), it was pictured standing on the head of an ant. Unfortunately, we have to use the past tense, because a couple of days before the images went viral on the Internet the real sculptures were destroyed, which is to be expected from art the size of dust particles.

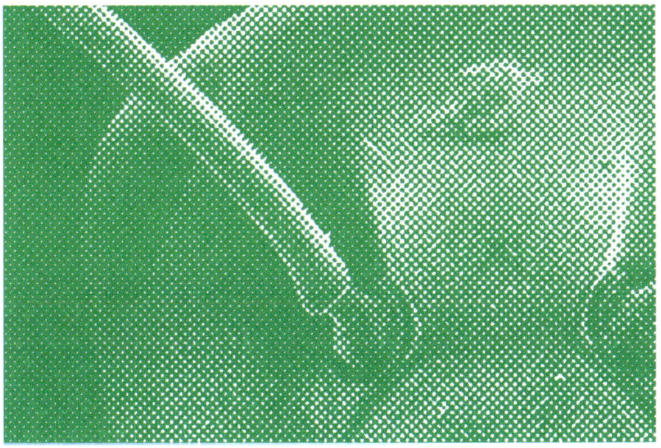

3D print of Psyche Revived by Cupid's Kiss on the head of an ant is 0.1 mm long

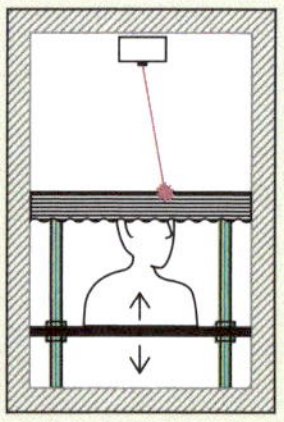

The first version to achieve some popularity was STEREOLITHOGRAPHY. The working material is a fluid thermoset that is cured by exposure to ultraviolet light. The machine consists of a vat filled with resin and a platform inside that can move up and down. An ultraviolet laser beam 'writes' and stacks up thin cross-sections layer by layer while the platform carrying the cured form moves down. Stereolithography is affordable now and still very useful for complex prototyping and visual checks, although the polymer is a bit brittle.

Thermoset powders, including good old Bakelite, like thermoplastics are suitable for INJECTION MOULDING. In principle the same type of machine can do it. The difference is that pressure and heat serve to fire up the chemical reaction in the thermoset to finish the material composition. There is no melting involved.

Now we enter the realm of typical thermoset product manufacturing and its use in making composites. It starts with RIM, OR REACTION INJECTION MOULDING. There are two containers with one monomer each, let's call them Tommy and Lee, to circumvent the eternal A and B. Tommy and Lee are mixed just before they are injected into the mould. There they react to become Tommy Lee. A reinforcing agent can be added to the mixture to make Tommy Lee stronger. This can consist of cut pieces of fibre or various kinds of powder. Here we're talking SRIM, OR STRUCTURED REACTION INJECTION MOULDING. The additive can also be thermoset granules from crushed products within a recycling scheme that saves new material by replacing part of it with used material of the same kind.

There is one other kind of RIM in which a woven or otherwise premade fibre structure is put into the mould before the Tommy Lee mixture is poured in. A product produced by RRIM, OR REINFORCED REACTION INJECTION MOULDING, will have a well-defined mechanical quality characterized by the fibres and their quality and direction.

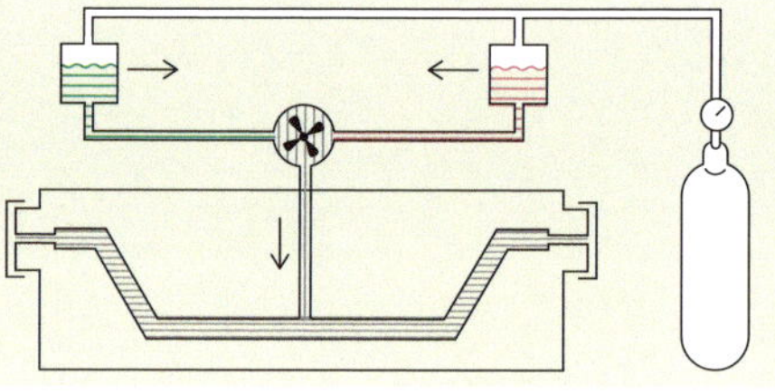

There is one last abbreviation: RTM, OR RESIN TRANSFER MOULDING, which is a low-pressure mould filling principle. There are several versions of RTM. Probably the simplest one is almost the same as rotational moulding for thermoplastic, but it requires no heat. The reaction generates it. It is a matter of injecting the mixture and rotating the mould while Tommy Lee is setting. The dose of resin doesn't have to be very precise, as the only concern here is to form an outer shell. You can try this at home, if the Internet is to be believed.

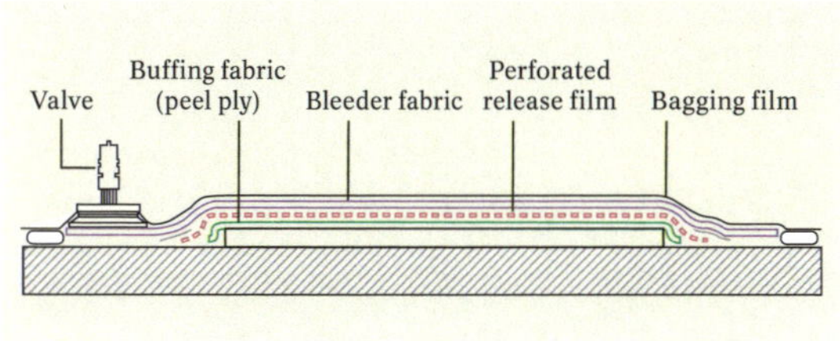

This is also true of VACUUM INJECTION, although you will need a vacuum pump. First you apply a thin layer of gelcoat to a mould that will make the object as smooth as that mould. Next, you drape glass fibre matting that has been cut to size over the partly dried gelcoat. Place a layer of foil over that with an airtight fix to the edge of the mould. The foil can be made to size and for repeated use it can be a soft silicon rubber cover. The set-up includes an air valve so that all the air can be sucked out and an entrance on the opposite side attached to a hose ending in a container of reaction-ready low-viscosity resin, usually epoxy. Now, turn on the pump. It will suck out the air and the vacuum will cause the resin to flow in, integrating the glass in the structure and reaching all the details of the mould. Setting may take 12 to 24 hours, or less when heated.

It will suck out the air and the vacuum will cause the resin to flow in.

This procedure has become quite common over the past years because it is clean. The emission of poisonous fumes is under control and vacuum injection is suitable for large components. Entire hulls for large yachts are produced this way. There is also the option of integrating a layer of foam to create a stiff, lightweight and possibly insulating structure for use in roofs defined by the buildings' architecture. This structure consists of a layer of hard foam milled to size and shape placed between two layers of glass matting. The vacuum process will then integrate the foam into the composite structure.

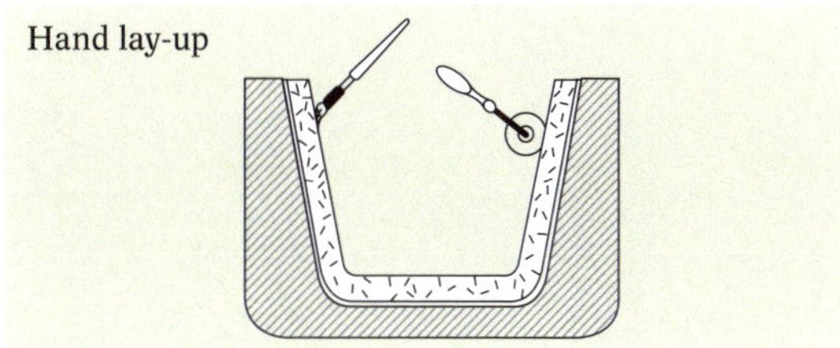

The obvious predecessor of vacuum injection is literally the most hands-on method of working with glass fibre reinforced polymer, namely HAND LAY-UP. The difference is that there is no foil involved. You simply apply the resin, usually polyester, vinylester or epoxy, with a brush, taking the fumes for granted. Hand lay-up is still in use but environmental rulings are likely to make it disappear from indoor production. It may well prove indispensable for repairs ■

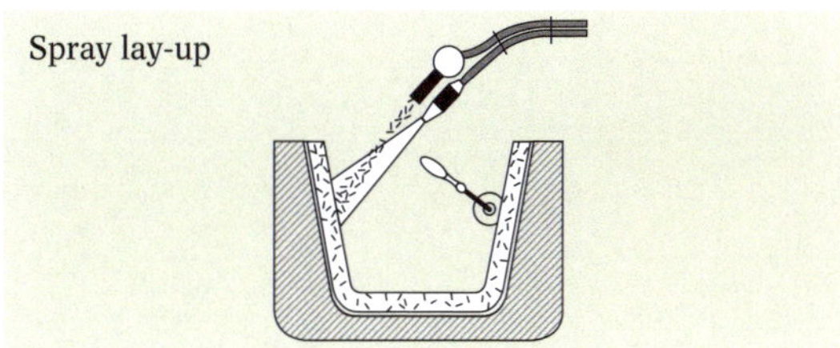

11.4 3D INFLATION

It takes a designer to drag 3D printing out of its comfort zone. In her graduation project 'Aera Fabrica', Arnhem design researcher Roos Meerman wanted to discover hidden qualities in plastics and decided to experiment with 3D-printed hollow shapes. Her idea was to heat and inflate them and then let them cool down again, to find out what would happen. It was a basic hands-on procedure requiring a bucket of warm water and a simple pump. The result consists of promising and colourful transparent objects and a new line of potential for discovery.

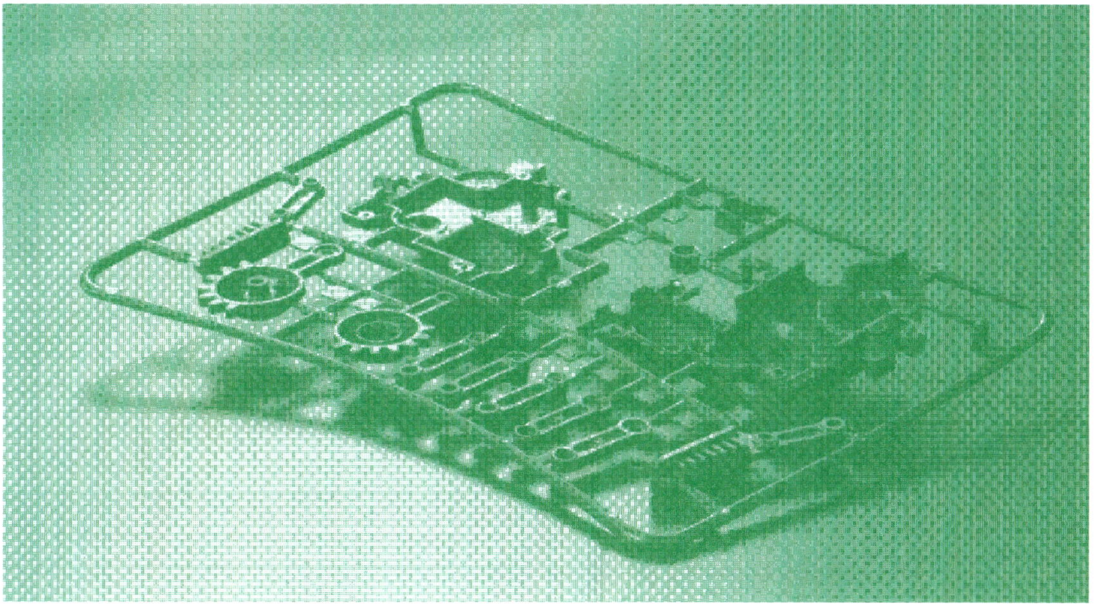

11.5 PLASTIC ADVENTURES

Thermoplastic properties depend on temperature and other circumstantial conditions. Plastic chopping boards, for instance, can absorb a considerable amount of water and if this happens on one side they will swell and become warped. The birth of a new product is the beginning of an adventure. If the designer hasn't taken into account what happens immediately after processing in terms of cooling in relation to form and material distribution, it will start its life already warped.

The thicker the material, the longer it will take to cool down. This means it will be softer and less resistant to the forces that thinner and stiffer parts will begin to exert. That's when warp arrives on the scene. There is software that can help optimize shape and proportions to prevent warp from occurring. Warp is found most often in assembly parts that are still connected to the runners in the casting process, say for miniature car models or air conditioning casings.

Another phenomenon directly related to the making process, particularly injection moulding and thermoforming, is 'crazing'. This describes the formation of cracks caused by internal stress within a material that is being deformed in one or more directions, for instance flowing from an injection point through the mould. The bond between parallel flows tends to be weaker in places where they have been brought close together. Think of a waterfall and a river flowing around rocks. What you see there is what happened inside the mould, except perhaps a bit slower.

Internal stress in thermoformed objects is made crystal clear by the following experiment. Take an empty thermoformed margarine tub and fill it with boiling water and behold: within seconds the tub will return to its original flatness. Be careful if you try this at home.

12. HANDLING FIBRES

You must have read earlier in this book that glass fibres were extruded by pressing melted glass through tiny holes in a die. This Owens Corning invention from 1938 marked the beginning of the targeted development of plastics with a reinforcing spine. Now reinforcement can take many forms, each with a different purpose. Some have already been mentioned. Later on, you will read about a minute contribution made to composites by a famous inventor.

On the least organized level there are FILLERS, granules of a chosen substance that adjust the material properties. Silica hardens, chalk enhances heat resistance, alumina improves wear resistance, and so on. Fillers may be nano-sized. ('Nano' gives them a Sci-Fi ring, but it's simply a measurement: 1 nanometre is one billionth of a metre). Particle fillers have little influence on processing principles. The tooling involved may have to meet stiffer requirements in terms of pressure, wear or heat resistance, but the working substance basically is the same.

The next step concerns the use of SHORT FIBRES, which are fibres cut into pieces. Adding those to a polymer provides it with a higher Young's modulus (stiffness) and σ_{max} (yield strength), which enhances its properties. The procedure is similar to processing plastics with a filler. It's cheaper and easier to process short fibres than working with the next level, namely ENDLESS FIBRES, or continuous filament fibres, which means they are produced in a continuous process that would be endless if left unchecked.

If endless fibres can only come out of machines, RENEWABLE FIBRES are produced from plants. There are many kinds of technical plant fibres and most of them have a history in textile production: flax, hemp, bamboo, ramie, nettle, jute, cotton, and more. They have a low density and at first sight they may look endless, ramie in particular, but in fact they are composites, small pieces of fibre from about 5 to 60 mm long with varying properties. Their performance under tensile load is less predictable than that of synthetic endless fibres. Because of this and for structural purposes it doesn't make much sense to organize them into a fabric. For other production purposes, however, this is a convenient possibility. In the Far East, composites of jute and bamboo are used for, among other things, corrugated roof panels to replace the more costly and much more corrosion sensitive metal ones.

Glass isn't the only endless fibre. CARBON is just as well known. Carbon fibre consists almost exclusively of carbon atoms and its specific tensile strength and stiffness, combined with favourable thermal and chemical properties, have made it very popular among engineers from all disciplines. Like most of the Lightness materials it has been around for longer than you would expect. Joseph Swan was the first to produce it as a filament for light bulbs, which were on the verge of being invented. Twenty-two earlier inventors have been listed. Thomas Alva Edison – here he is – initially tried to make filaments by carbonizing the likes of cotton and wood splints.

12.1 PULLED INTO SHAPE

In a book about lightweight structures, tension is taken for granted. All the same, it makes sense to examine the relationship between force and fibre structures. Some examples have been given already. A catenary is the shape you get when an equally distributed mass is accelerated, for example by gravity. It works its magic on a rope attached between two points. Span the rope and it becomes stayed to a degree, because its own weight can always come into play. Shapes defined by specific (constant) tensile strength and stiffness are called tensoids.

There are 3D equivalents of tensoids. These occur when membranes or fabrics are put under stress defined by spanning and by circumstantial influences, such as gravity and wind. Spanned tents and Frei Otto's Olympic Stadium are tensoids and so are the sails on a boat or a ship.

They are not that different from pressurized composite containers, vessels and kegs, which in a sense are just airtight sail filaments wound into a shape to contain liquids and gases. When used as containers they are usually cylindrical, not the best shape when it comes to structural efficiency and functionality.

One step further and we arrive at the sphere, the toroid (the car tyre shape) and more. These are special, because when pressurized the tension in the reinforcing fibres is the same throughout, which leads the way to weight reduction and more predictable behaviour. This type of filament-wound shape is described as isotensoid.

12.2 EMPEROR OF TENTS

This is not about textile or fibres but it comes close. Even before his career began, German architect Frei Otto must have been infected with some kind of tent virus while a prisoner of war (until 1947) in Chartres, France. There he designed and built camp tents with a minimum of resources. In 1948 he began studying architecture in Berlin and also spent half a year studying in the USA, where he met Frank Lloyd Wright, Ludwig Mies van der Rohe and Charles and Ray Eames, among many other celebrities.

In 1952, after working as a professor, he decided to become a freelance architect specializing in tent structures. He developed skills experimenting with fabric and nets and in 1967 was given the opportunity to build the German Pavilion for Expo 67 in Montreal. Around that time, the mayor of Munich had convinced the Olympic Committee to organize the Games in his city. The architectural firm of Günter Behnisch took part in the competition to design the stadium for the 1972 Olympics in Munich. It was a difficult contest fraught with disagreements and false starts, but in the end out of 104 drafts Behnisch and Partners were chosen to do the job. One of their employees, Cordel Wehrse, suggested involving Frei Otto, whose Montreal feat he had read about in a newspaper. It took a great deal of effort to convince the jury that a transparent tent would be the right mixture of unmonumental modesty and spectacular structural ingenuity. The structure is a net held in tension using cables and masts and clad with transparent acrylic panels.

12.3 THE SILK PROCESS

Fibres produced by tiny animals belong among the strongest in the world and can be woven into enticing fabrics. Bombyx Mori, the silkmoth, an insect bred in massive numbers, spends its larval state as the silkworm, which eats white mulberry and produces silk.

Spiders have always been an inspiration because of the webs they build. Spider silk is much harder to come by in sufficient amounts. It was thought that it would be ideal for bulletproof vests due to its strength. In 2016 the artist Jalila Essaïdi even combined spider silk with human skin and tested the result on its ability to stop bullets. It didn't, because besides being strong the material is also very elastic, or a spider wouldn't be able to catch prey with it.

Elasticity is also a property of butterfly silk. In Genghis Khan's time (c. 1162–1227), Mongol warriors wore silk undergarments and a leather harness, which were much lighter and more flexible than the iron plate armour then worn by their European counterparts. It was the Europeans' inferior speed and agility that caused them to lose the Battle of Legnica. Apart from its not entirely faultless protective qualities, the silk fabric had the advantage that if hit by an arrow you could pull this relatively easily from the wound by grabbing the surrounding silk along with it.

The spider silk the artist used in her work was made from the milk of a goat that had been genetically modified. The trouble with spiders is that, although they may be better in producing fibres, it is well-nigh impossible to control their behaviour. On the whole, scaling up fibre production from milk has not been a great success. Currently the better option seems to be to genetically alter yeast proteins and use those to extract spider silk from water in which they have been dissolved. It might just work.

12.4 HOMELY PLANT FIBRES

Plants, like hairy animals, produce fibres that we humans have used for centuries to make roofs, clothes and bedding. Textiles are our protective identity agents. In polymer composites, the requirements for fibres are more physical than they are in fabrics. Specific and constant strength, stiffness and elasticity are criteria when comparing them with their inorganic, artificial competitors. They do have renewability and biodegradability on their side. This doesn't necessarily imply that they are harmless. Let's put this another way. We may cause a lot of environmental damage by producing plant fibres and turning them into something useful, through the use of agricultural poisons and enormous amounts of water, in particular for blue jeans.

However, they do have potential for creating composite structures where stiffness is dominant. This is less the case where strength is concerned, since a plant fibre is like a chain. It consists of a sequence of short elements whose properties vary throughout its length. This causes differences in strength depending on where this is measured and the length measured. These differ from one plant species to the next. This table presents an overview.

Renewability bears the signs of being sustainable. But, as we see more often, this sustainability is not just a matter of growing fibres and using them. Processing is another factor, as is transportation. The look of a plant is particularly important when promoting the idea of responsible bio-design, or 'green bling' as some call it. But looks carry the wrong message when the 'green' fibres have travelled thousands of miles before being turned into a product.

We now have a very promising alternative: plant-based carbon fibres. These are made by carbonizing lignin, a very common complex polymer that occurs in the walls of plant cells. Research is now being done in laboratories across the world and the process will be slightly cheaper than producing fibres from the synthetic acrylonitrile polymer. In addition, lignin is abundant in paper waste. Black can turn green.

Ultimately his incandescent lamp with carbonized bamboo became the first real success, burning for 1200 hours. The ocean steamer SS *Columbia* acquired these lamps and became the first ship to have a dynamo on board.

The race for high performance carbon fibres got under way in the 1960s.

These early carbon threads were low on carbon content and a long way off from what would become today's strong fibre. The race for high performance carbon fibres got under way in the 1960s. Several companies and governments were after the right process to carbonize synthetic oil-based materials. Polyacrylonitrile (PAN) fibre was mass-produced as Orlon or acryl for heavy duty textiles, as distinct from viscose/cellulose fibres such as rayon. Rolls Royce took a tumble after developing its RB-211 jet engine with turbine blades consisting of a new carbon-based composite. Bird strikes and the belief that brittle fracture was more damaging than plastic deformation were a setback to development.

By the end of the 1960s Japan, where Dr. Akio Shindo was enjoying success with PAN as a raw material, had taken the lead. An agreement provided Union Carbide and Toray (Tokyo Rayon) with the licenses. From then on, carbon fibres steadily conquered the composite world – not that development has stopped. There are processing experiments under way to find a cheaper alternative for PAN. This could very well turn out to be lignin, a plant component often considered waste, mainly by the papermaking industry.

A totally different alternative for carbon is BASALT, which is made by extruding melted rock. As a fibre it is similar to glass, but with a composition that renders it slightly stronger and better equipped to deal with heat. It is more affordable than carbon. Its main application currently is in rebars.

It is unusual to see metal fibres combined with polymers, possibly because they belong to different conventions of design.

METALS also come as fibres. Compared to the materials described earlier they have the advantage of electrical and thermal conductivity, but they can also be more ductile, which implies that they can be bent and deep drawn to a particular shape relatively easily. This can be an advantage for the structural rehabilitation of building structures and has been tried as such. Metal fibres enable you to create a shape, either with or without a mould, and 'freeze' it afterwards with a resin or even with plaster. It is unusual to see metal fibres combined with polymers, possibly because they belong to different conventions of design.

ORGANIC OR POLYMER fibres, the last type in our list, can be found everywhere, as they are standard practice in the clothing industry. However, some have been designed for superior tensile strength. ARAMID is formidable. It outperforms steel in strength by about eight times.

The name is a portmanteau of aromatic and amide, meaning that it combines amide monomers and aromatic rings (hexagonal carbon molecules). The bonds create a very strong arrangement of atoms around the molecular axis. Aramid fibres are mostly applied in bullet protection requisites and in fireproof textiles, for which the fibre/volume ratio has to be 100 per cent, since resin is counterproductive in fire-fighting. In addition, aramids are used for polymer reinforcement, sometimes combined with carbon, which gives it a distinctive striped look.

Crystalline blocks alternate with very long straight molecule chains appropriately nicknamed the 'micro-shish-kebab' structure.

The strongest organic fibre is a modest polyethylene with a very precise molecular arrangement in which Crystalline blocks alternate with very long straight molecule chains appropriately nicknamed the 'micro-shish-kebab' structure. However, you need an electron microscope to see it. Generally, the material is known as Ultra High Molecular Weight Polyethylene (UHMWPE) but its brand name is Dyneema. Compared with other fibres, its integration in composites is more complicated. It requires special surface treatment. It has been interwoven with carbon fibres to drastically increase the impact strength of the resulting composite. One of its main advantages is resistance to mechanical violence, which is why UHMWPE is used to keep bullets from entering chests, heads and vehicle interiors. Army helmets, for example, are being produced by matched-die moulding thick composite panels. Both aramid and UHMWPE, however, are mostly used where strong and light ropes or cables are required, such as in shipping, yachting, windsurfing or kiting. DSM, the producer of Dyneema, has proposed a concept to stop a tsunami wave with a textile, a floater and cables. It would require little material and would leave beaches intact.

They tend to consist of sheets and plates, which are at the very root of their lightness.

Almost imperceptibly, we have begun to describe procedures to bring fibres and polymers together in thin composites. It is obvious that composite structures thrive on flatness. They tend to consist of sheets and plates, which are at the very root of their lightness. Fabrics from fibres exist in a morphological hierarchy, from random to dedicated. You can feed those structures into machines to integrate them into polymers. Random structures are known as non-wovens. These consist of chopped filaments that have been calendered together with the help of heat or a bonding agent. A special example of a non-woven is Sheet Moulding Compound, or SMC. This is a mixture of cut fibres or tapes and an uncured resin, produced as a thick sheet covered with foil. Regard it as a clever trick for preparing the right dosage for producing composite parts in a mould. First the right quantity is cut

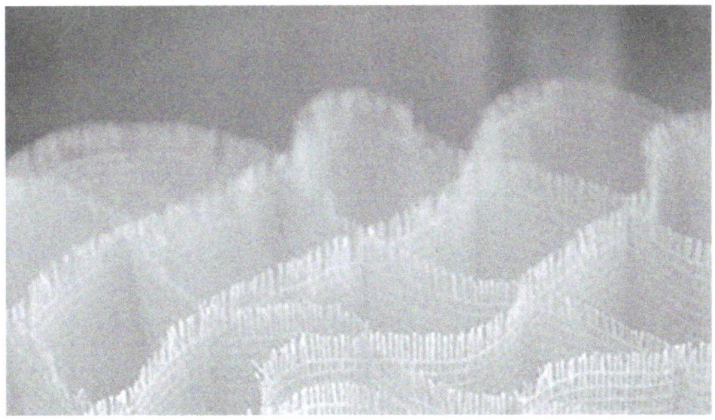

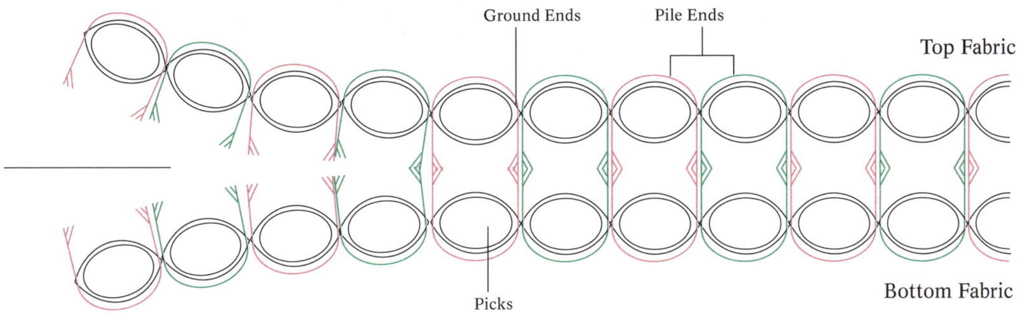

Left: Parabeam 3D woven glass. Right: Spatial fabrics by Samira Boon. Bottom: Velvet fabric manufactured by face to face principle. Side view

12.5 SPATIAL WEAVING

Flexible, soft, airy and on the thin side – woven fabrics deserve a better description! What we can do with a loom reaches much further into the third dimension than you would expect. One particular process is quite old. Velvet is woven with loop piles between two ground weaves by adding to the warp rods or 'picks' that are removed after weaving. Cutting the loops separates the ground weaves, resulting in two mirrored velvet fabrics. Forget about cutting and there you have it; a 3D (officially 2.5D) fabric with piles in the middle. A company called Parabeam produces this type of fabric with glass fibres, which is used to build product parts by hand lay-up method. What you get is a hollow structure, held apart by the piles inside.

Textile architect Samira Boon specializes in experimenting with spatial fabrics. The computer controlled Jacquard loom offers her many varied opportunities. Together, they're close to magic. One of her most interesting projects concerns the use of stretched elastic in geometric patterns. The elastic contracts after leaving the loom, giving it a waffle-like spatial pattern, for example. In another project, 'Architextiles', a whole range of adjoining spaces, each about 1 square metre in size, were woven in a single session. Each separated warp layer (there were five) could have its own colour or texture. These are principles that sooner or later will evoke ideas.

12.6 SEAMLESS FACADE

As entrances go, the one that welcomes you when you visit the Stedelijk Museum in Amsterdam is unique. This giant white object seems to float against the original building's former rear, which it almost entirely covers. A vast plastic object such as this is easier to design than to make, for it really had to be visually flat and seamless. In general single-surface structures are the most difficult to manufacture due to the sum of internal stresses.

This is extremely difficult for an outdoor surface 100 metres across because of thermal expansion. Generally, seams provide space for shrinking and expanding, so the designers at Holland Composites had to find an alternative that would give the least possible shrinkage and expansion, thereby obviating the need for seams. The trick was to use a composite skin of a single layer of carbon fibres in between two of aramid. Aramid (brand name Twaron) has a negative coefficient of thermal expansion, which means that heating causes it to shrink, and carbon (Tenax) lengthens only marginally when heated. Combined with vinyl ester resin, which is styrene-free, the sum total expansion over 100 metres is limited to as little as 1 millimetre per degree Celsius, a negligible amount. The resin can easily withstand the stress of counteracted expansion.

So, sandwich panels with a core of polyisocyanurate (PIR) foam were produced by vacuum injection in the factory, in a process very similar to prefabricating the roof panels for the Yitzhak Rabin Centre in Tel Aviv that the same company did earlier. The panels were then attached to a metal framework and the seams carefully sealed and smoothly finished. Now the entrance is doing its job and has got itself a nickname: 'The Bathtub'.

off and the foil removed. Next the sheet is folded to fit inside the mould, which is pressed together and heated. It is a relatively simple way to produce high quality parts. SMC can be considered a resin-saturated type of felt, a three-dimensional non-woven. Felt can consist of different kinds of material to be combined with a resin. If made from hair (sheep, llamas, humans) it will cohere after being treated with hot water and then rubbed and pressed, forcing the fibres to hook together. Among other properties, felt is good in sound insulation.

Endless fibres can be applied in strands, with a precured polymer coating, to build up forms in various ways. The next step is to pre-arrange them with an uncured resin parallel in 'endless' tapes, better known as UD (unidirectional) tapes. If you superimpose these UD tapes in different directions it gives you planar pre-impregnated structures or 'prepregs' consisting of flat tapes or round strands. Wide UD tapes – you could call them foils – can be laminated using a standard technology where each subsequent layer has a different fibre orientation. When arranged at 90 degrees to each other it is called cross-ply; angle-ply is the term for anything else. Moreover, the arrangement can be symmetrical above and below the central plane of the structure, meaning that the top and bottom layers of UD sheet have the same orientation and so have the layers respectively below and above those, and so on. Structures with designed mechanical and physical properties can be assembled using laminates of different materials. Lamination theory serves as a mathematical method to estimate those properties in a designed structure.

Basically, we are describing different approaches to designing and making textile 'wet' (polymer-coated) structures. Endless technical 'dry' fibres can be braided, woven and knitted like any other yarn. Strictly speaking, knitting by its very nature delivers a KNIT FABRIC, which is less strict than textile in how its shape is defined because it consists of connected loops rather than straight filaments. Be that as it may, all fibre structures are commonly called textiles.

The potential of 3D weaving with different yarns, including elastic ones, is only beginning to be explored.

Modern weaving techniques enable us to produce 3D textiles with glass and other endless filaments. There are industrial applications, beginning with velvet weaving. Velvet traditionally emerges from the loom as a two-layer 3D fabric whose layers are then cut apart, but for structural 3D weaving cutting is pointless.

An important principle when combining fibres and resin is convenience. That is why pultrusion is the first process to be mentioned. The second reason is that it is very similar to extrusion (mentioned in the first sentence of this chapter), and to complete the rationale, it was the earliest invention for applying endless fibres in a continuous process. W. Brandt Goldsworthy invented it in 1959.

As a word pultrusion is somewhat clumsy and contradictory, gluing English 'pull' to Latin trusion, which means pressing. Extraction would have been better but it has a bit of a dental ring to it. Nevertheless, the meaning is clear: a fibre structure is first soaked in resin and then pulled through a die to define the profile. Many different cross-sections can be produced. The lengths are usually dictated by how they are to be transported.

> *The evolution of composite structures is now moving in the direction of deploying thermoplastic technology.*

Winding, which we touched upon earlier, at first sight seems surprisingly simple as a method for manufacturing forms. It is not so straightforward in practice. A mandrel that turns, as in a lathe, is covered with tape by a robot that moves it appropriately, depending on the form and the layering algorithm. The variation in forms is limited, as you can't wind tape around just anything. It is possible to define a shape without a mandrel. You can define it by size and acceleration. The evolution of composite structures is now moving in the direction of deploying thermoplastic technology. In the end the shape will be the body of rotation of a catenary, the chain line caused by gravity when you suspend a piece of rope between two points. Centrifugal acceleration is just a different kind of gravity.

Noodles have been made in China for over 4000 years

Fibres not only contribute to strength and stiffness, but also determine composite processing limitations.

Fibre placement has by now become reasonably common for manufacturing objects by winding, with the fuselage of the Boeing 787 Dreamliner as a daring exploit in Automated Fibre Placement or AFP. From the perspective of robotics, however, we find another less precisely defined procedure. When the strand is wound around a mandrel, it is held under tensile stress. Fibre placement here is 'geodetic', which means that it closely follows the mandrel's rotation shape. Meridians on the globe are geodetic lines. This needn't be the case. Look at fibre placement as if it were 3D printing and suddenly there is more freedom to drape strands, say on a flat surface or even without support.

To return to the theme of thermosets and thermoplastics, up until now most composite structures by far have consisted of glass or carbon fibre and a thermoset resin. Polyester and epoxy are the resins of choice and if mechanical requirements are exacting, epoxy is the better polymer. Driven once again by convenience, and by the desire to make high specific strength and stiffness feasible for mass production, the evolution of composite structures is now moving in the direction of deploying thermoplastic technology.

Meltable plastics no longer hold up production through the need to wait for a chemical reaction to finish. Furthermore, it is possible to process semi-finished products by heating, bending or thermoforming them and – this is important – welding them. In a sense this transition can be seen as a partial return to metals because the processes look similar, although the principles of deformation are very different. Fibres inside the composite shear locally, causing swelling. Metals stretch and get thinner. There is a material similarity again in that thermoplastics are more ductile than thermosets and consequently offer better resistance to impact and delamination. Another advantage is that corrosion is no longer an issue. There are definitely greater differences in terms of conceptual consequences, and probably differences in behaviour that have yet to be discovered. The airplane and car industry are moving towards the thermoplastic composite production of parts. There is one more important advantage to thermoplastics: they are much easier to include in a circular system and may last longer ■

12.7 ACHILLES' EDGE

Composites don't deal with stress the way evenly distributed materials do. When they work together, fibres and the material that surrounds them can handle a lot of it, but stress concentrations may force them apart, particularly where fibres end, at free edges. In design, edges and transitions are always a matter of additional concern. In textiles, buttonholes get extra protection and free edges are hemmed.

Free edges in composites, particularly highly loaded composites, are the weak spots and need similar treatments to prevent fibres from moving around and triggering a process of delamination. To begin with, free edges have to be avoided wherever possible, for instance by folding them back and 'reintegrating' them in the surrounding structure. This is how window holes are defined in composite fuselages, with an integrated rim to hold the polymer windowpanes. The panes are fitted from the inside, so that the rim halts them when the cabin air pressure rises during the flight.

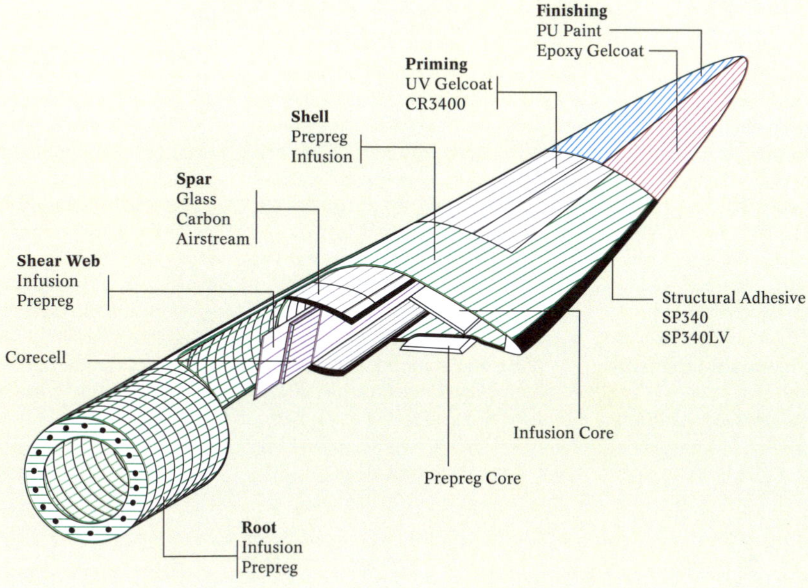

12.8 CLASSIC LAMINATE THEORY

Here's a surprise: the advantage of composites is that we can compose them to fulfil our every wish (well, almost). The drawback is that predicting mechanical behaviour is getting more and more complicated. However, in the 1950s a theory emerged from some early twentieth-century Russian books about the mechanics of sheet materials that are not equally strong in every direction, such as veneer: you can easily tear it apart in one direction, but turn it 90 degrees and it's impossible. The word for this property is 'anisotropic', which literally means unequally turned.

UD tapes are anisotropic, and they can be layered in different directions. You start with a tape consisting of carbon fibres embedded in a radically different polymer. On top of that you glue another tape of the same materials, in which the fibres run 90 degrees in relation to the first one. When you put this package under stress in the fibre direction of one of the tapes, this one will handle most of the excitement, whereas the other tape will mostly undergo load in the polymer matrix, which is much weaker and will hardly contribute to strength and stiffness. Now even out the differences and calculate the strain, in the awareness that in practice there will be more layers and different angles.

Deformation of the total package can vary from layers shearing off to torsion and saddle-shaped bending, which is like pulling opposing corners of a towel. Elastic warp doesn't have to be a sign of failure. It can be precisely what you're looking for. Wind turbine blades, for example, can be designed in such a way that aerodynamic forces adjust the blade pitch to prevent them from rotating too fast and getting overloaded. This is called aeroelastic tailoring, which means designing to interact. Here are some rules of thumb:

- Let laminates be symmetrical and balanced. Fibre directions and types are the same from the middle up and down and for every ply with a certain direction there is a mirror ply.
- Avoid large stiffness differences between plies.
- Avoid sudden free ends of plies ('ply drops') and if they're unavoidable let them happen one by one and not too close to each other (and cover them up).
- Keep it simple.

12.9 OBLIQUE CAN TAKE A PUNCH

It may be its deceptive simplicity, a view on style, or just a copied habit, but designers of all creeds tend to think in rectangular shapes, modules and endings. They live the Euclidean dream. This, however, is a perfect opportunity to quote British writer Douglas Adams in *The Hitchhiker's Guide to the Galaxy*: 'Reality is frequently inaccurate.' For there is at least one crooked alternative to be found in fennel, the sowbug and even our own hair, to name just three: call it oblique layering.

In laminates, layers are traditionally bonded parallel to one another. Oblique layering is different, because here the successive layers are attached not to each other but all to the same substrate. The principle is exactly the same as with the overlapping scales of a fish. These are all attached to the same 'sub-skin' of connective tissue. As a consequence, they are all at a slight angle to the sub-skin: this defines the obliqueness. Oh, and think of feathers: entire hierarchies of oblique layering to control body temperature and aerodynamics!

The Rotterdam bridge-building company FiberCore Europe (FCE) applies oblique layering in its own composite products, except that in the designs the bridge deck is itself an oblique layered structure. Its upper and lower skin, with ribs in between them, are both obliquely layered.

The advantage is that transfer of eventual delamination damage is minimal. It is very difficult for cracks to propagate from one oblique layer to the next. The funny thing is that the similarity between the engineered solution, which can withstand extended delamination, and the examples in plant and animal life was not discovered until after FiberCore Europe was established as a bridge builder in fibre-reinforced plastic. Often this is how biomimetics works: first the copy is designed and then the original is discovered.

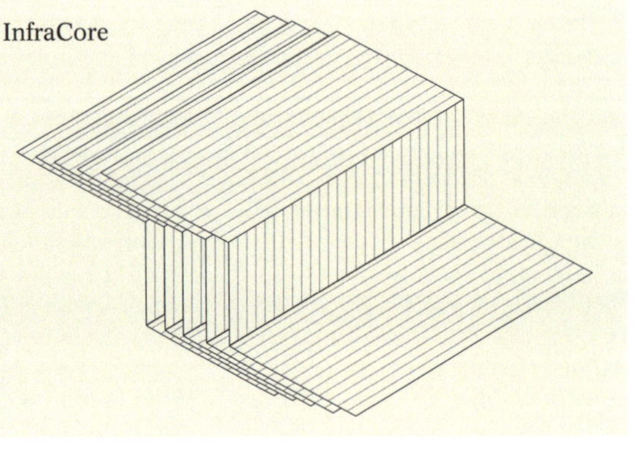

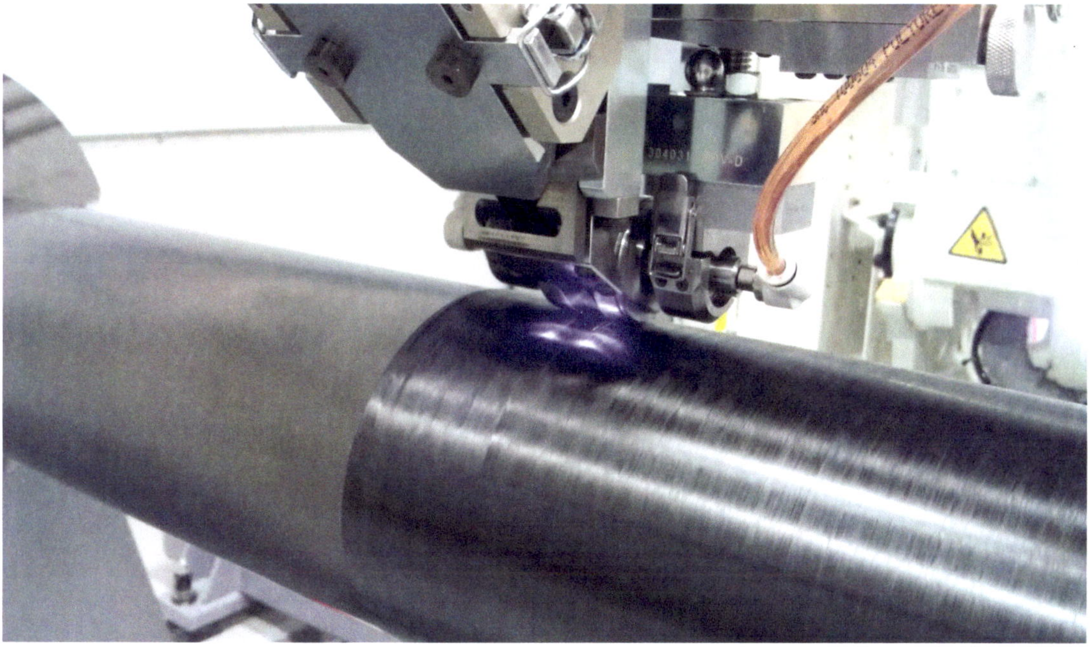

Thermoplastic composite laser welded fibre placement

12.10 COMPOSING PROCESSES

There can be setbacks in thermoset composite production, in particular when it concerns complex structures with masses of details such as aircraft and cars. In the world of thermosets, parts have to be connected with fasteners or they have to be cured together in an autoclave. There is also a restriction in terms of scale. Continuous fibre reinforcement is not easily formed and integrated in small parts other than by faking the carbon structure with a print. It doesn't help that it's hard to find machines for such tasks as handling fibres and attaching small prefabricated elements to other larger composite parts.

Fibre reinforced thermoplastics are a different matter, mainly because you can weld them. Welding principles are being used and developed by Kok & Van Engelen (KVE) among others. Fokker Aerostructures uses robots to weld ribs in wing noses for the Airbus A340 and A380. The melting capacity of thermoplastics is likely to advance the integration of welding, 3D printing, automated fibre placement (AFP), overprinting (3D printing directly on and around existing parts) and overmoulding, whereby elements are directly injection moulded on and around a substrate.

Thermoplastic AFP is a direct translation from its thermoset version. The difference is that attaching a sticky tape to build a structure before curing is just a matter of regulating forces, whereas welding plies laid one above the other requires precise heat regulation at the 'nip point' where the layers merge in heat. Research is also being done into induction welding, whereby heat between bonding surfaces is caused by eddy currents, which in turn originate from an alternating magnetic field. So this time the process requires monitoring, for which purpose integrated sensors are now being developed. One possibility is to 'build' an optic glass fibre into the polymer used for the structural tape.

Fusion bonding in 3D printing needs developing at all levels, from producing weldable filaments to developing machinery and software. And once you can handle 3D fibre printing, you simply have to find out how to apply it to a 3D object. So, here is the promise: thermoplastic composites require far fewer fastening procedures. It can be a step towards making composites more composite.

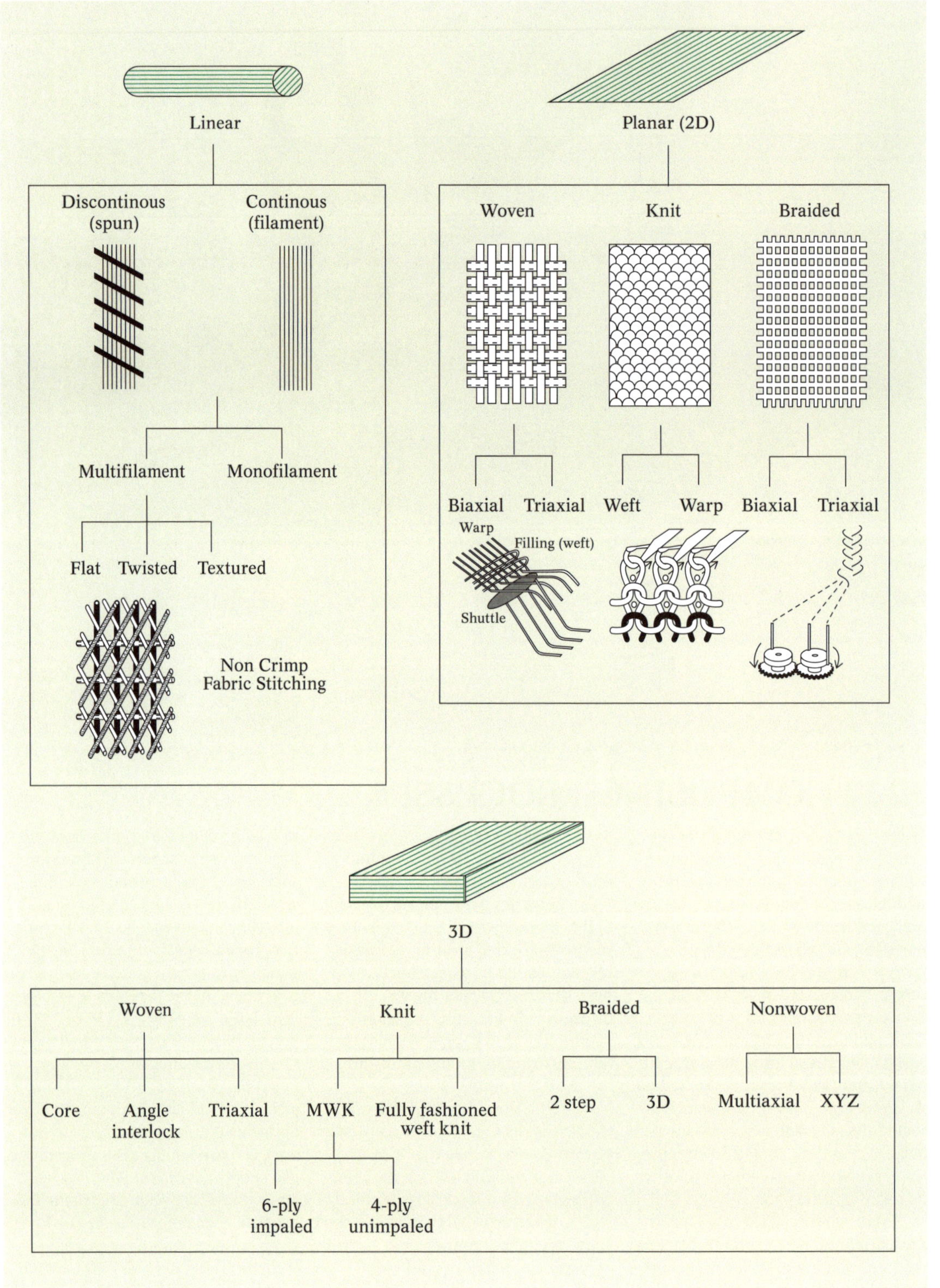

Ultimate Lightness
Textile structures in aerospace

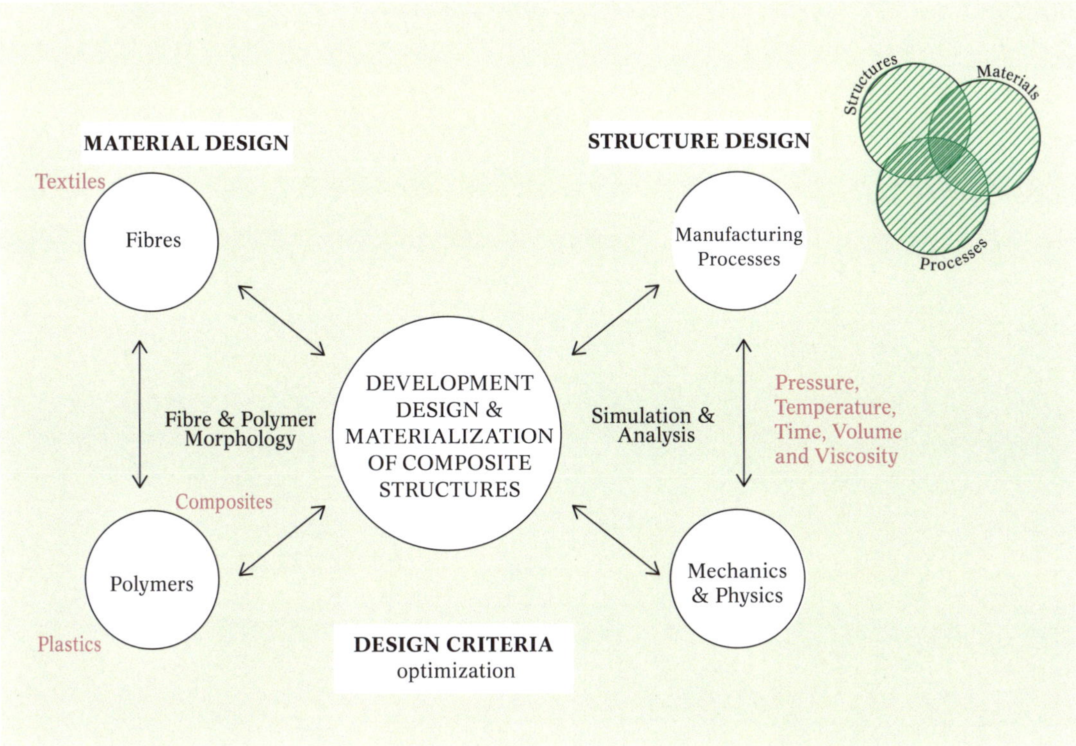

Elastic properties (specific strength & stiffness) of natural and synthetic fibres compared to steel wires

- ● Bekaert
- ● Cytec (Solvay)
- ● Zoltec
- ● Toray
- ● Toho
- ● SGL (BMW)
- ● Hexcel
- ● Mitsubishi
- ● Nippon Graphite
- ● Dupont
- ● Teijin
- ● DSM
- ● Toyobo
- ● Owens Corning
- ● St Gobain
- ● PPG
- ● Nippon

Material		Density ϱ 10^3 kg/m^3	Young's modulus E 10^9 N/m^2	Yield stress σ 10^6 N/m^2	Specific modulus E/ϱ 10^6 m^2/s^2	Specific strength σ/ϱ 10^3 m^2/s^2
● steel	piano wire	7,8	210	3100	27	397
natural fibres	jute	1.46	10 - 25	400 - 800	12	411
	hemp	1.48	26 - 30	550 - 900	19	490
	sisal	1.33	46	700	35	526
● synthetic	HT-carbon T300	1.76	230	3530	131	2010
● organic fibres	HM-aramide	1.45	133	3500	78	2410
● inorganic fibres	E-Glass	2.58	73	3450	28	1340

Lightweight Areas of Application

Carbon fibres	*light & fast structures*
Glass/Basalt fibres	*low-cost non-magnetic structures*
Aramide & UHMW PE fibres	*tensoids, light armour*
Metal fibres	*shielding & conductive structures*

Top: Development, design and production of composite structures. Bottom: Fibre materials & Structure efficiency Tensions Critical Structures: 'Tensiods'

13. COMPOSITE THINKING

Even though composites always consist of at least two materials, they are commonly mentioned and discussed as if a composite was a material in itself. There is no harm in that. Wood is a complex structure, steel can have a range of different structures, and yet they have always been known as materials. Nevertheless, as our knowledge and experience of materials and their properties and behaviour in relation to each other increases and we learn to incorporate those in design, it is time to normalize composite thinking and start appreciating the fact that for the full spectrum of convenience, identity and functionality, design begins at the level of combining materials.

Structures have been dealing with energy for thousands of years.

Different professions have different perceptions of composites. When a dentist applies a composite in a cavity the only fibres involved in the process belong to the dental floss used for cleaning afterwards. The UV curing acryl polymer they use has silica particles as a filler. These adjust material properties and the result is better than what polymer and silica can do separately. Engineers aren't inclined to take composites seriously until fibres and a polymer are combined in a meticulously designed structure. Here too the combination outperforms the sum of the individual components.

In both cases, the mechanical properties are deliberately enhanced to conjure up composites. Other characteristics, however, may change as well, on purpose or unwittingly, such as thermal expansion. Now suppose we combine two materials that wouldn't influence strength or stiffness but could store electrostatic energy, because together they would work as a capacitor. Hardly anybody would be inclined to call a capacitor a composite. However, as Wikipedia says, 'A composite material (also called a composition material or shortened to composite, which is the common name) is a material made from two or more constituent materials with significantly different physical or chemical properties that, when combined, produce a material with characteristics different from the individual components. The individual components remain separate and distinct within the finished structure, differentiating composites from mixtures, and solid solutions.'

This definition is much broader than a description of just one type of composite would suggest. Moreover, combining materials is becoming increasingly commonplace, as this technology has become more refined than just attaching parts to each other and there are often more than two materials involved. Energy-processing capabilities in particular are finding their way into structures. It is where the subtitle 'Structures for Saving Energy' becomes quite literal.

Structures have been dealing with energy for thousands of years. They protect us against heat and cold, sometimes through principles that are ingenious with hindsight. These date back to the early

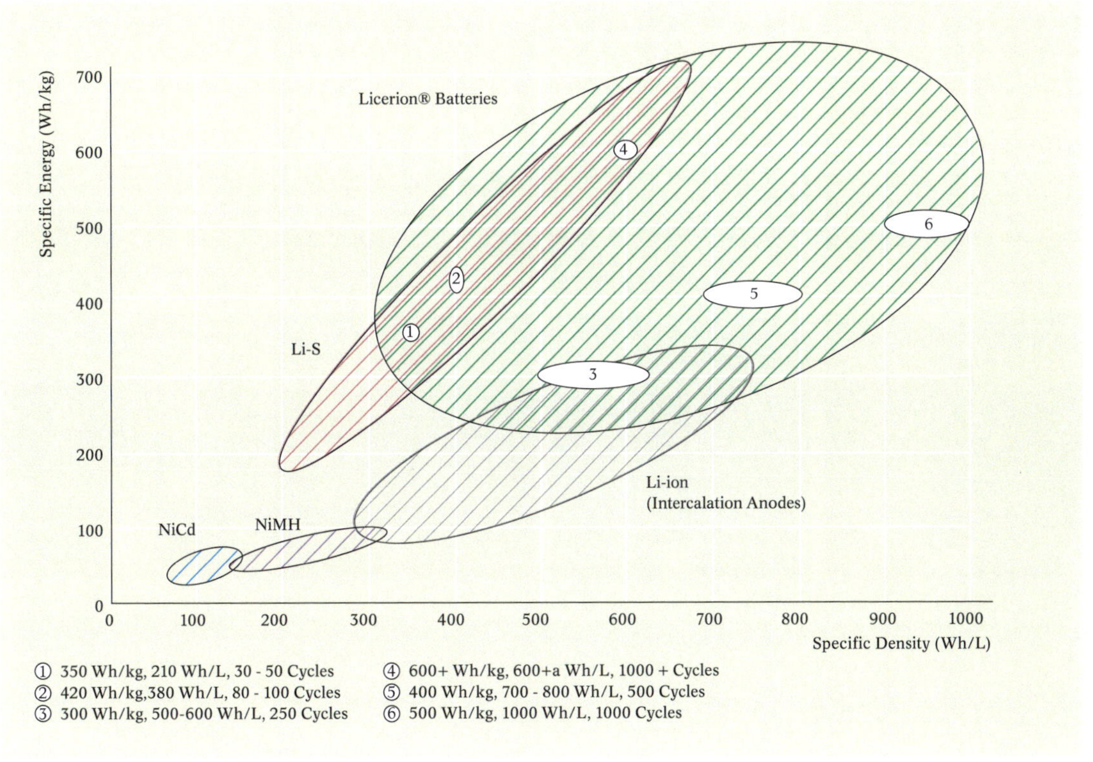

Qualities of different battery types

13.1 POWER PACKS

A serious battle for lightness is being fought in the field of power accumulator composites, better known as batteries. It looks as though electric cars are really taking over now and batteries with the longest range and shortest charging time promise to be the big winners.

The importance of battery weight is crystal clear in electric airplanes. We can use a fictional example to make our point. Suppose this Light Flyer has a 200-kilogram battery, 300 kilograms of empty weight, 500 kilograms of maximum take-off weight and a range of 150 kilometres. To double this distance, it has to carry a 400-kilogram battery, which means that empty weight equals maximum take-off weight: so forget flying. The effect for cars is similar but slightly less dramatic: the greater the range, the more difficult it becomes to get anywhere.

Currently the most popular batteries are lithium-ion batteries. These exist in several versions, depending on which lithium metal oxide is used. The cobalt oxide version is notorious for overheating. This type was chosen as an electric power buffer for the Boeing 787 Dreamliner, causing two of the first 50 new planes to catch fire. The entire pioneer series was grounded as a result. To prevent this from happening again the batteries were harnessed in an iron box, which in terms of weight alone is hardly ideal for airplanes.

The battle to improve performance is proceeding on two fronts. There are companies that try to improve Li-ion batteries, for instance by replacing the fluid inside by a solid. In general, the focus is on modifying the substance used, sometimes proudly showing off the nanoscale. Others look for radical alternatives. The Visual Capitalist, a website that represents economic changes in diagrams, shows 'hype cycles', waves of changing expectations for new concepts. So far there has been no sudden grand alternative and capacity increase is likely to remain in the seven per cent per ten-year range. But at this stage, anything can happen.

One thing is disturbing: in this era of growing attention to environmental and social side-effects, the focus is entirely on replacing the current fossil fuel system one on one, without any consideration for resources or for a thoughtful approach to mining. Electrical systems don't simply appear when you rub Aladdin's lamp.

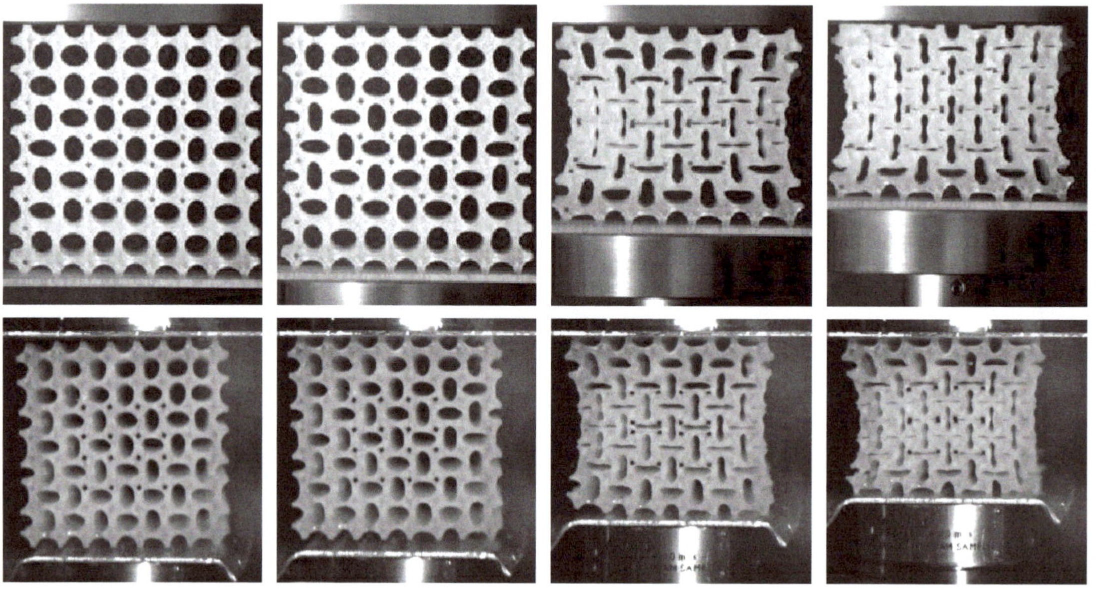

Metamaterial contracts under pressure

13.2 META-MAGIC

Since the end of the nineteenth century developers have been experimenting almost unobserved with the ability of manufactured dielectric material to fiddle with electromagnetic waves, for example to cloak objects using negative refraction. But it wasn't until the 1990s, when the stealth capacity of carbon materials was inexplicable even to Marconi Materials Technology, that physicist John Pendry was asked to investigate. He discovered that it was not a question of chemistry and molecular shape, which was the historically common assumption about light absorption. He observed that materials, or rather structures, physically interact with light on a wavelength scale far smaller than mirrors and lenses. Using shapes defined at this small scale (in the range of 0.5 micrometres) light waves can be made to do wondrous things. This grew into a research field of manipulating light and rendering objects invisible.

From the 1990s on, this new kind of material research gradually generated several derivates that explored the physical interaction between, say, sound or forces and so-called metamaterials. For one thing, metamaterials are not materials. Instead, they fashion regular materials into extraordinary modular structures. Metamaterials exhibit 'impossible' behaviour. For instance, you can build a material with a negative Poisson ratio that seems to shrink under compression. This seemingly counterintuitive behaviour looks like magic. But it happens simply because the structural elements are designed so as to allow trellising, shearing, folding and buckling in certain predefined ways. Numerous examples of such structures in two and three dimensions have been made. There are no applications yet.

days of pragmatism: wet leather or fabric cools the air when the water evaporates, simply because water can only turn into vapour at the cost of heat. It was discovered as a phenomenon long before the principle of desert cooling was understood. The same is probably true of black Bedouin tents, which consist of crudely woven goat hair. The hot desert sun heats the cloth and the air underneath. Hot air rises and can escape through the mesh, causing a gentle cooling flow of air. Tents with modern layered materials and a metallic reflective fabric on the outside don't really perform better. They protect against radiation, but air temperatures inside and out are practically the same. A much better way of regulating the temperature is to buffer heat with the help of phase change materials (PCMs are explained elsewhere).

Heat is a primitive form of energy when compared to electricity. For instance, research is being done on integrating capacitor functionality into structural composites in the interests of optimizing electric car systems, which are catching a lot of tailwind currently. The advantage of a capacitor over a battery, apart from lightness per amount of energy, is that its storage and release process is much faster than what a chemical battery can manage. It can deliver quickly, if in only limited amounts, and is used to whip out extra power during acceleration and store energy recuperated from slowing down.

Batteries are slower, but they can store more energy and are by no means out of the race as prospective contributors to structure. There are different ways of exploring how batteries can be 'entangled' with the car they energize. The most straightforward is to create a battery pack and apply it as a structural part, a beam or whatever. To go one step further: in 2013 Volvo published the idea of integrating batteries in car doors and other body panels. It hasn't happened in practice yet, but it might, since it has opened up a discussion of weight and energy consumption at the level of the car as a system. To arrive at innovation at this level means analysing the way functions interreact and then 'framing' them in different ways. Williams Advanced Engineering, renowned in the world of Formula One racing, is exploring the potential of sheet-shaped battery packs that can be folded. Engine cooling and aerodynamic and shock absorption are integrated in a bonded aluminium and carbon fibre reinforced polymer chassis unit. This is a complete revision of the familiar system, not only by including batteries in the family of chassis components but also by redesigning the battery as a composite.

Let us jump from storage to conversion, with a material property that we haven't mentioned so far, that of turning light into electricity, or the photovoltaic effect. This too is essentially a question of lamination. It is being applied in roofs of buildings, experimental cars such as solar racers (one of which has been developed for commercial availability as Lightyear One) and in experimental aircraft.

One example of the latter is Zephyr, a High Altitude Pseudo Satellite programme by the Airbus aircraft manufacturer in collaboration with the aforementioned Williams company. In aircraft, weight and aerodynamic shape call for the strictest requirements where integration is concerned. Planes are leading the way to system integration.

Clearly, there are reasons enough to open the composite doors to more extensive functionality.

There is more potential to be exploited. Electrical and light energy are what make electronic information networks tick. Circuit boards are laminates and the size of electronic and light processing components continues to shrink, so these could be integrated in structural composites too. Currently it is possible to print wearable elastic sensor circuits. Structures may have integrated circuits as well, including sensors, actuators and, as we saw earlier, batteries. Clearly, there are reasons enough to open the composite doors to more extensive functionality.

Cybernetics is becoming accessible as a kind of sophisticated version of 'elastic tailoring', the structural capability to interact with external forces. At the Korea Advanced Institute of Science and Technology (KAIST) they have developed artificial muscles, as tiny as insect wings. These are made from MXene, a compound, and of course a composite, consisting of layers of titanium and carbon several atoms thick, ionically bonded into a polymer. These muscles can be driven by electricity. At this stage it is wearable art, fake butterflies flapping their wings and expressing identity, but it has the potential to contribute to convenience.

Looking back into the history of composite development, its evolution matches the principle of continuous refinement. Whereas the first composites consisted of fairly large parts glued together, as in bows and chariots, we now have reached the level of entangling materials to the point where they are barely identifiable individually. One step further and they would get completely mixed up and lose their composite status ■

Electric muscles made from MXene flap the wings of 'butterflies'

13.3 SOLAR COMPOSITE

Glass and a transparent photovoltaic substance together are a good laminate for providing energy in a greenhouse. Marjan van Aubel sees herself as a solar designer and her aim is to find beauty in technical ideas. She has turned drinking glasses and ornamental windows into energy converters. And together with The New Institute, architect Emma Elston, researcher Yasmine Ostendorf, SmartSkin producer Physee and the University of Amsterdam she has created 'Power Plant'.

This is a greenhouse whose glass converts solar energy into the electri city that sustains the climate inside for growing plants hydroponically. The idea is that such greenhouses can be placed anywhere and make vegetable culture accessible to anyone. Glass harvests the energy to pamper the plants that we can eat.

14. ANTICIPATING LIFE CYCLES

Top: Pantheon in Rome. Bottom: Airplane turned into hotel

The hard part is to take responsibility for the return logistics and organize them accordingly.

Now that we can reduce the weight of everything by at least half, we have to work on the environmental side effects, since it is only now that we are entering the far more familiar territory of circular economy and circular design. Here everything, now much lighter, is supposed to go round and round in circles of value retention, from reusing complete products to reworking broken-down materials. This field of circular interest includes an arsenal of extra design and management requirements, extending into how we organize society.

> *One factor is still not sufficiently accounted for, and that's us humans.*

Circular Economy is the current label for what started out as a call for more recycling from the 1970s onwards, and via cradle-to-cradle design (C2C) evolved into the insight that maintaining product value in time through maintenance, repair, refurbishment, remanufacturing and recycling could lead to a system of managed obsolescence. One factor is still not sufficiently accounted for, and that's us humans. We're always after simplicity and because of this we're inclined to reduce everything to manageable technical issues. With its focus on technical solutions, circular design has given us some basic principles. Repairability, for example, presents itself as a solvable technical problem, although there is much more to it, such as financial viability, the organizing involved and the culture of immediate availability, which is why we are so impatient these days. Value, or the sense of potential, depends on much more than technical interventions. A very important aspect is reputation. In November 2019 Elon Musk, founder of Tesla, introduced his 'Cybertruck'. He claimed that the all-electric vehicle couldn't be damaged and during his theatrical introduction had the designer hit a window with an iron ball. With one bang he smashed it, and another one, causing the stock value of Tesla to drop by $770 million, which is more than it would cost to repair the window. Still, thousands of orders continued to pour in, which more than made up for the loss. Here we have an extreme example of a very important aspect affecting all the things we use, including the humblest ones. Six drinking glasses in the kitchen cupboard, for instance, are fine, but if one of them breaks spontaneously because of internal material stress, the 'honour' of the remaining unbroken five is jeopardized and they may be replaced because of that. Commerce is based on the creation of reputations. Even salespeople fall for its tricks when they buy stuff wholesale.

> *Commerce is based on the creation of reputations.*

The reputation of the Circular Economy itself suffers from the observation that currently it is fashionable, which brings it power, funding and attention, but also a certain practical shallowness. There is nothing wrong whatsoever with circular thinking as an instrument to further technological development in the interests of sustainability, but it suggests that there are principles of an easy way out, in which important aspects are overlooked. 'Circular', like 'green' and 'sustainable' has become an empty selling point labelled with the word 'recycling'. Chris Fleming from Western Sydney University addressed this phenomenon in his essay 'The Tyranny of Trendy Ideas' (*The Chronicle of Higher Education*, June 2019). This tyranny gives rise to preconceptions. In the context of the Circular Economy, it boils down to: 'We can make anything as long as we make sure it can be recycled'.

This has unjustly turned 'design for recycling' into the one and only benchmark for sustainability. It has become the ideal slogan for brands to be able to boast about their greenness and to suggest that sustainability is a consumer choice. 'Buy this bike! It's made of recycled plastic!'

However, recycling is a destructive and energy-consuming industrial activity, which for this reason should be postponed for as long as possible. The more we make, the more we have to recycle. Recycling has turned into an excuse for producing more than what is sufficient. Sufficiency should be more important than efficiency.

Recycling is only one part of the cycle, however. Furthermore, there is no need or obligation to recycle everything. Many objects and buildings have been made to last forever and indeed it looks as though they might. Some building structures were planned to be used for a limited time and have survived much longer. In 1889 Eiffel was given a permit for his Paris tower to stand for 20 years and look what happened. It was allowed to stay because it had a transmitter on top: this was radio architecture.

Airplanes are interesting in this respect. They are being recycled, but only slowly, which is fine because there aren't that many. For a major part they are handmade; maybe their production is a remnant of artisan culture. Something like 12,000 planes in special aircraft graveyards, most of them in the US, are to be taken apart in the coming 20 years. Some parts are more difficult to deal with than others. Aluminium recycling is easy and commonplace. Cockpit parts and wing sections can be reused in, for instance, education. One can order a slice of airplane, so to speak. Indeed, occasionally an entrepreneur will buy a complete used plane, turn it into a hotel and boast about being motivated by sustainability, which is futile since sustainability is about mass flows.

Fibre reinforced thermoset polymers are still only to be found in small

14.1 CIRCULAR DESIGN

The principles for keeping products within the Circular Economy are pretty straightforward. They take the product as a whole and hierarchically break it down into its component parts and elements. The following aims have to be kept in mind during the design process and when establishing requirements:

1. Attachment and trust are not the easiest of aims as they are about reputation and usage history. Designers have limited opportunities for control over their work.
2. Durability is partly a question of reliability, which can be estimated, and partly a question of perception.
3. Standardization and compatibility are where individual parts of a product are considered along with their ability to support continued use.
4. Ease of maintenance and repair is where many of today's products fall short. Product owners have insufficient access to their property.
5. Upgradability and adaptability are about resilience to changes in time and the availability of parts and information for new uses.
6. Disassembly and reassembly are familiar and closely related to the previous aims, although here the aim is very close to being a concrete requirement.
7. Decomposition is new and concerns the possibility of breaking down composites into their constituent materials.

Design is closely linked to business models and value cultivation scenarios. The most encompassing aim may very well be to plan and evaluate long before introducing a product and to consider more cycles than just one. A product made out of recycled composite material is all very well, but time doesn't stand still and there are subsequent steps to take.

14.2 BIO-COMPOSITE CHAIR

Label Breed is a small company that brings together designers and producers to ensure that the outcome can be put into production. The renowned designer Christien Meindertsma developed together with Enkev, a company specialized in renewable fibres, a composite sheet material consisting of flax – she has her own flax farm – and polylactic acid (PLA), a biodegradable thermoplastic. The sheets are heat-pressed to get the chair in shape and the legs and seat fit neatly into one rectangular piece to minimize waste. The use of a biodegradable thermoplastic composite places the chair at the cutting edge of design.

The Flax® chair is well designed, which leads us to an interesting paradox. It may be biodegradable, but it's not the kind of chair you would leave as a meal for microorganisms. Another interesting detail is that the chair's form was copied by a pretty big international furniture enterprise and produced with a mixture of 'renewable wood and recycled plastic'. Wood is of course always renewable and recycled plastic sounds green as well. The question is what will happen to it after that.

quantities in retired planes because structural composites in aircraft have only been around for a few years. They have proved difficult to recycle, firstly because of the need to separate fibres and polymer and secondly because thermosets won't melt. The only option was to shred the stuff and mix the milled composite with new resin, to somewhat improve its mechanical properties and reduce the required amount of fresh material. This has given composites an environmentally unfriendly reputation, which is not entirely wrong, but it isn't right either.

Progress continues to be made and at the end of the day anything can be recycled. It is more a matter of feasibility. This implies there should always be room for doubting that recycling composites is impossible. We may be close to recycling thermoset fibre reinforced polymers, even if it were just because of the value of saving weight and maintenance costs. There are two main principles for retrieving carbon fibres from their matrix. These are pyrolysis, or burning the resin, and solvolysis, dissolving it to free the fibres. These can then be reapplied and upgraded. The number of industries able to do this is currently growing. Retrieving glass fibres has not developed this far, probably because in the present situation new glass fibres are much cheaper.

For value droppers the emphasis needs to be on flow.

Progress is also being made in alternative matrices. Burning thermosets is a dirty way out, and their ability to dissolve may eventually become a better option. Nevertheless, the most important alternative is the use of thermoplastic composites, since separating fibres and matrix is then simply a matter of melting the plastic, although dissolving may work for some polymers. An important reason for the sharp increase in interest in thermoplastic composites is their recycling potential.

Of course, this coincides with the growing attention to recycling itself, as it is important to prevent mass-produced goods from cluttering the environment, as decluttering it is no simple matter. We can cope with the presence on earth of old dysfunctional airplanes, but mass-produced goods such as bikes, cars, furniture and particularly low-value stuff like fast fashion items, knick-knacks, disposables and single-use packaging all mean serious recycling business.

The hard part is to take responsibility for the return logistics and organize them accordingly.

Here we have a clear distinction between durables and 'value droppers', products that turn into waste very quickly. The range of products by and large coincides with series sizes or production quantities. So, on one side you will find small series of products that last long and on the other, things like throwaway mugs, syringes and bags for crisps. Durables thrive on cultivating value over time and need to be designed for an optimum maintainable lifespan. Maximum lifespan is not ideal since replacing old products, such as refrigerators, may reduce the environmental burden. For value droppers the emphasis needs to be on flow. This flow must be kept under control and the responsibility for it clearly defined.

Thanks to technological refinement, composites are present in increasing quantities throughout the entire range. In the middle you will find durables with a limited lifespan, say from a couple of years to ten or twenty. For these, easy recycling is an important requirement, which means that applied composite parts, which may include electronic components and textiles but also car body frames, should be easy to take apart. At the cheap end of the range, which in fact is expensive because there are costs attached to disposing of them, are packaging laminates, particularly metalized films, which cannot be recycled yet. Companies are experimenting with mono-material replacements. That would help but it still only covers the material and processing side of recycling.

The hard part is to take responsibility for the return logistics and organize them accordingly. Lastly, we shouldn't forget the option of reducing our own body weight by going easy on the packets of salted peanuts ■

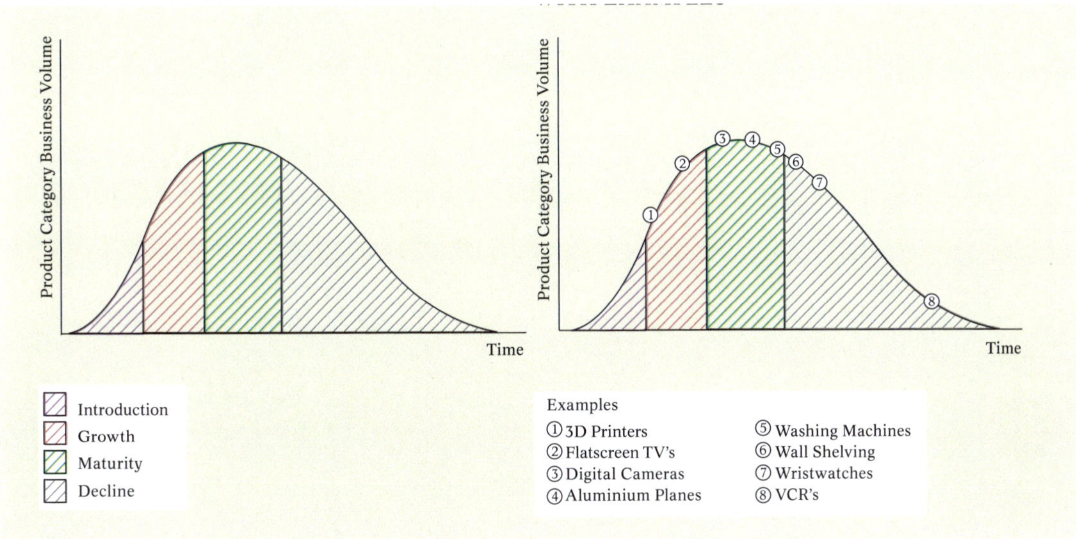

Left: Product category life cycle curve. Right: Product category life cycle curve with examples

14.3 CYCLES AND CURVES

The life cycle is an important instrument for measuring product lifespans. Or is it? There are different types of life cycles, each with its own interpretation. A well-known type is used to assess the environmental effects of certain artefacts. It adds up energy consumption, emissions and impact of waste in a so-called life cycle assessment (LCA).

More familiar to us is the bell curve, where the product life cycle is a simple representation of that product's turnover in time. It shows that a newly designed product doesn't sell well in the beginning, and then sales rise until a top level has been reached. After that the number of products sold gradually decreases until it stops selling altogether. But if you're smart you've introduced an alternative or a successor, even before sales started to drop, to increase the overall turnover and the profit. This scenario is the backbone of the Sell More Sell Faster business model, which generally ignores the life of products after they stop selling as well as the opportunities this new phase brings to make money by cultivating their value. Aircraft are under a certain maintenance and continued use after sales, Bluetooth speakers are not.

A third cycle type tells the most riveting story of all. It looks exactly like the previous curve, except that it shows the growth in use of a particular category of products, such as Bluetooth speakers, or a particular technical phenomenon, such as aluminium airframes. Most things in human culture can be represented this way. Suppose you want to participate in a market; the curve can help you to decide on your approach. If you are a pioneer, you will most certainly have competition and have to deal with adaptations and upgrades. Dynamics wear off at the saturation stage, so that adaptations will be superficial. The downturn stage can be defined by an emphasis on maintaining quality in the transformation to a service organization. The only other recourse is the jump to a better alternative. This is why the declining part of the cycle is often erased. Because of its shape the remainder is appropriately named the S-curve. It heralds change, for example from aluminium to composite aircraft.

EIGHT LIGHT TRADES

15. LIGHTWEIGHT IS THE WINNER

15.1 COMPOSITE CONTROVERSY
15.2 FOOTWEAR FASHION
15.3 VAULTING POLES
15.4 BENDING FOR A POWER ARM
15.5 STIFF COMPETITION
15.6 HELPLESS MONSTERS

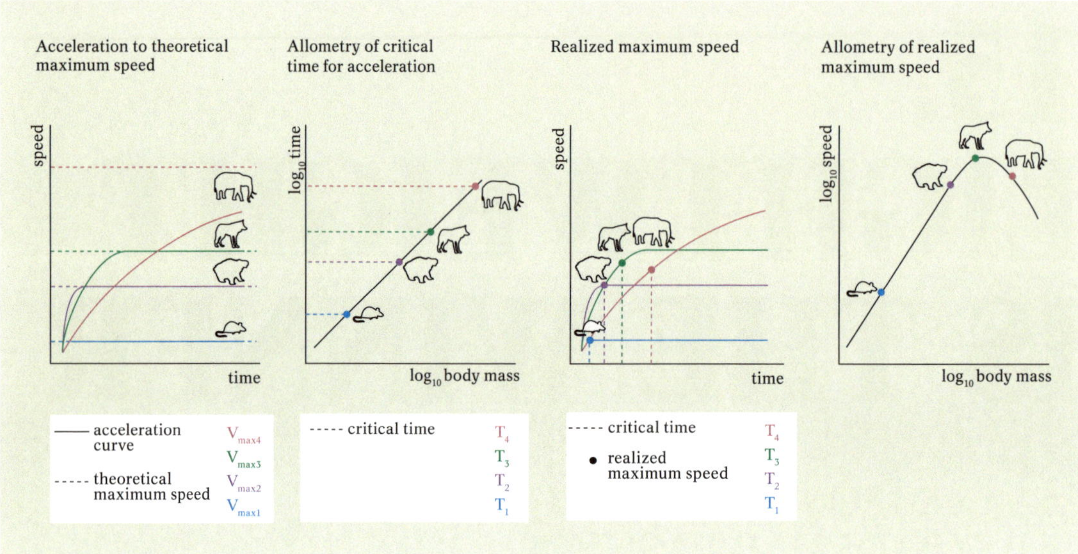

According to biologist Myriam Hirt, animal speed depends on the balance between weight and muscle power

How tempting it is to start with the fact that *Paratarsotomus macropalpis*, a Southern Californian mite, is by far the fastest animal in the world. This millimetre-sized micro monster can run 322 times its own body length per second, whereas a cheetah can 'only' run 16 times its length in that time. Yet the stupid mite still can't avoid being caught by a sluggish human, to be filmed in a laboratory racing alongside a ruler. It would be too simple to just relate velocity to body length, however. Mass and strength are important factors and you also need the right kind of body. Warfare requires superior equipment. However, in the end the smart lightweight trick triumphs over expensive heavy armament. In fact, computing may push fighting all the way into cyberspace.

Research has been done into this question of why the maximum speed of animals is not simply related to size. There is an optimum, defined by a good balance between size and muscle power. In 2017 biologist Myriam Hirt and her team at the German Centre for Integrative Biodiversity Research in Leipzig plotted the speed of over 470 different species, from insects to mammals, and found a hump distribution: animals in the top layer are powerful yet not too heavy. The cheetah and its prey, the springbok, fit the description perfectly. Hirt recognized the importance of accelerating mass and the time needed to reach the theoretical maximum speed, which quite simply is longer for bulkier beasts. Their muscles get tired before the maximum speed is reached. She proposed a formula that predicts maximum speed for different species reasonably well and that can even help estimate posthumously what dinosaurs could do.

It provides background information on the disadvantages of overweight. Subtle differences, however, are challenging for the formula, such as the slowness of humans compared to cheetahs. These big cats are faster than their body mass justifies.

The tools we carry have to be lightweight for the sake of speed and hopefully lead us to victory.

There is of course more to speed than mass and muscles. Different species happen to have different anatomies that have emerged through different evolutions in different environments, otherwise everything that lives would have the convenience of gills and wings.

One way or another, body mass is important in all human physical activity, because force is needed to compensate for gravity in all our movements. The tools we carry have to be lightweight for the sake of speed and hopefully lead us to victory, both in sports and in warfare, whereby the former traditionally serves as an exercise for the latter. Wrestling and fencing are forms of combat. Attack and retreat depend on our ability to run.

Identity became part of the deal.

As a first step in the following mass reduction hierarchy, let's take the human body and more specifically the runner's feet and legs. The shape of the leg alone contributes to the ability to win races. Many long-distance running champions belong to the Kalenjin people in West Kenya. Their genes provide them with thin limbs and high thin calves, thereby reducing the amount of mass of the two 'walking pendulums' we call legs. This doesn't imply that all Kalenjin people are fantastic runners, but this endowment does increase the probability.

15.1 COMPOSITE CONTROVERSY

These days a lightweight running shoe has a carbon fibre reinforced plastic plate integrated in its sole. Some argue that this should not be allowed, because the part is considered a device that provides extra push-off power. It has been compared with the Paralympic running blade that has empowered athletes with missing lower legs to run almost as fast as athletes with fully functional lower limbs. Dutch 'blade babe' Marlou van Rhijn set the Paralympic record for the 100 metres sprint at 12.79 seconds, which is only a couple of seconds slower than the mighty Florence Griffith-Joyner's 10.49 seconds. It is not unthinkable that this difference will become even smaller.

The basic question here is: are the sole plate and the running blade to be considered performance enhancing devices, or materials? In both cases there is a structure customized to provide quite user-specific functionality, which supports the 'device' argument. On the other hand, the device gets all its energy input from the movement and mass of the runner. There is no additional agent involved, which implies that it is mainly a material matter.

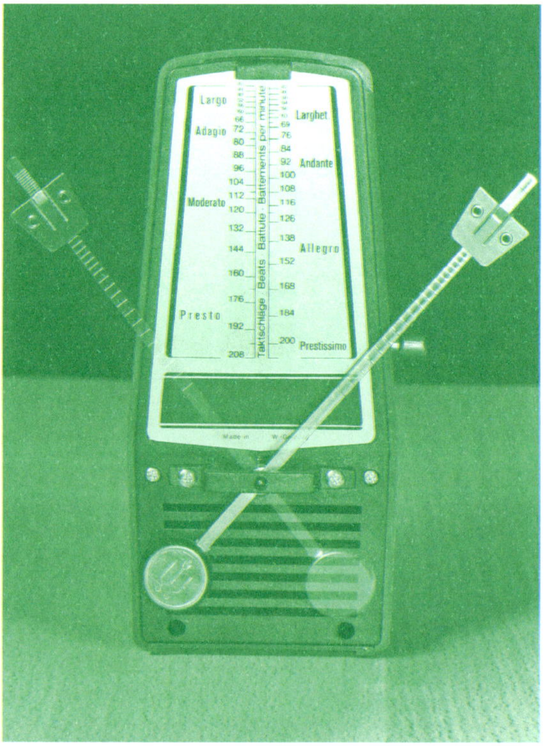

Right: The speed of a metronome depends on the placement of the weight

The first sports shoes for ladies (late 1880s); the crystal chain around the Gucci sneakers can be removed

15.2 FOOTWEAR FASHION

In 1974 track athlete Phil Knight and his coach Bill Bowerman came up with running shoes that had waffles instead of spikes underneath. Recently this first pair of Nike shoes – Nike was their brand – was auctioned for almost half a million dollars. They had brought a change in perception. Nike was the first to push running shoes into the world of fashion by developing a wide range of different applications for the running shoe format. Take a walk in the city, or anywhere else for that matter, and virtually everybody looks like an athlete of sorts. One can be 87 getting around with a walker and still wear colourful trainers. Prestigious fashion brands like Prada and Balenciaga sell spectacular trainers, some of which require special balancing skills because of the sheer height and volume of their soles.

Since expression has become so important, that is what technology is focusing on: flaunt more with less. Advanced colourful foam designs, built-in transparent fluid containers, patchwork, prints to give shoes and rubber plates a print-on carbon look – they're everywhere. Built-in LED lighting these days make shoes shine in the dark.

Mass consumption has turned trainers into a serious lightweight waste problem. Satirical science fiction writer Douglas Adams foresaw this when he described the future archaeological discovery of the Shoe Event Horizon. This is an era marked by a thin rubbery layer in the geological structure of Earth, during which humans bought so many shoes that they could no longer afford food. The word philosophers use these days is 'Anthropocene'.

Currently several brands are taking up the challenge of developing trainers that can be recycled and/or are biodegradable, which is admirable, except for the fact that it is not just material qualities that determine whether production and consumption leave minimal environmental traces. The main ingredient for that condition is responsible control of the material flow. Indeed, Adidas has recently taken a first step by introducing a deposit scheme.

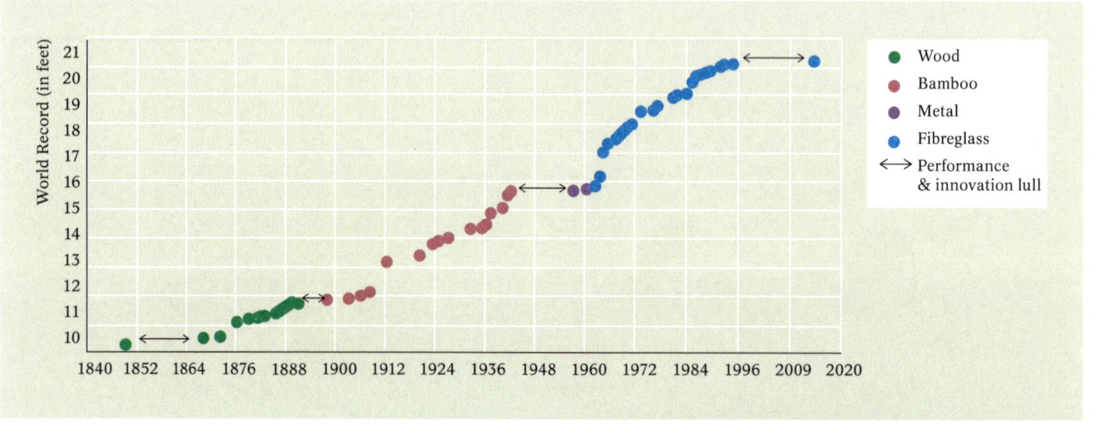

15.3 VAULTING POLES

There is a particular moment in history when pole vault performance made a spectacular jump of about twenty per cent achievable height increase. The sport began as a way to cross ditches, small rivers and channels without getting wet feet and without the need to build a bridge. That horizontal version of pole vaulting, which may involve pole climbing, still exists as a sport, mainly in the Dutch province of Friesland. Some Japanese athletes are interested.

The vertical version made its first appearance in Germany towards the end of the eighteenth century. It is much better known, and is now one of the most spectacular Olympic sports. Poles were wooden to start with but these were later superseded by bamboo and metal versions. Costa Mesa Pacific Laminates was the first company to experiment with fibreglass poles in 1949, when metal poles were commonly used. In those days the record was slowly rising towards the five-metre mark. A handful of athletes starting using fibreglass poles in the early 1950s but treated them as slightly lighter versions of the metal ones. According to Vasilis Grammaticos on the 'Rethinking Athletics' blog, this changed dramatically in 1961, when pole-vaulter Aubrey Dooley recognized the potential of bending the pole during his jump. That marked a new beginning. Pole vaulting turned into a sport of true interaction between athlete and pole. Before this, bending had been avoided, since it could lead to breaking. Fibreglass, however, doesn't break. The force generated when the pole straightens again provides the athlete with an extra push, all the way up to 6.16 metres so far (Renaud Lavillenie in 2014). The Russian Sergey Bubka was the first to jump higher than 6 metres. Poles are continually being improved. Combining different kinds of fibres, including carbon, enables them to be customized to a very high degree.

In ancient times the use of any form of equipment for running was not considered. In early Olympic games in Greece, some 2700 years ago, athletes wore nothing. But there were sportspeople from colder regions who wore sandals. These proved to have a better grip on the race track and soon the Greeks embraced the idea: the first step in the running shoe innovation race had been taken. Gradually sandals were improved and made sturdier, not just for sports, but also for warfare. Roman soldiers wore caligae, simple sandals cut from leather, to protect their feet during long marches over specially paved roads, a crucial element in itself in a system that accommodates speed. Over the centuries sandals gradually degraded in lightness and turned into boots.

In the eighteenth century the English were the first to introduce shoes specially designed for running. Sure enough, 1832 saw the introduction of the rubber sole, which less than thirty years later was given a canvas upper to facilitate the playing of croquet. The soundless nature of these shoes, and their eager acceptance by thieves, earned them the name 'sneakers'. Half a century later a female version was developed complete with high heels, a feature it was believed would prevent women from 'losing their femininity'.

From the 1850s onwards the industrial revolution really took off, bringing with it entirely new kinds of tools and products. As a result, the next shoe type was made suitable for riding bicycles. This new concept in turn became readapted for running in 1865 as brogues with one spike at the front and one on the heel. Shoes like these weighed a mere 280 grams. The first brand that produced – and continued to improve – running shoes to cater for specific demands and different kinds of running was J.W. Foster and Sons, which became Reebok in 1958. This was just after Adidas and Puma had started to make their mark as brands with characteristic symbols. Television brought added visual importance – and financial value – to functional running quality and profitability. Identity became part of the deal. In 1962 New Balance was the first company to introduce a scientifically tested shoe. This weighed only 96 grams. This is within the 90 to 100 gram range for fast running shoes today, which typically have mesh fabric uppers and synthetic soles that include a carbon fibre composite plate.

Agility therefore often tends to lose out to protection, providing opponents with opportunities to fight fast and 'dirty'.

In warfare, fighting and weight reduction have always been in conflict. As a soldier first and foremost you have to be 'safe'. Agility therefore often tends to lose out to protection, providing opponents with opportunities to fight fast and 'dirty'. Swords were made heavier to the point that wielding them became almost impossible to sustain for an entire skirmish and iron harnesses brought warriors to a state of near immobility. Then an enemy comprised of agile horsemen arrived from the east dressed in light silk and leather vests and armed with daggers and short powerful bows and arrows. This enemy proved almost impossible to defeat. Archery also created distance between opponents. Killing became more abstract.

With hindsight hockey sticks and tennis rackets could have guided warriors to an easier life. The impact of hand weapons depends less on weight than it does on stiffness. For tennis rackets there is additional value in frame strength: a high string tension provides the player with a larger 'sweet spot', the area best suited to hitting the ball.

Tennis has never had any practical equivalent beyond competitions and fun. The game had an initial primitive stage in the Dark Ages, when it was played with bare hands only. Later, players wore gloves until the appearance of the first rackets in the sixteenth century. From then on, rackets consisted exclusively of wood (mainly ash) until the end of the 1960s. The disadvantage of wood is that it is a living material, so that wooden rackets can behave unpredictably. Still, after ten years of experiments with metal alternatives (aluminium, magnesium and titanium), top players still preferred wood.

A major advantage of fibre reinforced structures is that they are customizable to precise requirements.

Nevertheless, its supremacy quickly declined after racket designers started to use composites, with carbon – or 'graphite', as it is also known in tennis circles – as their principal component. Rackets could be made very stiff and still dampen vibrations sufficiently. A major advantage of fibre reinforced structures is that they are customizable to precise requirements. Rackets now mainly consist of fibre reinforced polymers, which has also made it possible to modify their shape and make them larger. No doubt this has gradually changed the game, but not in ways that are easily measurable. It might be interesting to watch a time machine match between Billie Jean King in her prime and Serena Williams in hers.

In the eighteenth and nineteenth centuries guns became the weapons of choice in a way that is totally incomprehensible now: regiments would stand bolt upright opposite each other and shoot simultaneously. They would repeat this until the regiment with the most soldiers left standing had 'won' and could move on. Something as obvious as the trench had still to be invented; this happened during the Crimean War (1853-1856). The First World War turned the trench into a symbol of the futility of warfare. But it also saw the rise of fighting vehicles – armoured cars, tanks and airplanes – motorized wagers of war that hitherto hadn't existed. These included fake wooden versions, particularly of tanks, which were used to draw airplane fire.

It meant a powerful boost to the continuation of the arms race. This is as old as humanity, an unceasing effort to overpower and outwit the enemy with deadlier weapons, stronger protection and dirtier tricks – and more impressive vehicles.

'Rupert' dummy paratrooper as used by the Allied Forces during the invasion of Normandy

WWII inflatable decoy tank

And now the race had become powered by mass industry and fossil fuels.

Warfare is rapidly getting more awkward and cheapness is becoming more powerful.

After World War II and into the Cold War the arms race continued with the production of absurd amounts of bombing power. Subsequent conflicts became ever more entangled with mediated reality, giving more weight to the phrase 'The first casualty of war is the truth'. There was US Secretary of State Colin Powell, who in 2003 'proved' that the Iraqi dictator Saddam Hussein had the power to deploy weapons of mass destruction, which he hadn't. A few weeks later Iraq was invaded, and the news networks showed footage of precision bombings, as abstract as if you were playing a first-person shooter. Journalist Joris Luyendijk in his book *People Like Us* about the Middle East wanted to witness riots in Ramallah. When he arrived, everything was quiet. When he asked what was going on he was told that the riots were scheduled to start at 2 PM.

Warfare is rapidly getting more awkward and cheapness is becoming more powerful. Recently an attack by relatively cheap drones and cruise missiles reduced Saudi Arabia's oil-producing capacity by half. The sophisticated Saudi systems that were supposed to offer protection just weren't designed to counter the simple slow weapons used for the attack. Two years earlier, US General David Perkins had already proved this point: a $2 million Patriot missile had successfully brought down a drone, the $300 variety that anyone can buy anywhere. Deploy twenty of those and you're a winner at an affordable price. This in itself has become a means to conquer the world. Stimulate mass consumption through mass media and you won't need violence at all.

The experience of violence is being innovated out of conflicts anyway. There is hardly any difference left between a control unit for remote warfare with drones and an up-market gaming cockpit. The next step was announced on BBC News last year: 'UK military fears robots learning war from video games'. But first robots will have to learn how to walk properly. We wouldn't want a clumsy person to fire rockets, now would we? ■

Striking similarity between gaming console (left) and drone control unit

15.4 BENDING FOR A POWER ARM

Bows and vaulting poles have a way of storing energy than can be put to more kinds of use than just flinging arrows. Think of leaf springs. Two lightweight bows made of carbon fibre reinforced polymers, one for the right arm and one for the left, now have become the crucial parts of an exoskeleton, the Skelex 360, which supports the arms during repetitive overhead work, as in the case of operators in an automotive assembly line.

The shoulders are spared, because the device saves energy for lifting. According to Skelex it enables the full natural movement of arms and torso. 'The device creates a sensation of weightlessness in the arms when working far in front or overhead by providing an adjustable lift force from 0.5 kg to 4 kg.' The weight of the Skelex 360 itself (2 kg) is negligible.

Left, 'Kimera' and right, 'Kinsei' by Koga

15.5 STIFF COMPETITION

Bicycle track racing is about power and precision. And these have to be in balance. Dutch bicycle producer Koga introduced the 'Kinsei', a new instrument of speed and the successor of the 'Kimera (2006)', which earned a few medals but too often lost out to mainly British competition. It served as the perfect benchmark for the new bike. Everything was tried and tested scientifically.

The Kinsei is 34 per cent less susceptible to drag and 23 millimetres longer, which improves the rider's position. Even reducing the thickness of the rider's forearms was considered, but not tried. That would have gone too far! More importantly the new design is 15 per cent lighter, 35 per cent stiffer and weighs 6800 grams, the exact current minimum weight for a bike. A frame must be able to withstand the opposing forces of pulling the handlebar on one side of the bike and pushing the pedal on the other. Stiffness is considered crucial to make sure that each and every ounce of racing energy is turned into movement rather than elastic deformation. Its predecessor's frame already consisted of relatively wide thin-walled tubes to do this job.

15.6 HELPLESS MONSTERS

Money is not always put to good use in the development of army products. A good example is the Abrams tank. Where to begin? Well, when it was sent into Iraq its engine, a not very efficient gas turbine, spent most of the time idling, implying that its efficiency was less than 1 per cent. This makes a military operation quite costly, since on the battlefield, which during Operation Desert Storm happened to be oil-rich Kuwait and Iraq against a backdrop of burning oil fields, fuel has to be brought in at a cost of approximately $600 per gallon, or €140 per litre, 240 times the normal price. This and the lack of appropriate transport caused the invasion of Iraq to be delayed by over a month.

Moreover, the Rocky Mountains Institute estimated in 2000 that in a confrontation between 30 Abrams tanks, each weighing over 60 tonnes, and 30 Baja dune buggies armed with precision-guided munition, each weighing less than 1 tonne, three tanks would survive as against 27 buggies.

16. ON ROUTE TO THE FUTURE

16.1 FOR FLUIDS AND GASES
16.2 EVOLUTION OF BRIDGES
16.3 THE WIND TURBINE AS INFRASTRUCTURE
16.4 HUMBLE SMARTNESS

'Maybe they want this too!' has to be the driving force behind global travel and trade. All over the world there is evidence of several thousands of years of exchange of goods, knowledge, slaves, animals, plants and one-celled organisms between people of different regions. Some exchange was accidental. Shipping tobacco from America to Britain, for instance, was associated with worm transfer the other way. Worms came as stowaways with the ballast on board empty tobacco ships.

To facilitate transportation, we created a fantastic infrastructure that never seems finished. It started with the sea and rivers and flat land that were all just there and continued with constructing settlements on coasts and riverbanks. Places where a river branches out were particularly well suited. Many of these old harbours have now sprawled into cities, some of them quite extensive urban areas. Of course, rivers can't reach everywhere. That's why at a certain point we also started to build roads and dig canals. Moreover, water has certain disadvantages when it comes to crossing it. Bridges solved that problem. New flows were also created, of oil, gas, water, sewage and electricity. These all need their own routes, often more in line with the literal meaning of the Latin word 'infra' ('below'), although they all have versions above ground.

Walking in cadence can jeopardize the structure of a bridge

Instead of building bridges to cross rivers with freight trains and trucks, it is smarter to sail those rivers and canals.

Worms came as stowaways with the ballast on board empty tobacco ships.

More infrastructure arrived for engine-driven rail transport, which in the beginning merely consisted of trains and trams, the first tram engine being the horse. The introduction of the horse-drawn tram into England by the American entrepreneur George Francis Train failed at first, despite his name. The word 'tram' is derived from a Middle Flemish word for the wooden beams that were used to even out tracks before there were rails. The systems that Train introduced had rails on top of the roads instead of built-in, which was highly inconvenient for other traffic. Once this was redressed, trams became an accepted mode of transport. Steam engines took over from horses. And in 1880 a Russian, Fyodor Pirotsky, invented the electric tram.

There is one last top layer of infrastructure, namely the air and the airports that serve it.

There have been attempts to introduce alternatives for railway tracks. One is the 'monorail', preferably provided with a magnetic levitation principle to avoid the use of wheels for very fast transport. So far, the 'Maglev' has not been applied on a large scale. It isn't cheap, and will have to compete against the now firmly established high-speed train.

There is one last top layer of infrastructure, namely the air and the airports that serve it. It includes a part of the infrastructure one is inclined to overlook: the radar guidance system for aircraft and, come to think of it, satellite navigation for just about anyone.

Our mesh of infrastructure is not carved in granite. It is growing continuously, and it keeps on teaching us how to make improvements. An important lesson is the fact that we humans have no exclusive right to space, something that motorways in particular would seem to suggest. Wildlife crossings are springing up all over the world. And particularly in the Netherlands, a country that would be sea if it weren't for an elaborate water control system, it has become clear that all too rigid water-level regulation is counterproductive and may even cause floods. Rigidity also complicates life for flora and fauna. It is in fact logical and more sustainable to provide space for flooding and safer for areas where flooding could be a threat. If the American story of Hans Brinker with his finger in the dyke was once considered crucial for survival, these days it is opening sluices at well-chosen moments that provides safety as well as an incentive for biodiversity. It is a lighter approach that may be suitable for other water-rich regions in the world.

The smallest barge type carrying just 14 containers easily outperforms 14 trips by truck.

A much thornier problem, it seems, is the choice of route for transportation. Efficiency is often confused with speed. When it comes to large amounts of goods, barges are a very efficient means of transportation. They have low specific drag and a large load capacity. One of the more questionable projects in the Netherlands was an expensive freight train line from the Port of Rotterdam to the German border. Before construction had even begun, the chairman of the barge operators' union said, 'I can beat that train with 50 ships.' He was right. That's why the European Union is currently restoring old canals. The smallest barge type carrying just 14 containers easily outperforms 14 trips by truck. This implies a reduction of pressure on the utilization of resources. Instead of building bridges to cross rivers with freight trains and trucks, it is smarter to sail those rivers and canals. Barges don't have to settle for transporting sand and waste. They can handle cargo of much greater value, such as the Airbus parts that are brought to Toulouse by ship.

Still, we need bridges, since rivers and canals need to be crossed, and differences in height need bridging too. Bridges tell a wonderful history, and have the advantage that they reveal their 'working method' by performing and, on occasion, by failing. The transition from stone to iron shows an almost literal translation of the principle of parts leaning against each other. The influence of steel was more radical in jumping towards a bridge structure dominated by tension in suspension, with stays for the support and torsion for the deck. Iron and steel bridges are hugely dependent on maintenance. Some spend their entire lives being repainted.

New and upcoming bridges are of the composite variety. Of the four bridge-building companies in the Netherlands, one has made a biocomposite bridge for a new Adventure Zoo.

These ultralight fibre reinforced polymer structures hardly require maintenance and are virtually indestructible.

FiberCore Europe is the most active of the four. It guarantees its bridges for 50 years but claims they can last a century. These ultralight fibre reinforced polymer structures hardly require maintenance and are virtually indestructible. They weigh just a fraction of what at this point are still conventional bridges, and hardly need foundations. It takes little effort and energy to place them and if necessary to lift them and move them elsewhere. They can be made to support any kind of load, from pedestrians to heavy trucks. Vertical applications needn't be all that different. The same company produces lock gates. These products are light and transportable enough to be suitable for export. This will require an infrastructure of its own ■

16.1 FOR FLUIDS AND GASES

Not everything has been settled yet on the subject of wind turbines. The energy they produce may be renewable, but there are still issues with the machines themselves regarding the materials required and whether blades should be reused or recycled. Lagerwey is currently addressing two other issues. The first concerns the construction of large turbines with rotor diameters in the region of 120 metres. In a conventional situation a very tall crane is brought in. Its reach has to be sufficient to allow parts to be mounted accurately up to a height of 135 metres. It also has to be stabilized. This takes up a considerable amount of space alongside the turbine's tower and costs a lot of money. Lagerwey's alternative is a crane that can climb the tower, attaching itself hydraulically to the segment ridges. This takes up less space and also far less transportation capacity. Just three trucks are needed for what might otherwise require a hundred.

The second issue is the interesting option of directly using the converted energy to produce hydrogen. There is sufficient space inside the tower and the advantage is that the energy is immediately stored with the potential to produce electricity using fuel cells. A hydrogen infrastructure is not very complicated to build. Indeed, the turbine would be part of it.

Pont du Gard

Brunel's bridge at Maidenhead

16.2 EVOLUTION OF BRIDGES

Arch bridges date back to Roman aqueducts. The stonemason's skills would increase over the centuries to follow. Designed by the British engineer Brunel, the railway bridge at Maidenhead (UK) had such wide arches to accommodate shipping that the railway company directors feared it would collapse when the timber frame was removed. Brunel was instructed to leave it in place. Instead he decided to lower it to make it look as if it were still functioning. Later a flood washed away the frame and nothing disastrous happened. The design was approved.

The structure of the Iron Bridge (1779), the very first bridge in cast iron, is closely related to its stone predecessors, with its parts leaning against each other from two sides. Theoretically there could have been a crown stone in between. There is a structural similarity with the famous cantilever railway bridge (1889) across the Firth of Forth near Edinburgh. It is much longer (almost 2.5 kilometres) and was designed

Iron Bridge

Armstrong hydraulic bridge

to withstand wind forces. It consists of three very large truss structures that serve as stable cantilever supports between four smaller bridge parts.

The Golden Gate Bridge (1937) is probably the best-known steel suspension bridge. Special carts were developed to carry the wires across that would form the cables from which the deck would hang. The cables are not wrought but parallel to prevent them from damaging each other and to reduce bending stiffness. Shortly after (in 1940), the first Tacoma Narrows Bridge was built. It starred in the most spectacular bridge disaster ever caught on film. Several versions are on the Internet and no computer graphics have ever been better. Tacoma Bridge collapsed a little over five months after the opening in very windy circumstances. The cause was simple. The deck lacked torsion stiffness. The upshot was aeroelastic flutter, vibration with increasing amplitude, which eventually destroyed the bridge. The only casualty was the dog of a

Forth Bridge

Test model for the Forth Bridge

newspaper editor who was right in the middle when the bridge started to move. Something similar happened to the London Millennium Footbridge over the Thames, although with less catastrophic results. The bridge started to move in line with the cadence of people using it, once again due to insufficient torsion stiffness. The structure had to be modified.

The suspension bridge over the River Severn near Bristol (1966) is much smarter than both its predecessors. Firstly, the entire bridge is lighter than one Golden Gate tower. Secondly, the deck consists of steel tubular elements that can float. All deck elements were towed along the river like pontoons to their location and lifted into place.

The construction of the spectacular Millau Viaduct in Southern France designed by Michel Virlogeux and Norman Foster was quite similar to the fire ant process. The central pylons are taller than the Eiffel Tower.

Firth of Forth model

The Golden Gate Bridge, San Francisco

Composite bridges are rapidly becoming very successful. They have a disarming ease about them. Their main advantage is sustainability. Production requires very little energy compared with steel and concrete bridges. From a report on replacing all 169 bridges in the Province of Utrecht with composite structures, it was estimated that the energy saved would equal that consumed annually by 27,000 households. The standard question about recyclability is overruled by the potential of perpetually reusing these bridges. And they are surprisingly light. FiberCore's first in the series, a 24-metre-long carbon fibre reinforced pedestrian and cyclist brid-ge, was transported from the production facility in Rotterdam to JEC World in Paris, before being returned to the Netherlands to be placed in Dronten. Hoisting it onto the river banks took something like half an hour.

First Tacoma Narrows Bridge

Millennium Footbridge

Severn Bridge

Millau Viaduct

Fibre reinforced golf cart bridge by FiberCore Europe

Inflated ski bridge, Val Cenis, France

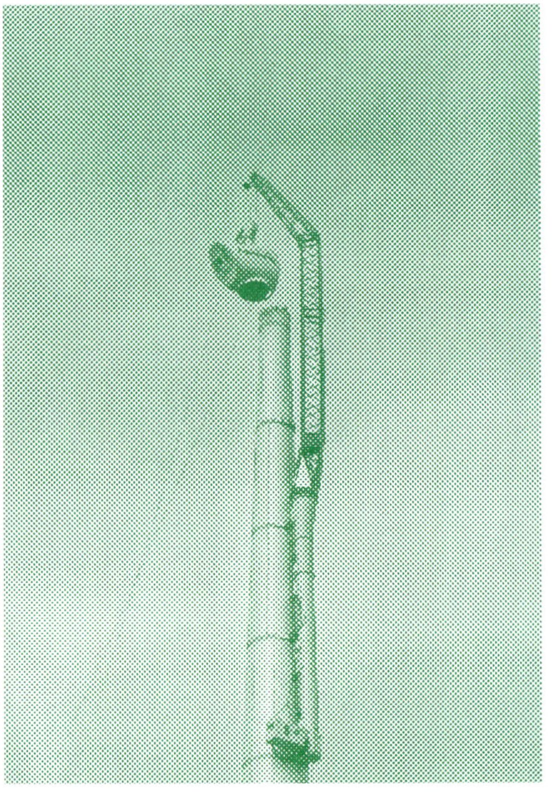

16.3 THE WIND TURBINE AS INFRASTRUCTURE

Not everything has been settled yet on the subject of wind turbines. The energy they produce may be renewable, but there are still issues with the machines themselves regarding the materials required and whether blades should be reused or recycled. Lagerwey is currently addressing two other issues. The first concerns the construction of large turbines with rotor diameters in the region of 120 metres. In a conventional situation a very tall crane is brought in. Its reach has to be sufficient to allow parts to be mounted accurately up to a height of 135 metres. It also has to be stabilized. This takes up a considerable amount of space alongside the turbine's tower and costs a lot of money. Lagerwey's alternative is a crane that can climb the tower, attaching itself hydraulically to the segment ridges. This takes up less space and also far less transportation capacity. Just three trucks are needed for what might otherwise require a hundred.

The second issue is the interesting option of directly using the converted energy to produce hydrogen. There is sufficient space inside the tower and the advantage is that the energy is immediately stored with the potential to produce electricity using fuel cells. A hydrogen infrastructure is not very complicated to build. Indeed, the turbine would be part of it.

16.4 HUMBLE SMARTNESS

Manholes suffer horribly because of their low status, but also because sewage gas corrodes their walls, which leads to concrete washing away, leakage and ultimately sinkholes. Sewers therefore have to be repaired, which is a heck of a job, with streets needing to be closed for days on end. Smit Composite has developed a contemporary update that takes up far less time.

First the manhole is scanned to get a 3D model of the situation. Then the replacement parts are 3D printed in a polyester composite at the factory. Lastly the actual repair work is done in less than a day. The repaired drain is not susceptible to sewer gas corrosion and designed with a smooth surface to accommodate drain water flow. As a next step, drain covers are now being developed with built-in sensors. These can provide information on what is going on in drain systems.

Left: Medieval Persian drainage system in Isfahan, similar to current ones
Right: Smit Composite advanced drain repair system

17. ELECTRIC WHEELS

Tourists on Segway personal transporters

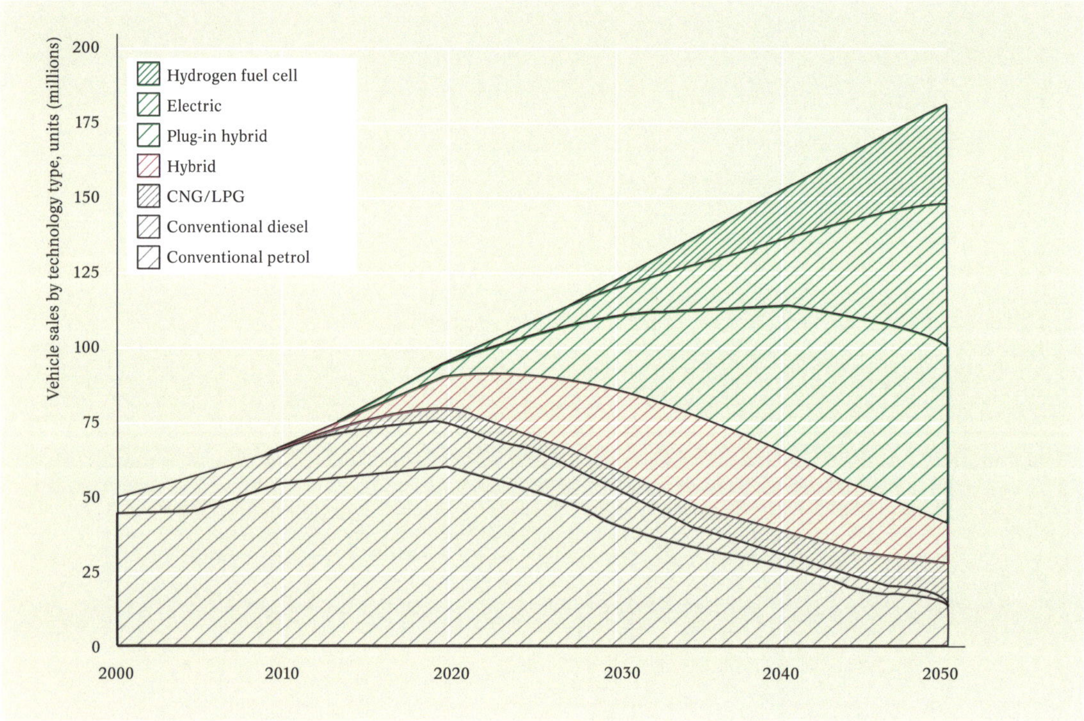

Expected sales of vehicles by energy type

Watch out! Electricity is coming! Electric current is making its mark on all kinds of road-related traffic. Pedestrians, skateboarders, cyclists, other two-wheelers and slow and fast drivers of small, medium and large four-wheeled vehicles are feeling the power of the change of power. Obviously, the impact is not the same across the entire spectrum, but the effect of lightness is more directly experienced than before, in terms of convenience, range and costs. The energy system behind all this movement has yet to take shape, both legally and in practice.

> *But even at this level of smallness battery weight can be an issue.*

Disney's inventor character Gyro Gearloose saw it coming in the 1950s with his motorized unicycle. Segway began in the early years of this century with two wheels side by side, a smart balancing system and a handle, which always looked a bit odd. The tall version was a way of identifying tourists in cities and service personnel in a rush in hospitals and airports. Later the enterprise introduced smaller, lighter, portable and more playful offspring in the shape of hoverboards, monowheels, one-wheel skateboards and low carts. These are much more attractive and readily accepted, mostly by young people. And Segway is no longer the only producer of these gadgets. But even at this level of smallness battery weight can be an issue. It is possible to equip a one-wheel personal vehicle with enough electrical energy to take you 240 kilometres from where you started, but the battery required would weigh almost 30 kilograms, and when the wheel's power source is flat, you're going to have to carry the thing. Legislation for these little human movers is lagging behind. In some countries they are not allowed in public areas.

The same is true of electric scooters. In many cities, however, they can be rented by the minute. Their advantage is that they are easy to ride and that recharging them is outsourced. The deal is that you can leave them anywhere for service staff to pick up and 'juice', which these freelancers usually do at home. The market for this service is considerable. In Los Angeles (CA) alone, there are eight companies competing with on-demand bikes and scooters. According to *The New York Times* (25 October 2019) one of the companies, Lime, hires about 60,000 juicers in the 100 markets where it is currently active. Juicers get about $3 to $10 per retrieved scooter. The environmental impact of the cars juicers use for the purpose is as yet unaccounted for. Convenience evidently outweighs the side effects.

Electric bicycles, or pedelecs as they are also known, are a different story altogether. Traditionally bikes have long been commonly known all over the world, either as affordable means of transportation or for sports. These days e-bikes are really beginning to make a mark as person movers, whether for commuting or for recreation. Hilly roads and headwinds aren't much of an issue when you're on an e-bike. Its range is best kept short but if

The cycling route to the summit of Alpe d'Huez

17.1 FASTER PER KILOGRAM

What is true for cars and airplanes is also true for bicycles. The heavier they are, the slower they go.

The cyclist is the most significant contributor to the moving mass. They are payload, battery and engine all rolled into one. This mass is all the more important when climbing.

Suppose a racing cyclist climbs Alpe d'Huez, a 13.2-kilometre-long ascent to a height of 1071 metres. Hundreds of cyclists do this all the time. That's how we know.

If this racing cyclist weighs 72.5 kilograms and the climb takes 60 minutes, we can calculate the energy required for the ride. Now we can calculate the time needed for the same cyclist weighing 2.5 kilograms less, which is 2 minutes shorter. All in all, this implies that the cyclist is 48 seconds faster per kilogram weight loss. This does not imply that all a cyclist has to do to become a super champion is to return to early childhood.

17.2 SERIOUS LARGE-SCALE LIGHTNESS

Most car brands are bringing out electric models now. They can't stay behind in the trend initiated by Tesla. The classic sports car brand MG, which has been in Chinese hands for fifteen years, has launched an affordable electric SUV.

Nevertheless, in the current early stage of drastic car renewal, only BMW is making serious efforts to develop the mass production of lightweight structures. The BMW i3 is the first consumer car with a full composite body structure, following up the experience gained by BMW with braided structural CFRP parts (EuroCarbon NL) in earlier models.

The basic chassis, which literally includes the battery, also holds the main mechanical parts and is glued to the frame above it. An almost fully automated system produces this body frame in a resin transfer moulding (RTM) process, with plates stitched together from strands of carbon fibre produced in the US by SGL and BMW at Moses Lake, Washington, because of the available hydroelectric power. The roof consists of recycled carbon fibre waste removed during production of the body frame. Inner door panels are of hemp fibre reinforced polymer.

That BMW mean business is apparent from the way they use this car to explore technologies. It already boasts a CFRP thermoset (epoxy) floor panel overmoulded with thermoplastic (PA) stiffeners. To stimulate bonding, the epoxy part is locally pre-treated with a laser that superficially removes a thin layer of epoxy, exposing the fibres. The thermoplastic likes bonding to these. And it saves fibres for bending stiffness.

One step further is still at the experimental stage. This is an overmoulded alternative for the current RTM frontal upper part of the windshield frame. It consists of a skeleton of four pultruded thermoplastic bars with thermoformed ends, with all the reinforcements and attachment points for functional elements integrated in it. Making the skeletal alternative saves production time and exceeds the RTM frame in all respects but one: torsional stiffness, which is only to be expected from such an open structure. No doubt this requirement will be included in follow-up steps. This is what experimental projects are for.

Full composite body structure of the BMW i3

17.3 COMPOSITE SAFETY

It is very difficult to change what people believe. Fibre reinforced structures are not easily trusted because they behave differently and that takes getting used to. An important difference between metals and composites is that metals can dent, through plastic deformation, whereas composites won't yield that way. They break instead.

Not that they break that easily. It may require a huge amount of energy, depending on the design, much more energy than it would take for steel to give way. Before you know it there is an advantage to breaking. Instead of tightly encapsulating the driver's limbs, these are freed. That is the reason why Formula 1 racing cars are probably the safest of all, perhaps with the exception of the new less noisy Formula E class.

Dutchman Federico Kroymans crashed in 2004. The car broke, but it suffered no hazardous deformation

Challenger Class Nuna solar car designed by TU Delft students (p273)

17.4 SOLAR RECORDS

Student teams from four Dutch universities take part in the World Solar Challenge, a biannual competition in Australia that is a part of the larger Global Green Challenge. A 3000-kilometre race from Darwin in the North to Adelaide in the South, it was held for the first time in 2001. Of the ten races run so far, Delft, sponsored by Vattenfall, has won seven times in the Challenger Class, which is about speed exclusively generated by the sun. They came in second twice and in 2019 unfortunately their car caught fire.

At least as impressive is what the Eindhoven team has accomplished in the Cruiser Class. This is truer to life, as the car has to be approved for normal use on public roads and must be able to carry passengers. The four consecutive versions of the Stella car all turned out to be winners, not in speed, because that isn't the point, but in efficiency and convenience. It is meant to be a family car. Indeed, the cars all have coffee mug supports on board and the 2019 Stella Era can function as a power source for other vehicles and of course for an espresso machine or any other electrical appliance. The empty weight of a Stella, which can carry four people, is 375 kilograms. It has a range of 1200 kilometres in accordance with the Worldwide Harmonised Light Vehicles Test Procedure and 1800 kilometres when optimized for efficiency. It is no wonder that the Stella laid the basis for the development of the Lightyear One described elsewhere in this book.

the battery does run out you can continue on your way with a bit of extra effort, since it has pedals like a normal bike.

These days e-bikes are really beginning to make a mark as person movers.

In the cycling nation that is the Netherlands, e-bikes were mainly for the elderly for their first few years. The change came at a price: more cyclists got involved in accidents. Easy speed is treacherous. The weight of electric bicycles is not as important as it is for non-electric racing bikes, although getting it into or out of a rack can be tricky. The market is currently opening up for all ages. Carbon electric racing and mountain bikes are rapidly appearing on the market too and particularly electric racing bikes are indiscernible from powerless ones, because the engine and the battery are well hidden inside the frame. It seems identity and the idea of magic propulsion are getting more important than healthy effort. Electric cycling is becoming a lifestyle signature and the carbon look is part of that.

Despite the growing concern with the energy issue and growing interest in transportation, cars lean heavily on expressing identity. Martí Guixé from Barcelona, who calls himself an 'ex-designer', came up with a fantastic idea for bringing this phenomenon to light. In 2008 he proposed placing large mirrors along roads so that drivers could watch themselves go by in their cars. Driver mirrors should have been everywhere by now. Before anything else, an auto (from 'autos', Ancient Greek for 'self') is a very heavy device that just happens to have wheels and at least one engine. Since cars became mass products,

Lightyear One Commercial solar car, designed by GranStudio

they've gained a lot of weight, perhaps with the exception of the first years after WW2 due to material scarcity. A Ford model T used to weigh about 550 kilograms. Today an average family vehicle easily weighs more than double that figure.

SUVs are double the weight of regular cars, which are far too heavy as it is.

Anyway, twenty or thirty years ago, when you inquired about virtually any new car of any brand at a car fair, the sales representative would say: 'It has all become much heavier since last year'. There are generally two reasons – or excuses, if you like – for this weight gain. The first is safety, which for steel means extending the crumple zone and increasing the mass. The second is gadgetry, or convenience as it is generally known: electronic gizmos that do things and distract the driver. There is a third very important reason, the reason that sells cars. It is known as 'design', which really is an expression of who you think you are. But it's too easy to just call a car a 'status symbol'. It also expresses what kind of person you are, sloppy or careful, clean or dirty, and the interior is an extension of your home, where you can relax and listen to the radio while stuck in a traffic jam. But the cream of the crop is that it gives you a sense of your position in the traffic, preferably high up, with a view across the roofs of neighbouring cars.

This must be the one overriding reason why SUVs in particular are so attractive these days. They are double the weight of regular cars, which are far too heavy as it is. As it happens, SUVs and other heavy expensive cars (cars have a higher price tag per kilogram weight) are also the forerunners of electrification. Many products follow a similar line of introduction. They start upmarket and then gradually trickle down. There is also an element of 'rebound effect' in there. This is the phenomenon whereby money saved by consuming less energy is used to buy more energy consuming products, for instance LED lamps. Similarly, driving on batteries is cheaper and the money saved is spent on extra weight.

Things are moving forward now, because it is well understood that weight comes at the cost of range, which is an important selling point. That is why small electric cars are becoming more attractive and also why BMW is putting a lot of money and effort into developing a production system for composite car bodies. This strategy includes early proposals for composite recycling. Of course, the mass production of composite products requires a thorough analysis of their entire life cycle.

City buses are rapidly becoming electricity consumers.

City buses are rapidly becoming electricity consumers as well. Because of the kind of service that a city bus provides – short distances, regular stops, modest speeds – a clean energy system is an obvious requirement. Some exploiters believe that the range and battery weight can be limited, with one or two charging intervals every day. Some 300 cities have had trolleybuses for a long time. The Shanghai system dates back to November 1914. Gdynia in Poland is embarking on a combination: the new hybrid trolleybuses have batteries to extend their range into areas without overhead lines.

Trolleybuses lead us briefly to trams and trains. These are mostly electric now, but so far there has been little incentive to reduce energy consumption by saving weight. It is likely to happen, particularly in high-speed trains, although their colonization by composites is lagging behind.

> *So smelly fumes are still around but outsourced.*

As for electrifying long-distance buses, batteries would add too much to the vehicle weight. The hydrogen alternative seems a lot more feasible. FlixBus is a long-distance operator that will soon start using hydrogen-powered vehicles. Hydrogen fuel cell buses are already being introduced for local services in cities all over the world. In London even double-decker buses will run on hydrogen. Apparently, cities are quite eager to advertise themselves as green, even when most hydrogen production depends on fossil fuels. So smelly fumes are still around but outsourced.

Whether trucks can be equipped with batteries depends on what they do. Battery-powered urban delivery trucks and dustcarts have been on the market for some years. For long-distance trucks, electricity provided by fuel cells rather than batteries would be better in terms of weight. The reason is simple. Trucks have a maximum weight of between 32 and 50 tonnes (about 10 tonnes per axle) depending on national regulations. To achieve a reasonable range the weight of batteries would put too much of a burden on the amount of payload. Come to think of it: batteries are costload. Developments in electrification are very promising but they have to be handled with an awareness of side effects. Electricity is not just a matter of an engine here and batteries there ■

Ex-designer Martí Guixé's Car Mirror concept (2007)

17.5 LIGHTWEIGHT BUSES

Electric buses are on their way to becoming the norm rather than the exception. Beijing, for instance, just bought 2790 of them and Rotterdam now has ten. A new Dutch electric bus company, appropriately named Ebusco, used to work with Chinese companies until recently but has since begun production in the Netherlands and is doing quite well.

The important step it took was to develop lightweight buses with a CFRP chassis and body. The resulting 35 per cent weight reduction allows the vehicles to carry more passengers with a longer range (450-500 kilometres), long enough for them to go without a recharge during a day service. It prevents the inconvenience of buses standing idle during charging and wasting valuable driving time.

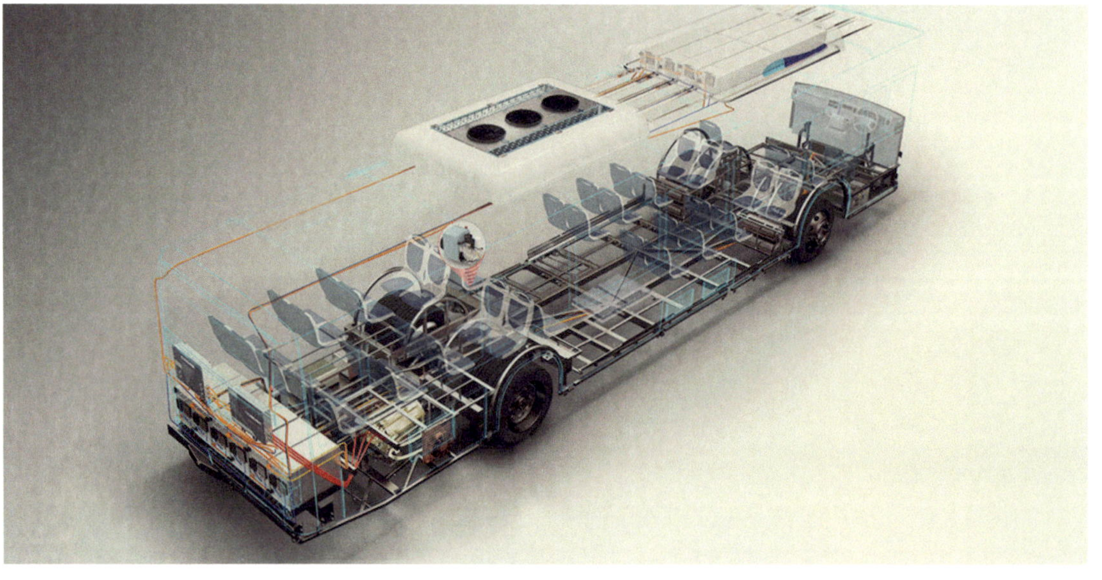

Art Deco styling of HCD-6 Neptunes by Hyundai

17.6 HYDROGEN TRUCKS

Batteries are too heavy for long-distance trucks. Their weight considerably diminishes the payload the trucks can take. So producing electricity from hydrogen and oxygen using fuel cells is an attractive proposition. Several concepts for hydrogen-powered trucks are out in the open now. Introducing a new system calls for cooperation. Interestingly, the way this system is introduced differs per region.

The US prefers the start-up approach with the firm of Nikola, which happens to be the given name of the engineer Tesla. The company is promoting three hydrogen fuel cell trucks (ONE, TWO and TRE) and three electric power vehicles (NZT, RECKLESS and WAV). T-shirts and caps are readily available.

Europe has started in a more European way with a Dutch-Belgian organization called WaterstofNet (Hydrogen Network), which cooperates with a great many partners. It coordinates cluster projects on all aspects and segments of hydrogen-fuelled transportation, and it has a newsletter. As part of the H2Haul project it will have sixteen trucks ready by 2040 for demonstration in Belgium, France, Germany and Switzerland.

The South-Korean car manufacturer Hyundai introduced its concept for a hydrogen fuel cell truck at the North American Commercial Vehicle Show. The HDC-6 Neptune is part of Hyundai's 2030 Vision, with a design uncomfortably similar to that of the New York Central Railroad's Mercury locomotives, designed in Art Deco style by Henry Dreyfuss in 1936. Neptune and Mercury – global modernity cannot escape the power of the ancient Roman gods.

18. BUILDING AND CONSTRUCTION

Lightness in a geologically dynamic tropical region differs from lightness in a tranquil rich watery country.

A building is not regarded as a transportable entity. But it should be, or it wouldn't be there. Its construction involves moving materials and parts in large quantities, usually too large since there are leftovers in the region of 10 per cent of the total amount of waste in affluent countries. During its useful life there are modifications made that require materials being brought in and out. Demolition at the end is part of the process and quickly converts value into rubble. No less than 30 to 40 per cent of all waste in Western regions consists of demolished buildings.

> *Architects, engineers and building companies are very similar the world over.*

It is therefore crucial to reduce material flow. First and foremost, this requires organization and improvements in design, which in terms of architecture, building construction and cultivation of value is not simply a matter of replacing steel with composites, which isn't easy anyway. It requires a different perspective on the implications of building, which depend on what people think and do; in other words, the culture of the entire cycle.

Building is a cultural activity, determined by an amalgam of desires and requirements, civil tradition, architectural conventions, location, available materials and technology. And, of course, by influence and money. Context is important when considering the long-term cultivation of value using a minimum of materials. Lightness in a geologically dynamic tropical region differs from that in a quiet rich watery country. Only one thing is certain, that reducing the material flow as applicable to building is quite a challenge. The culture of building is lagging behind in refinement and value cultivation compared to other trades.

To see where we stand, we can best start by considering input, use and, ultimately, output. The most important part of course is what goes in. One has to be vigilant, to prevent the process from becoming wasteful. Material processing and design are determined by available resources and tradition, which itself is a crude mixture of cultural habits and opinions nourished by the region and by education. A simple assessment shows that cultural differences *within* regions, or countries if you like, are much larger than those *between* regions. For building and construction this implies that specialists in this field – architects, engineers, building companies – are very similar the world over. This is a corollary of the notion of International Style, which emerged from modernism and was defined in the Museum of Modern Art in New York by Henry-Russell Hitchcock

Haut wooden apartment building in Amsterdam

and Philip Johnson in 1932. It forged a convenient link between the prevailing idea of architecture and the economic climate. It lasted until about 1970 but the manner of expression never really went away. In his BBC documentary *On the Brandwagon* (all his documentaries are essential viewing) the British architecture critic Jonathan Meades introduces the Regenerative Community, a group of well-known and less well-known architects and designers repeating the same modernist mannerisms all over the world. It looks very similar to the expression of early functionalism, except maybe that it has been turned into a convention to impress the observer with extravagant simplicity. From a structural and societal point of view functionalism and minimalism have all but left the formal playing field.

> *Contractors want to buy cheap and the consequences reveal themselves afterwards.*

By far the most of what humans build, however, is informal. People build what they like, from a catalogue or what they can afford, with whatever they can get their hands on. Or they go for something in between. Architects have a different kind of influence on all these layers. For the poorest people they can help set the conditions to build their own communities, through advice and through help in providing access to basic material needs. For affluent customers they design complete buildings and help organize their construction. This process of putting up a building can be quite complicated, since it involves the architect, the contractor, any subcontractors and the resources for materials and parts – and we mustn't forget the client. They all have their say during the process, which sometimes leads to disagreements or financial issues, a different point of view resulting in a fresh start or a serious slow-down. A complete project shutdown is not exactly an exception, with half or completely finished 'ghost' structures standing around looking useless. There are books and websites crammed with spectacular casualties of such misfortune, including complete cities in China, a long overdue airport in Berlin and a banking tower in Caracas that was taken over by squatters and after their eviction severely damaged by an earthquake.

This observation only concerns the results and effects of projects. Wastefulness, however, starts with the low value of useless leftover parts and materials that are expensive to get rid of. Contractors want to buy cheap and the consequences reveal themselves afterwards. The most important difference with other industries is, generally, the crude assembly process divided among a fragmented constellation of contributors. Rather than the precise and seamless assembly of a single product, construction brings together an assemblage of products in various stages of evolution in an arrangement that is kept upright with the help of untold quantities of low-grade material, including the spray can of PUR foam to shroud the need for a finishing touch.

Cardboard tubes carry more value than their money's worth.

This is by no means a new and original observation. There have been plans and projects based on the idea that buildings should be mass-produced, like cars. The fact that buildings, unlike cars, are personal beacons in our daily life is overlooked. Buildings provide orientation and are a means to appropriate space. Large series of identical prefab houses never really made it. Even repetition under centralist regimes is scarcely if ever rooted in a prefabrication industry.

If construction is well prepared, adaptations will be part of the expected process.

On the other hand, the character and identity needed for individual homes and buildings do not rule out industrial production entirely. One of the most prevalent, if not the most prevalent industrial product is the brick. And there really are such things as home building kits. The point here is that value is determined by the degree of building clarity. The best person to explain this is the Japanese architect Shigeru Ban. He has created many buildings – schools, offices, religious

An *enamelled steel Lustron house on the move*

18.1 THE LUSTRON HOUSE

The time seemed ideal. After WW2 the metal once used for fighter aircraft could be used for other products. There was also a huge need for housing because of all the GI's returning home to start a family. So it was that the industrialist Carl Strandlund, who was experienced in constructing filling stations, acquired the funding to begin mass-producing enamel-coated steel homes in a new company named Lustron. Based in a former airplane factory in Columbus, Ohio, it had an impressive array of tooling along more than 12 kilometres of conveyor belts and 11 enamelling furnaces each 50 metres long. Special trucks were constructed to deliver the homes.

The houses were designed as straightforward steel frames, with insulated steel plate walls, hot air heating from the ceiling and smart storage and kitchen features. The house was maintenance free, and promised to be something of a time saver for housewives.

Lustron was scheduled to produce 45,000 houses in the first two years (1947 and 1948). Things got difficult, however, because of production delays, poor distribution and rising prices of production due to the considerable investments. Moreover, some municipalities had strange rules, such as not allowing steel chimneys. Of course, there were also conspiracy theories. Whatever the exact causes, Lustron went broke in 1950. Between 1500 and 2000 units of the historic batch are still in use. One is in a museum in Columbus, featuring the Thor Automagic machine which could handle both laundry and dishes.

18.2 DYMAXION BATHROOM

Richard Buckminster Fuller was indisputably a designer. He was always discovering scientific principles that could make life more convenient. When he was in the navy, he used to work in the engine room of a ship. One night – this was in 1917 – he felt hot and greasy and decided to go on deck for a breath of fresh air. It was cool and foggy outside and very much to his surprise the dirt started to disappear from his skin. He figured that this might be turned to good use as a new way of washing. He patented the fog gun in 1927 and built a prototype in 1949.

In those same years Buckminster Fuller worked on the development of a new kind of lightweight '4D house'. The first version of Fuller's house was to be displayed as a scale model at the Marshall Field's department store in Chicago, but it needed a better name. They hired a copywriter, Waldo Warren, who after a few days came up with 'Dymaxion', from DYnamic MAXimum tensION. It was to become Buckminster Fuller's life-long brand.

The Dymaxion House was a long-term project. Famous science-fiction writer Robert Heinlein ordered one but never got it. The Wichita House was the most successful of the several versions built. For his airplane-age aluminium dwelling Buckminster Fuller designed a prefabricated Dymaxion bathroom pod. It had a built-in fog gun. A restored Dymaxion House is on display in the Henry Ford Museum in Detroit.

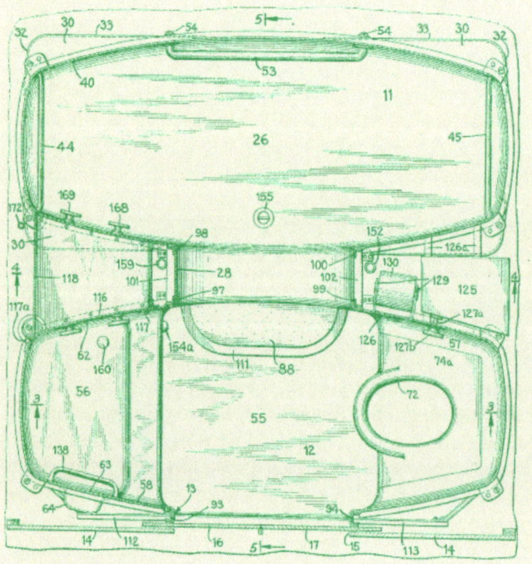

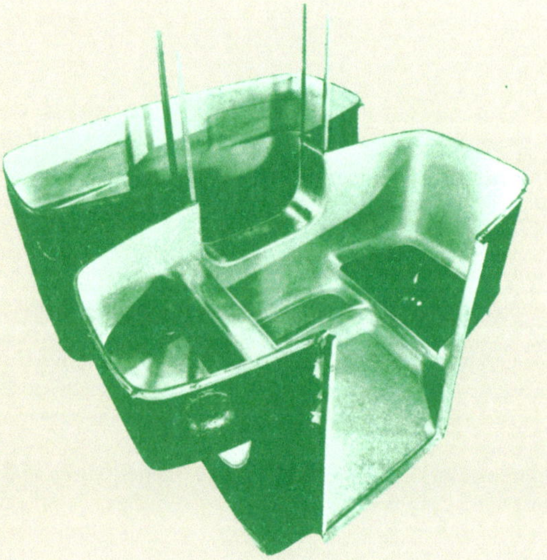

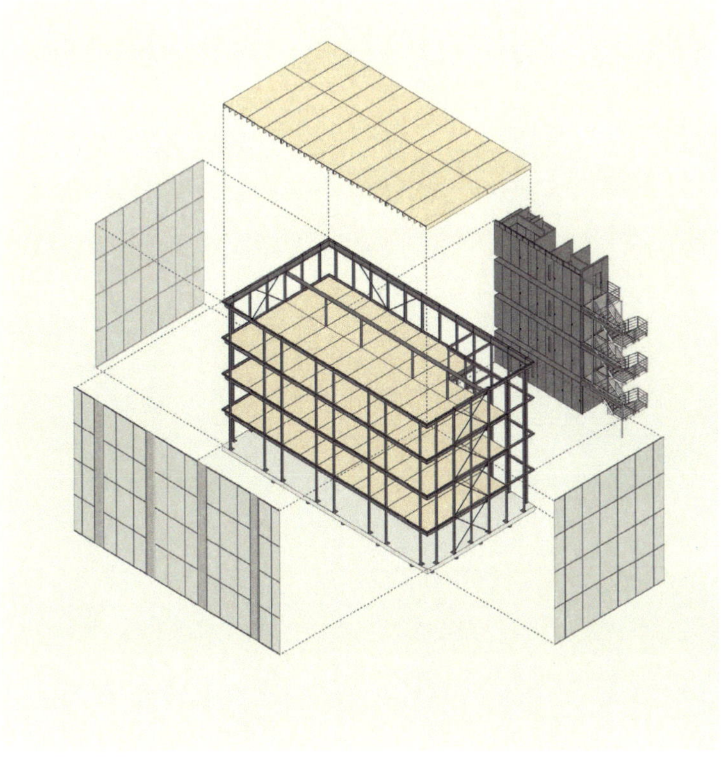

18.3 THE SMARTEST KIT

Lightweight building above all depends on organizing the construction in such a way that there is no waste. This is a matter of design and it defines the goal of cepezed. This Delft-based architectural firm seeks to create comfortable and flexible spaces ('flexible' being one of those language issues mentioned in Chapter 3). One of cepezed's key desires is to find ways to provide sufficient daylight. These are standard requirements amongst architects and their clients.

The way cepezed achieve these goals is special. They design building kits, rather than buildings. Their focus is on lightweight structures, but they don't go so far as to compose materials for a particular application. They do try to reduce the depth of the foundations. This is significant, as foundation depth can be considered part of the typical construction machismo that extols heaviness.

Cepezed design all the parts and every detail to the point that there is no superfluousness to distract from pure function and that furthermore the entire kit can be assembled without the intervention of anything wet, such as cement or glue. This implies that construction takes less time and that it isn't complicated to take the kit apart or replace elements later on when changing or upgrading the building. Moreover, it means that the firm sometimes avoids working with a contractor, who may be inclined to avoid non-standard solutions, whereas parts suppliers may be keen to develop new products and be part of an innovative culture.

Recently cepezed added a new building to their studio. This 'demountable' glass block is a clear example of the work they value. The facades are extremely simple and consist of double-glazing panels attached directly to the steel frame. Floor and ceiling panels consist of wood that lies directly on top of the frame. The panels have local stiffeners but are hollow when seen from below. Utilities fit in between the stiffeners where needed; additional layers dampen the sound. To build homes using this design would mean taking further measures – either that or Dutch regulations should be made less rigid.

Mobile office made of cardboard tubes by Shigeru Ban(2004) in Milan version (2019)

buildings and many dwellings in disaster areas – whose structure largely consists of cardboard tubes attached to each other with wooden nodes. Cardboard tubes are very cheap, but as laminated primary structures for building just about anything, they carry more value than their money's worth – price and value are not the same thing – in particular because they're not as 'anonymous' and abstract as bricks and require a very specific and recognizable treatment in construction. In many cases these structures last longer than intended.

As usual, saving costs is often the reason why buildings are constructed the way they are, particularly in the short term. There have been a number of attempts to turn a complete dwelling into an abstract mass-produced machine for living, Lustron houses being the classic example. This never worked. But certain relatively complex components did become successful. The bathroom pod, a complete bathroom designed as an industrial product to be installed in a living space, is a popular product with a huge market, mainly for student housing, hotels, healthcare facilities and residential purposes. Kitchen pods are on the increase as well. The advantage is that prefabrication ensures better quality, faster installation (convenience) and lower rates of failure, which in building and construction work are still considerable.

Over the years, reducing the weight of bathrooms has become more important, in line with saving costs on building and construction, which means that the floor strength has also been reduced. Until the mid 1990s pods consisted of reinforced concrete and weighed 3 tonnes on average. Then came the switch from concrete slabs to steel frame structures. Still more weight reduction was required, which accelerated the development of glass fibre reinforced polyester. Pods made from FRP had the added advantage of hardly requiring any maintenance, which made them ideal for student housing and budget hotels, especially because of the change in building arrangements, whereby contractors were now responsible for exploiting buildings as well as getting them onto site.

Currently all three material concepts – concrete, steel and FRP – are in use. The gradual take-over by composites is clearly visible and for now depends on process control, weight and the need for maintenance. The same thing is happening in facade systems, except for the fact that additional features of composites enter the picture. Apart from the earlier mentioned advantages, we have insulation, which is obvious coming from plastics, and there are new opportunities for expression. Architects tend to overlook these, because they are not accustomed to consider relief and texture as designable properties. FRP cladding panels are a fast-growing market in relation to speed of construction, an advantage of weight reduction that is often overlooked. It might be an idea to construct buildings not only within a financial budget but also a strict time limit so as to enforce weight reduction, a smooth process and the most thorough preparation.

Composite thinking has yet to reach the level where it contributes to the structure. There have been modest attempts made with unorthodox roofs. Unexpectedly, wood has come close in the form of Cross Laminated Timber. In principle this is plywood, except that the plies consist of planks rather than veneer. The timber panels can be as much as 400 millimetres thick. There are many advantages to wood construction, if only for the reason that woodwork is traditional. The idea of laminating timber to create very large panels dates back to the early 1990s and it has proved possible to build more than twenty storeys high with CLT, providing the central core is concrete.

If construction is well prepared, adaptations and upgrades during use will simply be part of the expected process, and the scenario of what will happen afterwards will be clearer. For this a systematic approach to material flows is indispensable. This includes the continued use of building parts. It has been said earlier: we have to start preparing for more than one cycle. The crudest form of continued use is to stop demolition altogether and look at existing urban structures as an existing landscape to build on. The cleanest way to create a new building is of course to make it float on water, mooring it where it needs to be and towing it away when it is required elsewhere. And on that aquatic note we have tumbled into the next chapter, which is about ships and boats ■

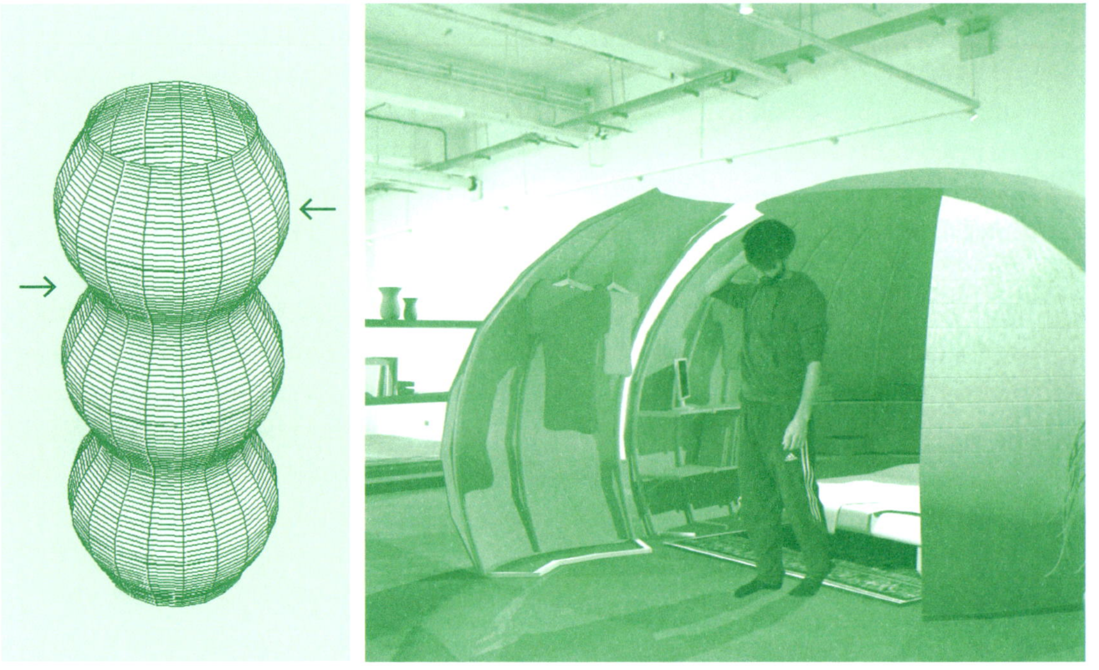

Left: Form of a wound structure that can be pressurized to become infinitely stiff. Right: Concept for a portable and foldable room by DRS22 Marcel Kock (2014)

18.4 LIGHTWEIGHT CHALLENGES

One would like the tradition of architecture, building and construction to be more open to new ways of thinking about structure. In general architecture is focused on the creation of form and function (in the architectural sense of the word) and ways to make them happen. It is rare for architects to consider new technical principles, apply these to arrive at construction and pragmatically take it from there. Time, then, for some speculation.

It just might, for instance, be possible to create 10-metre-tall lightweight but extremely stiff columns, which could be transported in a small van because they are inflatables. It would be quite a lot of work designing them, up to and including the production process. Manufacturing them would be a matter of robotically winding the material and giving it a foldable skin, according to the principle shown in box 16.1. Once designed, they would make a very convenient alternative. However, their visual expression would be highly unconventional, shaped as they are like a row of bobbins. This could help to initiate research into new means of visual expression, taking lightweight structure as a starting point instead of form as a goal.

Another principle that could lead to much simpler designs is to leave the functional programme to the users. A room could be a lightweight object that one could buy or order, to unfold it wherever it is needed. A kitchen or a bathroom needn't be a special space as long as the equipment, which can be mobile, is available and can be connected to energy, water and sewage systems anywhere.

Flexipol Photovoltaic facade panels

18.5 PICK YOUR PANEL

Composition is about bringing properties together and before you know it you have composites. Flexipol is a company that engineers and produces composite building parts: balconies, roof edges, awnings and also cladding. The latter in particular is a good example of the possibilities presented by different combinations.

The options start with the outer layer. A fibre reinforced skin is enough in itself to greatly improve a traditional inner panel, reducing maintenance costs and increasing the freedom of form for architects. These can then add the appropriate detailing and expression. Needless to say, mounting such a combination on the supporting frame can be time consuming.

One step further is to develop a complete composite panelling system, including the interior finish, water barrier, window frames and insulation. Such panels can be attached in just one go. But the planning has to be very precise.

There is a difference, when meeting fire safety regulations, between just a composite top layer and a complete system. In the latter case the panels constitute the entire facade and have to abide by those regulations.

With insulation included in the panels, there is another possible enrichment to potentially render facades more sustainable and truly up to date. Composite thinking enables photovoltaic functionality to be integrated into the building envelope.

19. THE FLEET OF THE WORLD

Cruise ships are not really vehicles. It wouldn't explain their gross architectural obesity anyway. Think big is the name of this game. The largest floating mega-resort currently in existence is the *Symphony of the Seas*. It can accommodate a maximum of 6,680 passengers on top of its gross tonnage of 228,081. This implies that every person gets 34.1 tonnes and, assuming that a person with luggage weighs 100 kilograms, that every kilogram of human occupancy gets approximately 341 kilograms of cruise convenience, which amounts to an empty weight per unit payload somewhere in the region of a one-way trip to the moon. Never mind. We already established that a cruise ship is hardly a means of transportation, with all its swimming pools, cinemas, gambling facilities, bars and restaurants. Instead it belongs to the flotilla of grand ocean polluters, burning the lowest grade of crude oil (except for two now that use natural gas) and dumping its waste in the sea. It really is a wandering 'luxury building', a lightweight version of the standard skyscraper mentioned in Chapter 1, except that it moves on water and has to make do without municipal dustcarts. Most waste is probably disposed of outside territorial waters, since plastics can't be dumped within 25 miles of the coast. In fairness, some cruise liners do have their own on-board recycling system.

Experiments occur in upmarket yachts because these are bespoke products.

Weight has been of some concern for these ships. The advantages of energy conservation have been recognized, although the reduction in fuel costs achieved by using FRP for the top five decks these days may be translated into the possible addition of an extra half deck, which simply undoes all the energy saving.

Nevertheless, saving weight in favour of speed and reduction of energy consumption is not uncommon as a principle. Ships and boats have a long tradition behind them of mostly wooden structures. In some categories, composites have really taken over, particularly in ocean racers, where a lightweight structure could make you a winner, and in very large luxury yachts, where ingenious sails and rigging in composite masts enable handling by small crews. On the other hand, employing a large crew is part of a show of ostentation, until you get jealousy and rows due to insufficient insulation between cabins. So you have to choose: either a smarter ship or a bigger crew.

Yachting is quite interesting, because there prestige outweighs costs. There is room for experimentation, which may or may not be inspiring to the real world. Some concepts are just too far off the grid. There are unexecuted designs in the billion-dollar league, for a yacht in the shape of a 'tropical island' (with volcano) and for a manoeuvrable copy of Monaco (complete with go-kart circuit). So far, not even the filthiest rich have fallen for these.

Experiments occur in upmarket yachts because these are bespoke products.

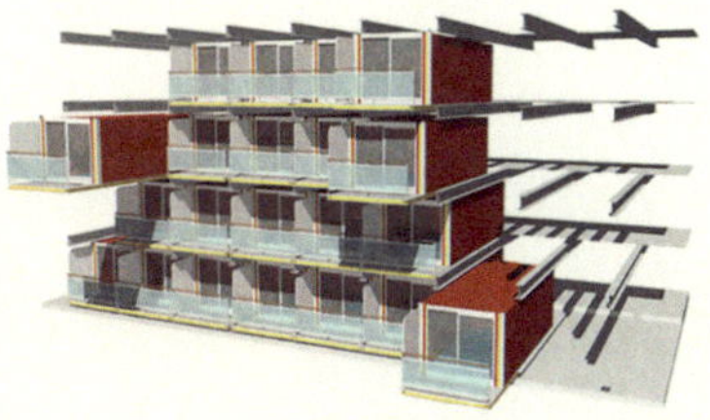

19.1 1001 CABINS FOR THE NIGHT

Cruise ships benefit from production uniformity during their construction. It is quite common to equip them with prefabricated cabins, with an open floor to attach them to the steel deck. A certain amount of thought has been devoted to ways of saving weight, since the rapidly growing cruise world is aware that its carbon footprint has to be kept low. The use of lighter cabin modules could contribute to this as well as to stability, which is an issue in cruise ships with a tall superstructure.

Several experimental projects are being executed as we speak. There is no final outcome yet, but estimations point in the direction of 50 per cent weight reduction per cabin. Known requirements that were inherited from steel cabins are easy to fulfil. And improvements can be made: the need for maintenance has been reduced and there is greater resistance to damage. The only remaining drawback is the scale of production. Builders should be able to overcome this, since every new ship needs another couple of thousand cabins and one cabin manufacturer can work for several cruise ship builders.

19.2 THE TALLEST STARCK

Grab your magnifying glass and take a look at the stern of this sail assisted motor yacht. If you're lucky you can just about discern two people. They give you some idea of the size of this Sailing Yacht A. The Russian oligarch Andrey Melnichenko owns it and the French designer Philippe Starck designed it. He also did Steve Jobs's yacht. His name rose to fame in the early 1990s when he designed a seriously eye-catching lemon squeezer called 'Juicy Salif'. This yacht is eye-catching too. Built in Kiel, North Germany, by Nobiskrug under the direction of its owner's project leader Dirk Kloosterman and his team, it's the largest design Starck ever made and probably will ever make.

The ship is over 140 metres long and sails with a crew of 52. The middle of the three carbon fibre reinforced masts gives the vessel a staggering height of 100 metres. Produced by yacht mast pioneers Magma Structures in Portchester, UK, they are the tallest free-standing masts ever, anywhere. And they are not just very tall. Attached to the spars is a CFRP casing over the full height that conceals the mechanics and the sails. All the helmsman has to do to unfurl the sails is push a button and up she rises.

Composite structures for very large yachts built in the Netherlands are not standard, because customers have their own personal requirements. For example, Arabs allegedly don't want yacht designers to take away weight from the interior, since they prefer silence and privacy. The Dutch Feadship yard built the *Venus* for the late Steve Jobs in aluminium, which is appropriate for a deceased Apple CEO. Royal Huisman, also from the Netherlands, can build very large yachts in aluminium (up to 90 metres) but also in carbon composite, or a combination, if that is what the customer wants. It's all about how a ship behaves at sea. There, a carbon fibre hull can be rough and noisy compared to an aluminium one. This of course depends on the design and the requirements. Rondal, a subsidiary of Royal Huisman, can even use an entire manufacturing hall as an oven (at 80 °C) that staff can enter in special suits to check that all's well with the UD tapes.

Inland waterway freight transport is currently making a comeback.

Plying the waters in a private yacht is a relatively new phenomenon. It dates back to the beginning of the previous century, as does the yachting industry. Royal Huisman began in 1884, producing wooden fishing vessels and workboats. They switched to pleasure boats when the Afsluitdijk causeway was put in place and the Zuiderzee east of Amsterdam lost its connection with the sea and effectively became a lake.

Contest Yachts in the Northwest of the Netherlands build smaller (up to 25 metres) seaworthy sailing boats in a limited range of customizable models. They produce exclusively vacuum-injected GFRP hulls for customers all over the world. Buying such a boat is not a matter of picking one from a catalogue. As a customer you are involved in all the facets of manufacturing, which can easily take a year. You get to understand your purchase, or you send the captain you hired to learn the tiniest details. At their yard they also carry out maintenance and repairs on all the yachts they build. Owning a high-quality boat gives you a personal relationship with the firm. Yachting is still mainly a male pastime. Female customers do exist, but they are extremely rare.

All at once thermal insulation is an important issue.

Yachting on inland waterways began with traditional boats, these gradually being replaced by small recreational craft in wood, metal and later GFRP. Boats are built to last and traditional former fishing and transportation boats are still a familiar sight. Some are true antiques. Every year there are sailing races for old 'botters', schooners, 'kotters' and Frisian 'tjalks'. These flat-bottom boats used to carry freight before steam and diesel engines made their mark. After WW2 trucks and trains took over much of their workload.

Inland waterway freight transportation is currently making a strong comeback. The demonstrable efficiency of barges of different types has reinstated their importance. Currently the EU is putting money

Boskalis' Black Marlin carrying 18 inland vessel hulls

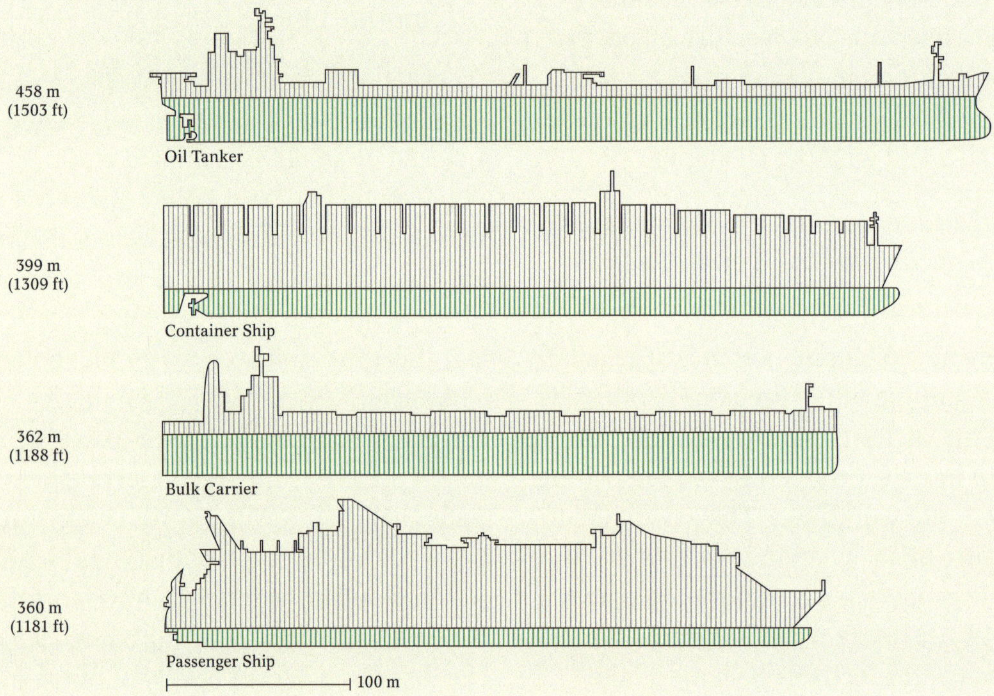

into restoring its waterways. There has definitely been a recognizable interest in weight reduction, but there is also a fuzzy clash with tradition. The idea of a composite barge was put forward more than ten years ago, but the Dutch world of inland waterway transport has a hard time understanding the implications. Such structures are made differently. Welding has to be replaced by gluing – there may be an opportunity for thermoplastic composites here – and the new rules and regulations are as yet unclear.

Inland skippers are hesitant but may become convinced by the increasing interest. They could look at examples in other shipping segments. Recreational sailing is an inspiration, also in terms of the convenience of living on a barge. And navies everywhere would be lost without composites these days. Obviously, there are advantages in speed, fuel consumption, load and maintenance. All at once thermal insulation is an important issue. Naval vessels spend a lot of time in ports with the crew on board. A ship needs to be comfortable if you're living on it, which is why fuel consumption takes up a considerable part of the 'hotel costs'.

There are other specific navy functions that benefit from composites. Radar transparency (stealth) and, particularly for submarines, invisibility to infrared detectors and sound insulation are indispensable. There are constructional advantages too. Damen Shipyards and SAAB are developing a concept for a new submarine with composite segments. Functional elements such as crew accommodation and the command centre are included as separate modules. Because of this there is all-round access for assembly and testing.

The submarine proposal is a more universal version of the Swedish A24 submarine, which was specifically designed for the Baltic Sea. The project is illustrative of the global nature of shipbuilding today. Damen began as a company that took over Dutch shipyards that were suffering from the steep business decline due to competition from the Far East. Currently the enterprise is a large cluster of shipyards, organized internationally, with one in Antalya (Turkey) that specializes in the serial production of a whole range of glass fibre reinforced polymer workboats for patrolling, transportation, search and rescue, and other applications.

International trade in ship parts has really become quite spectacular. For example, Damen ordered 18 inland vessel hulls in Shanghai and these were transported to Rotterdam using the Boskalis semi-submersible heavy lift vessel *Black Marlin*. The *Vanguard*, another such Boskalis vessel and the largest of its type in the world, once lifted the *Carnival Vista*, a 4000-passenger cruise ship, and transported it to a shipyard for its engines to be repaired. The ultimate in heavy transporter firms, Boskalis claimed that this load weighed the equivalent of 300 Boeing 747s. At this point the relationship between heaviness and lightness becomes mind-boggling, particularly because 300 Jumbo jets between them can carry 140,000 passengers ■

Top left: Damen Shipyards and SAB proposal for a submarine with composite modules. Top right: Vacuum injection of the hull of a Damen Shipyards waterbus in Turkey. Bottom: Waterbus Rotterdam

Left: PortLiner's EC52. Right: CompoCaNord

19.3 BARGES ON THE VERGE

There is an urgent need to make greater use of inland waterway transportation but getting more efficient ships developed for that purpose is clearly no easy matter. CompoCaNord was the name of a 2007 consortium that received Dutch government aid to develop an 'innovative, multi-purpose, lightweight composite barge', to replace small conventional steel ships. The consortium consisted of a European partnership of transporters, two companies and a knowledge centre.

It developed a rough concept setting out the main measurements. The place for the engine and a car was to be in the middle of the 45-metre ship, leaving ample living space in the stern. The total weight was to be 133 tonnes and the maximum cargo weight 917 tonnes, which is impressive. And now a brief remark about the word 'innovative'. There is a tendency to see this as a quality, whereas it can actually distract from making progress. New isn't always better.

Anyway, the project failed to materialize. Several reasons have been put forward as to why it fell through. Too many questions remained unanswered, about regulations, classification and feasibility. Turning knowledge into practice is a difficult business. The consortium fell apart because of differences in opinion on the marketing strategy. A consortium is always tricky, because this collaboration between parties (obviously a good thing) is bound to precipitate a clash between idealism and opportunism (not a good thing at all). Often it is the failure to agree that brings about its demise. More recently Europe subsidized the Dutch company PortLiner to develop six battery-electric barges. So far, their introduction has been postponed several times. The concept is interesting in the sense that electrification implies additional cargo space as well as the opportunity to decouple the wheelhouse from the hull and provide it with a mechanism that lowers it behind the load. However, it is disappointing that there is no mention of the barge's weight. It might compensate for the extra burden of batteries. Moreover, in this day and age, there must be smarter ways to oversee the ship than a moving wheelhouse. One cause of this missed opportunity is the current governmental focus on the 'Energy Transition', which tends to blur the view of the entire concept.

THIN RED LINE AEROSPACE

20. FOLLOW THE FLOW

Despite the reduction of material mass per unit, the sum total use of materials has increased with turnover.

Foil, paper, laminates, sachets, envelopes, blister packs, cans, bags, boxes, cases, tanks and containers are the apparel of whatever we take from one place to the next. These products enclose all that we value (or maybe just tell ourselves we value), with protection against all the convenience-threatening dangers they meet on the road and emblazoned with graphic proclamations to spread the messages of handling and identity. At the same time packaging has to be light and unobtrusive. Packaging is the humble servant of mass trade. And it is the industry that screams lightness, because you wouldn't want to transport materials in a way that increases both the costs and the hassle of unpacking after delivery. Because of its overviewable short-cycle functionality, packaging can serve as an example for other industries.

Packaging is the humble servant of mass trade.

The packaging industry has done very well. In general, it can perform better per packaging unit with less material, even on a yearly basis. So material reduction is profitable too. This seems to be what designing lightness is about. However, we run into a fundamental paradox, because despite the reduction of material mass per unit, the sum total use of materials has increased with turnover, helped by the consumer's appreciation of smaller packaged portions: a freshly packed biscuit with their cappuccino. This implies that material consumption keeps on growing. And what better to curb this increase than the background challenge of lightweight design. This requires long-term development, which means designing for the right balance between longevity and circularity, combined with a drastic increase in concern for unwanted side effects.

The effort that goes into adding functionality and at the same time subtracting amounts of material is considerable. If only this were always the case. When you order, say, a toothbrush at an online store, you may get it the next day in a box so large that it would feel quite comfortable even to a grumpy kitchen chair.

The cause of this awkward mismatch is that in this example packaging is a process in a very complex setting. An army of workers have to pick out items in a huge warehouse with anything from air fryers to marmalade to zip ties, scan their respective barcodes and put them on a conveyor belt. This brings the items to a packing station, which recognizes their individual size (from the barcode) and the box that each of them needs. Because such a warehouse contains thousands

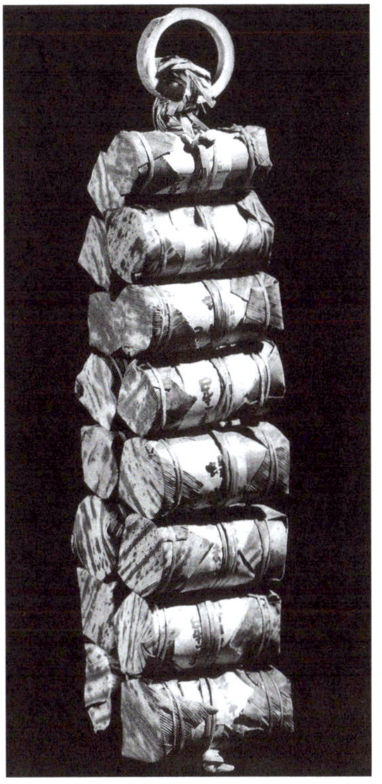

20.1 TSUTSUMI

One can put something in a box or a wrapper, fix the loose ends with sticky tape, maybe put a ribbon around it and call it neatly packed. The most inspiring alternative is to consider packaging an art and really make the best out of it. Tsutsumi is the Japanese art of packaging.

Here the package is the message, not what is inside. A long time ago there used to be *tsutsumi* ceremonies where the gifts were not even meant to be unwrapped. It just had to be clear that the contents were safe. That was the point. Currently *tsutsumi* is about exchanging gifts.

There are special considerations for different kinds of contents, as we can see from these two passages from 'Tsutsumi: the Japanese art of packaging' by Luisa Canovi (*Perini Journal* 28):

'Foodstuffs such as eggs, vegetables, fish, tofu and pasta made from rice often find housing not only in paper but also in other flexible materials, such as leaves, straw, rope, etc. By wrapping, tying and intertwining, small protective architectures are created where to place eggs, for example. Even though they are clearly visible, they are still protected by a veritable anti-shock packaging. Grids of careful knots support fish, crustaceans and vegetables so that they can be hung to favor ventilation. But this packaging is also safe for transport, for selling and for use. Foodstuffs packaged in this way remain visible and one can appreciate their aesthetics and freshness.'

'Contemporary design has taken ideas from all these Tsutsumi for today's industrial packaging. Starting with traditional natural materials used to their utmost potential through extremely refined elaborations using paper, wood, rope, etc., to recover – innovating at the same time – antique forms to contain things.'

Egg packaging is especially ingenious, since the structure of an egg and its particular strength are part of it.

20.2 HEAT IN, HEAT OUT

The protection of goods is not always a transportation issue. Thermal blankets protect us from getting too cold and we can extinguish a fire by throwing a blanket over it, cutting off the oxygen supply.

Recent years have witnessed the emergence of an entirely new packaging concept, which is to pack snow and keep it safe for the skiing season. It came with a new expression: snow farming. Actually, saving snow for when it is needed may well involve transporting it. In 2019 snow was brought into Moscow by special delivery to provide the city with a wintrier ambience during Christmas and the New Year celebrations.

of different products, and a packaging machine can't produce every size of bag or box because that would mean too much discarded cardboard, assumptions have to be made regarding the type of product and package size. Here we arrive at a major shortcoming of programmed machines: there are always built-in 'what if's' and these inevitably lead to system stupidity.

Packaging is a verb.

Anyway, the toothbrush box has served to illustrate an important realization: packaging is a verb. It is part of the process to transfer an object or a substance from one place to another, where it is going to have to be unpacked. What happens to packaging after that, whether it's continued use, recycling, dumping, burning or being left to hungry bacteria for composting, is of major concern and needs to be dealt with within the concept of material flow. It isn't enough to state that your material can be, or indeed has been, recycled. That's not the point. Dumping waste on landfills or in the sea is harmful, because it takes up space and there is no control over side effects. And by now we are well aware of the effect on the atmosphere of burning waste.

The current mission therefore is to bring packaging under a systematic regime.

The current mission therefore is to bring the massive flow of ever lighter packaging under a systematic regime. This consists of three principles brought together in a transparent network of circular trajectories: continued use, recycling and biodegradation. Such a network already exists but needs to be more clearly defined. The three principles don't necessarily exclude each other. An item that has been designed to last for any number of years can still be shredded and turned into something new. And maybe that long-lasting item requires biodegradable support materials, or a certain kind of plastic. Everything has its own trajectory.

Setting up such a regime requires the clear division of responsibilities that is now beginning to emerge. Governments need to set rules and regulations that help to manage flows. In the Netherlands, law has forced the government to take adequate measures to reduce emissions. This may see the Dutch government focusing more proactively on individual industries such as packaging. Currently producers pay a certain amount per kilogram waste to make sure the government can take care of it. This arrangement still needs refining, in particular with regard to the flow of different plastics used for packaging. Technically all plastics can be recycled – in fact any material can – but retrieving everyday polymers such as polystyrene and polyethylene from a mixed flow is much more expensive than retrieving the virgin granulate.

Technically all plastics can be recycled.

Biodegradable plastics are complicating the process at present due to a counter-intuitive phenomenon. Composting installations have been made to work much faster over the past years, so much so that biodegradable plastics haven't been able to keep up. They have been consigned to the 'residual waste' category for the time being. In countries without a waste collection system, biodegradables can help to reduce the flow, at least for now.

Composite design adds functionality to packaging materials, which have to protect products from whatever may damage content. A very common protection composite for dry foodstuffs, such as tea, biscuits and snacks, is metallized film as mentioned elsewhere. It is difficult to handle because it is lightweight, and separating a few microns of metal from slightly more microns of two layers of different polymers for recycling is not entirely impossible but costly when compared to dumping it and producing fresh laminate. Recycling companies are looking into possible alternatives.

> *Flow organization can also be a business model.*

One option is to replace two different plastics with one, which allows for better flow organization. Another is refillable packaging. This used to be the norm in the days when most food wasn't processed in large factories. It can work again for that kind of product. The story is far more complicated for crisps and chocolate bars. There is a rationale behind packaging that needs redefining. Another question that occupies producers is whether consumers are prepared to accept a reduction of convenience. One answer is that not all issues are best left to consumer choice. We humans are not very good at choosing, as Nobel Prize winner Daniel Kahneman shows in his best-seller *Thinking, Fast and Slow.* Regulations are likely to help. Governments all over the world have banned free plastic shopping bags. Such measures now need refining.

Flow organization can also be a business model. The TerraCycle company began life at Princeton University in 2001. Now it is a world market leader in recycling materials that were first thought unrecyclable. You can tune in to different material flows for recycling, some of which are sponsored by companies and others you have to pay for yourself. The smart part of the principle is that it tempts customers to select the right flow. TerraCycle takes care of the rest and can even handle cigarette butts.

Of course, there are also transportation services that own all the recycled products and will simply reuse them over a longer period of time. CHEP, for instance, owns millions of pallets and containers and provides pooling services to companies all over the world. A company like CHEP benefits from cultivating the value of its system. It would be interesting to see if a similar set-up is feasible for consumer products. But probably the most important issue is to address ways of taking packaging apart as well as the question of what happens to it after delivery ■

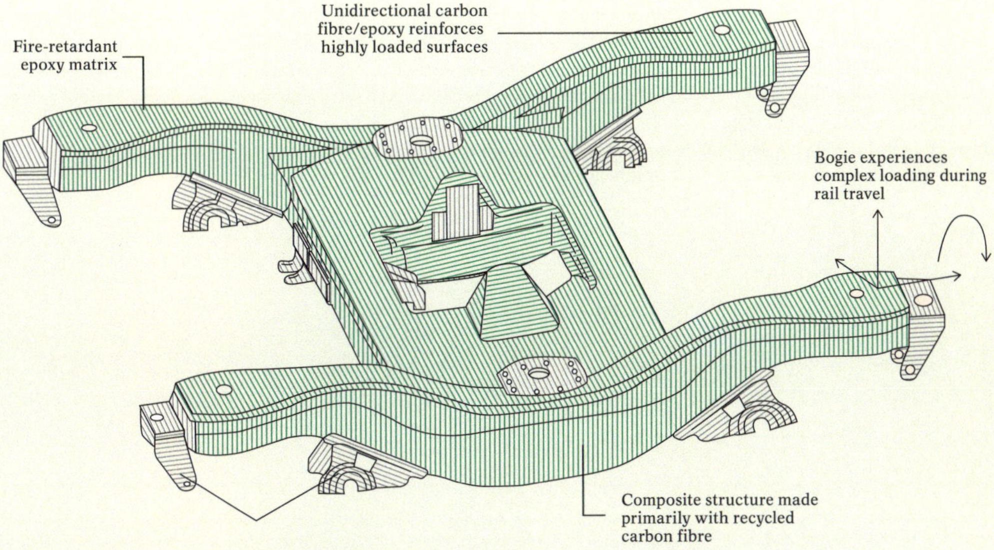

counterpart to accommodate fixtures.

DESIGN RESULTS

Carbon fibre-reinforced rail bogie

- Basic frame structure 590kg (64%) lighter
- Bogie frame and fittings: 36% weight reduction in prototype; up to 50% in future versions
- Up to 40% reduction in wheel rail transverse loading
- Reduction in cost and enviromental footprint through recycled carbon fibre

Body in white (BIW) weight for different materials

Conventional	Advanced Steel	Aluminium	Carbon Fibre
			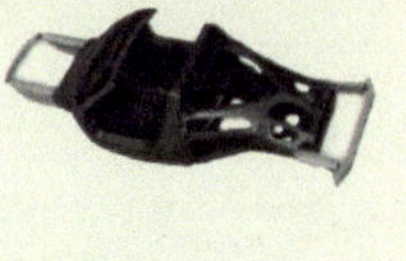
Weight BIW 300kg	Weight BIW 195kg	Weight BIW 214kg	Weight BIW 150kg

20.3 SPECIAL ACCUMULATORS

Batteries are packaged quantities of energy. There are different ways to put power in a wrapper. In China's Shandong Province it is not uncommon for villagers to steal natural gas from an oil plant to heat their homes. They collect it in enormous plastic bags that they carry or attach to a bike.

An entirely different way of putting energy in a skin is to compress air into a very strong underwater balloon. A prototype was developed by the CFD research group and Thin Red Line in Chilliwack, Canada. The pressure force of the water will be great enough to squeeze out the air. All you have to do is let it happen. The basic idea is that a wind turbine pumps in air, which when released drives a generator. These 'energy bags' would be anchored at a depth of about 600 metres, where the pressure is extreme.

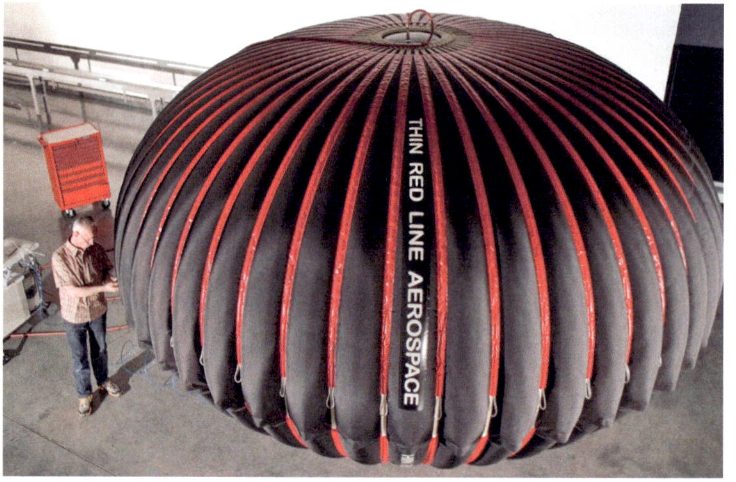

20.4 COMPOSITE CONTAINERS

The largest standard packaging and transportation device, as mentioned in Chapter 8, is the container. Saving weight is an issue of increasing importance. The use of composites is obvious where cheap steel containers are less suited to the job. Steel is heavy, provides no insulation and is prone to corrosion. Cargoshell in Rotterdam is the first company to introduce three types of composite containers. The first is foldable, a response to the fact that much transportation is one-way, meaning that containers have to travel back empty. Since it weighs 25 per cent less and can be folded to a quarter of its normal height, it is possible to transport four such containers in the space normally occupied by one and weighing about the same as three empty ones. The second has been approved for transport under Customs seal and the third can be refrigerated, benefitting from the fact that composites are good insulators. Also, there is no corrosion or moisture condensation. The absence of metal allows for remote monitoring and a built-in GPS sensor.

Composite Production Technology BV, located north of Amsterdam, was already producing wound composite products when it decided to focus on composite tank containers under the name Tankwell. The weight reduction is almost 40 per cent, allowing a payload increase of over 3000 kilograms to about 36 tonnes. It can carry fluids that you can drink, but also industrial chemicals. Another obvious advantage is that composites provide better insulation than stainless steel.

Composite containers are an obvious choice for air freight in terms of weight reduction, provided their design is based on an awareness of the conceptual differences between composites and metal.

21. CLEAR THE AIR

Lightness is by far the most obvious requirement for flying structures and sure enough the airplane industry has been the front runner in the development of lightweight structures since its early days. Airplanes belonged to the mythology of the era before and during WW2 and established the characteristics of streamlining as a decorative style that is still shown off to express nostalgia for technological progress. Aircraft development is much more complicated than it used to be, when a company could bring out a new model in a year or so. It is beginning to lag behind other fields of interest. These days a new plane is a once-in-a-lifetime experience for an aircraft designer. This is due partly to aircraft not being mass products and partly to safety regulations. But there have also been surprises: rising pressure to reduce the environmental side effects of flying gained an unexpected emphasis on electrification because of what is happening in the car industry, and there has been the sudden Rise of the Drones.

Airplane manufacturing also used to be at the forefront of developing vehicle technology, with aluminium technology setting examples for design in other fields. Today it is a well-organized industry that has spread all over the world. There are hardly any companies left that produce complete airplanes. Brands focus primarily on components for assembly. Adding value has fragmented and value has increased. Aircraft producers have their very own 'silk route', complete with specially developed airplanes and ships.

These days companies outsource part production and no longer produce entire planes themselves. Even wings and complete fuselage sections are brought in from elsewhere to the assembly hall. For example DTC, an abbreviation of Dutch Thermoplastic Components, produces high value limited sized airplane parts from continuous fibre reinforced engineering thermoplastics. One of its Japanese customers might use these to produce airplane doors and supply those to Boeing in the US. But DTC also has Airbus as a client. This spreading of production is happening in industry in general. It is the consequence of looking for optimum procedures in a world that has become small for manufacturers of high value products.

When aircraft making was in its pioneering stage, you had these adventurous men with tiny companies. They just wanted to be as free as a bird and tried to use anything they could lay their hands on to create their flying contraptions. Otto Lilienthal built a range of beautiful gliders and copied birds' wings and tails in wood, metal and textile. In 1903 Orville and Wilbur Wright were the first to successfully build and fly an airplane with an engine, the Wright Flyer, also called Flyer 1 in retrospect to distinguish it from its successors. They worked in an environment with machines of various kinds and from their experience with making bicycles they believed that with a bit of practice, trial and error one could learn to fly. They built a primitive wind tunnel to test the effects of wing deformation and used those principles in their design: no hinges or ailerons, just warping as in birds' wings.

> *In technological development there is always an element of familiarity.*

Thirteen years later Junkers in Germany built the first all-metal plane. Before that it had manufactured heating systems, which was still visible in the structural parts the company used, namely pipe fittings. It signifies pragmatism in technological development in general. There is always an element of familiarity. It is one of the reasons why it is taking such a long time for gluing to be accepted, and for composites, being reinforced glues.

This is not just a matter of gaining trust, but also of understanding change, which leads us back to the main principle of Designing Lightness. Materials never travel alone, but always come with a process and a concept, within a context. Time and again a material gets replaced with little or no thought for the implications. CFRP plates have been riveted to replace aluminium, for instance. Riveting is always damaging, but particularly in plates where the structural integrity is compromised by cutting fibres and increasing local stress.

Conceptual mistakes can also happen at the scale of complete structures, as part of the process of composites colonizing load-bearing parts. Recently a test was

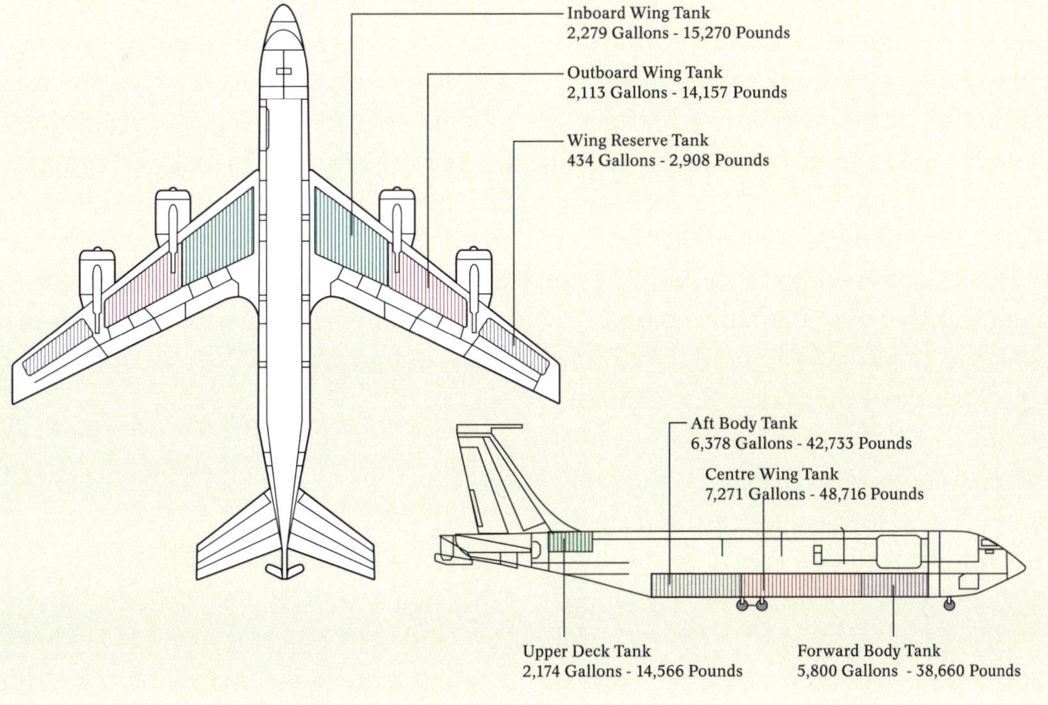

Airplanes are the robots that do the work in the factory that produces flights between airports.

carried out with a Boeing 777, a very successful wide body dating back 25 years, in which aluminium wings were replaced by composite ones, clearly to save weight and maintenance costs. During the static ground test with the '777X', in which the fuselage was pressurized and the wings were loaded, a door blew out and the fuselage split. In earlier tests the aluminium wings snapped, just above the required 1.5x maximum load. The carbon wings didn't snap. Instead the fuselage decompressed at just under 1.5x maximum load. Luckily this was a static ground test. At the very least it is an indication that replacing the wings changes assumptions about static load acting on the structure as a whole. Dynamic testing may reveal issues too, for carbon wings have different 'personalities', as discussed in the section about bending.

Those carbon wings for an existing airplane, together with two fully composite planes, the Boeing 787 and the Airbus A350, are a clear indication that composites are now serious business and no longer limited to non-primary load-bearing segments. Nevertheless, there are still signs of a building tradition that harks back to shipbuilding principles. ('This is your captain speaking'. Airplanes do have a naval background.) The 787 fuselage is a closed convoluted fibre placement structure. This means that everything inside the fuselage must fit through the doors and that access is limited. The A350 fuselage consists of curved panels placed together. The interior remains entirely accessible until the tube is closed. This approach is less radical, but more convenient.

Thermoplastic composites have found their way into airplane structures too and the blessings of welding are multiplying. Whereas DTC produces fibre reinforced thermoplastic parts from textiles produced by Ten Cate Composites (recently taken over by Toray), Airbus is now discovering ways to weld complete thermoplastic fuselages. Because of the potential of mass production, engineering plastics are really beginning to make their mark. GKN Fokker Aerostructures has been welding wing and nose panels to ribs for some years already. The move towards welding may signify a new wave of composite colonization.

It seems that batteries will always be too heavy to thrust hundreds people to another continent.

Aircraft construction has mostly remained a craft. Robots do contribute here and there, such as in GKN Fokker's welding setup, but conveyor belts are rare in production. They help load and unload

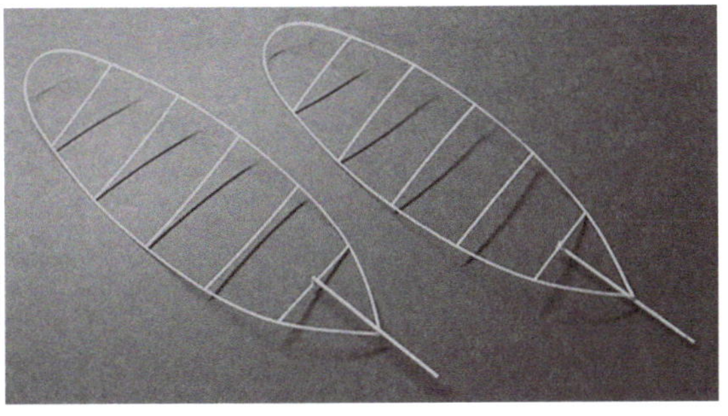

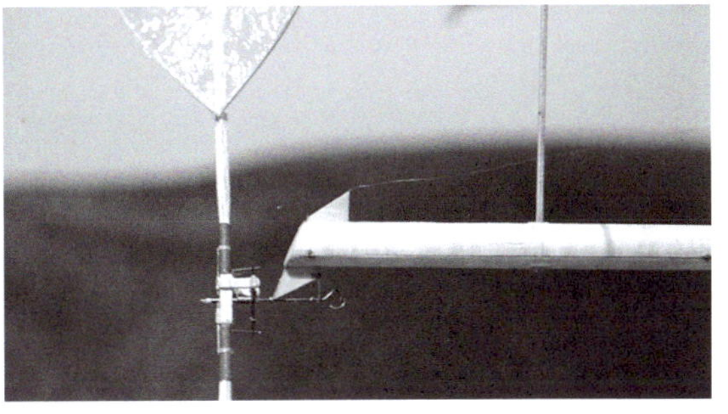

21.1 THE LIGHTEST OF THE LIGHTEST

This is a recommendation, just to amaze you. Competitive model flying can be divided into several classes, including gliders and planes powered by little engines of elastic. The aim is always to stay up in the air longer than your competitors. The most beautiful class is called F1D.

Look at these specifications: the minimum weight is 1.4 grams and the maximum wing span 550 millimetres. They're made from balsa wood, a little fibre (boron and carbon) and a skin of plastic film less than 5 micrometres thick, like a soap film but without any torsional connotations. Power comes from 0.4 grams of rubber in a loop that can be wound 1500 times, with the stored tension energy generating torsion. You can – no, you must – watch competitions on the Internet. They fly so elegantly, as if in slow motion.

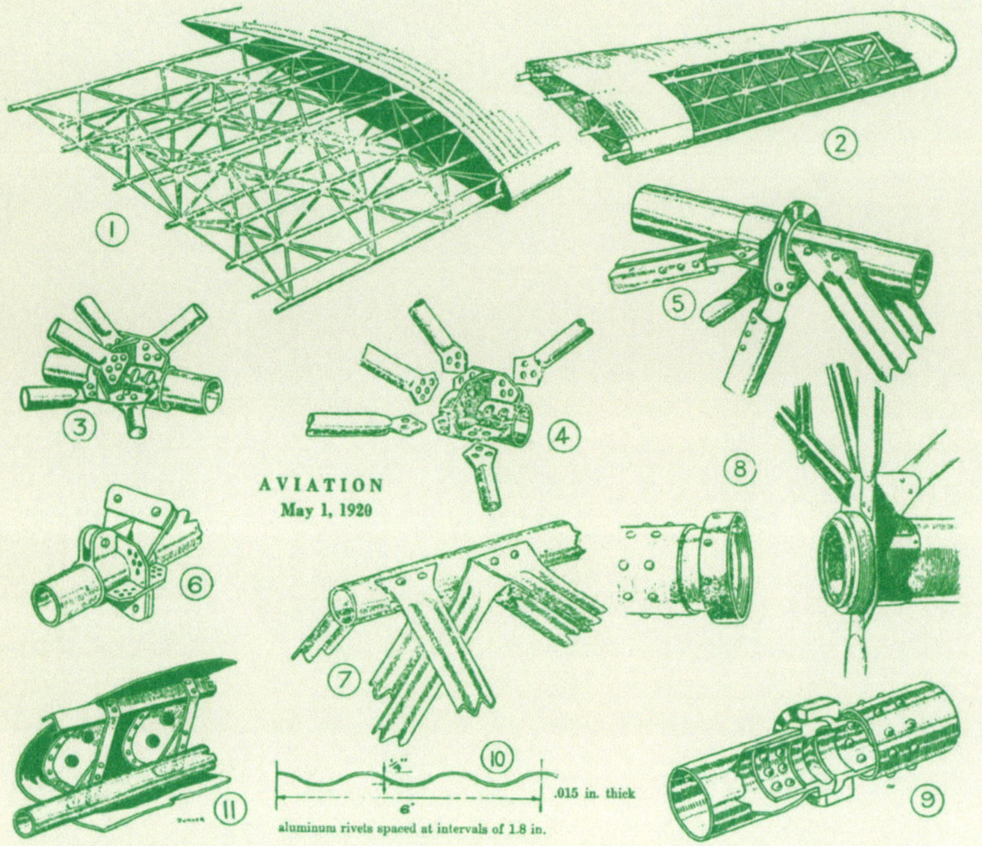

CONSTRUCTIONAL DETAILS OF THE JUNKERS WING: (1) AND (2) GENERAL CONSTRUCTION; (3) TO (7) DETAILS OF WING BRACES; (8) AND (9) DETAILS OF WING ATTACHMENTS; (10) CORRUGATED SHEET COVERING; (11) LEADING EDGE

21.2 THE BEST STRUCTURE

Junkers originally made its airplanes from the parts and materials it had in stock from when its founder Hugo Junkers produced heating appliances: tubular steel, threaded connecting parts and steel sheet. His firm did make corrugated aluminium but couldn't afford to use it for airplanes. Instead they sold it to a colleague, Hans Reissner, who used it to build a monoplane, the Reissner Ente, Ente being German for Duck.

In 1914, at the beginning of the war, Junkers began with a 0.2-millimetre outer steel skin, stiffened inside with corrugated steel, which is like corrugated paper except much heavier. It didn't take long for Junkers to make the switch to a single layer of corrugated aluminium. This wasn't ideal in terms of drag, but compared to other airplanes of those early times, with two or even three stacked wings (the Red Baron's Fokker DR1), Junkers planes were very fast. There was another advantage that is unthinkable from today's perspective. In 1919, during the Baltic War, Junkers fighter planes had no trouble with rain. Planes made of wood and linen, on the other hand, couldn't take off if they were soaking wet.

people and luggage in the travel factories known as airports rather than contribute to airplane assembly. The air travel market is expressed in chairs per trip rather than numbers of products. Air travel is a service industry and one could say that airplanes are the robots that do most of the dangerous and difficult work in the factory that produces flights between airports. And it's a full-time job.

The stunning productivity of airplanes currently carrying some 2.7 million passengers each day – and that number is increasing – is a major cause of pollution. They produce noise and CO_2 and also contrails, thin clouds of ice that has frozen around soot particles, which according to meteorological research contribute more to global warming than CO_2 emissions. The effect is stronger but not as persistent. Unlike CO_2, which hangs around for years, ice disappears within hours, unless it is replaced by the next flight.

In terms of efficiency, flying is not much different from cars per seat kilometre, but the pollutive effect is more concentrated and of course related to speed and distance covered. Over the past years speed has not been translated into costs, environmental or otherwise. On the contrary, flying is ridiculously cheap.

The societal pressure to do something about this has been with us since about 1970, to little effect. Recently, however, now that global warming has been acknowledged, the urgency of change has gone through a sudden increase. There is not one simple cause for this, but a major part of the noticeable change in mentality, exemplified by the Swedish word *flygskam* (shame of flying) and the impact of young Swedish activist Greta Thunberg's choice to travel to the US by sailing boat, is a follow-up to Elon Musk's demonstration that 'electric' can be made feasible and attractive. The – dare I say – disruptive rise of electric cars has been the springboard for the idea that in the foreseeable future airplanes will be electric too.

If this will really happen across the board is as yet uncertain, but many new possibilities are now presenting themselves, each with a different time scale. The first manned free flight in an electric plane took place back in 1973. There have been many experiments since then with light planes, batteries and fuel cells. Siemens built the Extra 330LE, an adapted fast acrobatic airplane and the first electric plane to tow a glider. Solar Impulse 2 was the name of the first completely solar-powered airplane. It flew around the world with one long intermission due to battery damage.

It looks as though drones are the technological front runner.

Currently concepts are being tested everywhere, more than 200 of them. Airbus is testing an electric turbine on a hybrid jet plane called E-FanX. Whether the electrified planes of the future will have the same capacities that are prevalent today is anybody's guess. As for now, it seems that batteries will always be too heavy to thrust a couple of hundred people to another continent. Most projects currently under way are for planes performing taxi-like services for a limited number of passengers to be transported over short distances, generally no more than 10 people within a range of 300 kilometres.

Saving weight is of course paramount for these planes, particularly if they fly on batteries. But there is more going on. Electric engines are lighter and smarter to control. It's not that hard to plug in a few extra engines, so to speak. Unexpectedly, aircraft configuration has become open to experimentation. Lilium, a new German brand, is developing a sleek 36-engine canard-winged aircraft capable of vertical take-off and landing (VTOL).

There is a connection between such developments and what is happening in the originally unrelated world of drones. These unmanned devices have long been part of the military world of reconnaissance and autonomous torpedoes. The drones currently conquering the air in vast numbers are mostly four-propeller 'quadcopters', often with built-in cameras. The principle of the quadcopter, believe it or not, dates back to the 'gyroplane' designed in 1907 by Jacques and Louis Breguet, the second of whom went on to found an aircraft company. Similar designs by other pioneers were to follow and in the 1960s wireless control started to make inroads on unmanned flying. In 2001, after the attack on the Twin Towers, the US began flying armed drones over Iraq. Drones really took off from 2006 onwards, when the US Federal Aviation Administration began issuing commercial, non-military drone permits. Together with ever lighter and smaller electronics and sensors, quadcopters have literally become household products and can be bought very cheaply complete with built-in cameras. In 2010 the French firm of Parrot introduced the first smartphone-controlled drone. Package and pizza delivery are on the way to being taken over by drones, wherever safe, outside urban areas. Improvements are continuing and here we are in Shanghai watching the 2020 New Year's celebrations (actually enacted on 28 December 2019) where a swarm of 2000 drones with remote-controlled coloured lights on board have taken over from fireworks.

The drone market is so promising that companies often buy one before they actually know what they're going to use it for. And drones are being developed all over the world. In the Netherlands there are some small firms that make special purpose research models.

Drones can also carry people. Ideas and plans are emerging to develop unmanned taxi services. It could be that moving people automatically in the air is safer than on the road, because it is much easier to block a road, say by playing basketball on it, than it is to stop a quadcopter once it has reached a certain height, except perhaps with another drone. It looks as though drones are the technological front runner now, starting a new life cycle curve with a combination of sensing capabilities and flying. But we have to be careful. Materials and energy can come at a price ■

21.3 LESSONS LEARNED

In 1971 Fokker, together with the German consortium Vereinigte Flugtechnische Werke, introduced an unusual 40-passenger airplane. The VFW 614 had its engines mounted on top of the wings. There were several ideas behind this configuration. The engines would suffer less from dust and rubble on badly maintained runways, drag would be reduced, there would be more space in the cabin and it would be safer during crash landings without low-hanging engines making the first touchdown. The first prototype crashed within a year due to torsion flutter, fatal rotational vibration of the entire tail section because of which some of the control cables became tangled. The design was modified, but only fourteen were sold and the project was axed in 1980.

Towards the end of the 1980s Honda began work on a business jet with a similar above-wing engine placement. Built in the US as a prototype, the Honda MHO2 was the first all-composite business jet. Development continued in Japan and concept testing was completed in 1999. A proof-of-concept version of the HA-420 HondaJet made its first flight in 2003 in the US. In 2010 the first FAA approved model flew and the following year GKN Fokker Aerostructures was chosen to produce the complete composite fuselage. The first production jet flew in 2014 and is currently in production.

The HA-420 HondaJet has a very stiff fuselage compared to the earlier VFW model, as the tail and nose are composite sandwiches and the tube in between consists of stiffened panels. The wings, pylons and empennage are metal. From 1971 to 2014 is rather along time to develop an unusual concept.

Tupolev TU-155 hydrogen fuelled prototype

21.4 THE HYDROGEN EXPERIENCE

Hydrogen for air travel is making a belated recovery from the setback of the notorious disaster when the Hindenburg LZ127 crashed at Lakehurst, New Jersey on 6 May 1937 and went up in flames. It was the largest of the zeppelins, none of which was a success. But now we know there is so much more you can do with hydrogen in aviation besides exploiting its low density. It has by far the highest energy content per unit mass of all the elements and its risks are manageable because it is so light. It is highly inflammable, but when it catches fire the flames will rise quickly. This can even be seen on the newsreel of the Hindenburg accident, where most of the passengers survived.

The option that is most seriously being considered right now is the slow reaction between hydrogen and oxygen in a fuel cell, which produces electricity and pure water. Airbus is experimenting with this principle initially to power the aircraft cabin. ZeroAvia and others want to use this power to drive engines.

The most obvious way for airplanes to use hydrogen energy is to burn it in adapted jet engines. There are plans for a Liquid Hydrogen Fuelled Aircraft (LHFA). It will be bulky, because of the space needed for cooled hydrogen tanks. The disadvantage of burning hydrogen directly is that the process is not as clean as one would expect. The heat also supports a reaction between oxygen and nitrogen – about 80 per cent of the air we breathe is nitrogen – to form nitrogen dioxide, which is poisonous and contributes to acidification.

There is some measure of experience with such a plane. Towards the end of the 1980s the Soviet Union built the Tupolev TU-155. It was an adapted version of the TU-154, to be used as a testbed for alternative fuels (hydrogen and liquefied natural gas). It flew about 100 times. The project was cancelled when the Soviet Union collapsed.

21.5 STUNT SHOES

On 14 July 2019, a French national holiday commemorating the beginning of the French Revolution in 1789, the whole world saw him for the first time performing an extremely spectacular stunt. Franky Zapata flew over the Parisian crowds on a tiny jet-propelled platform, his Flyboard Air. He had stunted before on his similar water-propelled Flyboard. It seemed impossible to actually fly in this way, but it worked. The Belgian artist Panamarenko had made similar contraptions, but it was never his intention to succeed.

The inventor of this fantastic device then announced that he would cross the English Channel eleven days later, to match the exact date on which Louis Blériot flew from France to England for the first time.

Zapata's first attempt was unsuccessful because his refuelling stop misfired. But on 4 August 2019 he succeeded, in 22 minutes. To cross the Channel in this way is of course a phenomenal stunt, but it remains doubtful whether the Flyboard Air is suitable for other tasks. The little machine is quite noisy, and you have to be a skilled daredevil to fly it. On a more serious note, the Flyboard is low efficient since the person standing on it increases the drag by a factor of at least seven. And you can't have the pilot land every ten minutes for a refill. Maybe the wearable fuel cell will offer solace at a later date.

22. INFLATABLE SPACE

This mutual embrace of science and culture has continued to this day.

Six, five, four, three, two, one, NOW! You probably think that the countdown is an obvious ritual, even for televised cookery competitions to mark off the last few seconds of permitted activity. Actually, it was invented for dramatic reasons by film director Fritz Lang for his 1929 science fiction movie *Frau im Mond* (Woman in the Moon). Hergé, who drew the Tintin comic *Explorers on the Moon*, must have seen Lang's movie, judging by the cartoon rocket's interior.

For the necessary scientific precision Lang hired Hermann Oberth. This German pioneer of rocket technology would later be assisted in his work by Wernher von Braun, the man who developed the V2 for the Nazis in WW2. Later von Braun was in charge of the Redstone Arsenal team that built the rocket that sent Explorer 1 into orbit in 1958. He also led the NASA team that developed the range of Saturn launch vehicles for Project Apollo. Von Braun worked for Disney Studios as a technical director of television movies made to convince the US government of the urgency of Von Braun's plans for space colonization.

The bond between fiction, reality and of course prestige is particularly strong when it concerns conquering space. Explorer 1 was a direct response to the launch of the Soviet Sputnik 1 exactly four months earlier. Russia had its movie pioneers too. Pavel Klushantsev is regarded as the godfather of visual effects. He made some wonderful educational movies, such as *Road to the Stars* (1958), in which, among many other sneak previews of space travel, we get a guided tour aboard a space station by a lady scientist. Particularly sweet are the cat and the flowers on the table in front of the square window, which is not very smart in a pressurized cabin. There are uncanny similarities with Stanley Kubrick's *2001: A Space Odyssey* (1968) and the vehicle that lands on Klushantsev's Moon looks like an early blueprint for the Lunar Module used by NASA.

This mutual embrace of science and culture has continued to this day. The *Star Trek* franchise, for example, employed André Bormanis as a science consultant. Apart from producing, writing and some acting, his task was to safeguard the series' scientific plausibility. He did similar work for other science drama projects. The reverse has happened as well, although not quite as often. There has been a Dutch project entitled Mars One, which originally planned to send humans to Mars on a one-way trip in 2026, preceded two years earlier by life support equipment. Financially the project was to be kept afloat on the revenues of a reality TV show. There were no less than 200,000 applications worldwide, from which a small selection was made. Currently the project is broke. There are more realistic plans in the pipeline for travelling to Mars. Plans for new lunar missions, fifty years after Apollo, are under way in China,

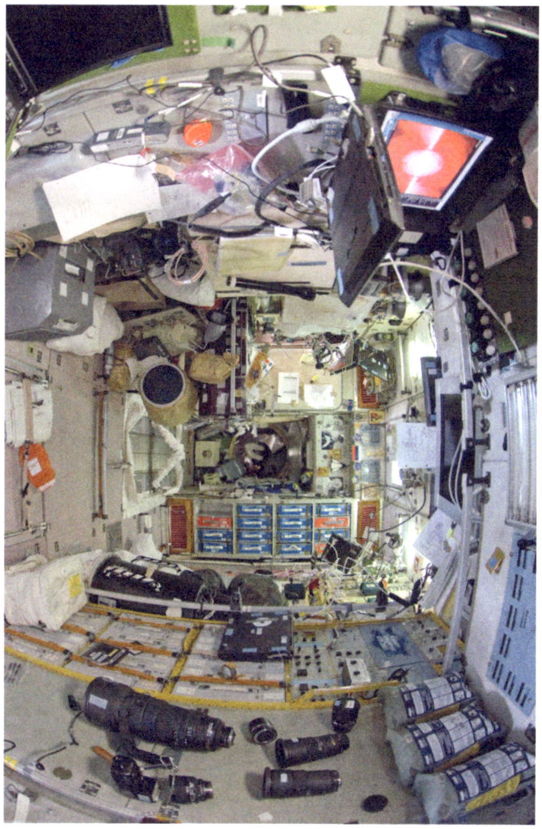

Top: BEAM inflatable workspace. Bottom left: MetOp satellite. Bottom right: ISS interior

22.1 THE ROCKET SPY NEXT DOOR

Wernher von Braun developed the A4 bombing rocket, better known under the name Nazi Propaganda Minister Joseph Goebbels gave it, 'Vergeltungswaffen 2' or V2. First though, the Germans used its cruise missile predecessor the V1. But the British found a way to topple these from their trajectory by pushing them aside with the wingtip of a Spitfire fighter plane. The V1s and V2s terrorized London and other parts of England when London was too far away. The V2 had the advantage of mobile launching.

One of the locations where V2 rockets were launched was The Hague. As it happened, a talented Delft chemistry professor, J.W.H. Uytenbogaart, was living there at the time. After completing his studies and working at a Dutch Rayon company, Uytenbogaart had led a research institute attached to the Vereinigte Glanzstoff-Fabriken (United Rayon Factories) near Berlin. He was aware of rocket experiments being carried out nearby and was interested in propulsion systems. When he sensed war was imminent, he decided to return to the Netherlands and settled in The Hague. He received a request from the London wartime authorities to acquire information on Nazi terror weapons, which is what he did. He collected V2 parts after failed launches and even discussed them with Germans. He found out everything he could about them in a secret room in his villa, analysing them and taking measurements, and sent the information to London by courier. His neighbour was a Dutch spy working for the Germans, who never noticed Uytenbogaart's double life. The work he did was extremely dangerous, because of failing V2 rockets and ammunition depots in the neighbourhood; twelve members of his resistance group were executed. By the end of the war, Uytenbogaart knew all there was to know about the construction of the V1 and V2. He received two decorations for his resistance activities, one for science and one for bravery.

22.2 BIO-LANDER

Nothing much happened to the InSight Mars probe during the 6.5 months between its launch and its landing on 26 November 2018 – except that it didn't travel entirely by itself. It flew simultaneously with two CubeSat MarCO satellites, the first time that a lander had relays nearby to monitor the landing. InSight is collecting data on the geology of Mars and thus of the rocky planets, including Earth.

Landing InSight was quite a different matter. The 5.5 km/sec had to be brought down to slightly more than 2 m/sec in 6.5 minutes, which would have been rough for a living entity. Its safe landing in an almost non-existent atmosphere was facilitated by retrorockets, parachutes and a heat shield made of SLA-561V (that's Super Lightweight Ablator 561V in NASA-speak), which had been used for earlier Mars missions. Surprisingly, the super lightweight material mostly consists of cork. The advantage of cork is that it can be thick enough to withstand the possible abrasion caused by sandstorms and still weigh very little.

Russia, India and the US, not necessarily in that order.

But let's return to the part of the Universe that we know best because it is conveniently close: planet Earth. Here we're struggling with structural lightness and the battle is at its fiercest when we send things into outer space. The reason for this is that for every kilogram you launch you need fuel, and for every kilogram of fuel you need another kilogram of fuel. Fortunately, fuel loses weight when it is being burnt, or nothing could ever reach space. The bottom line is that we need 500 kilograms of weight to send one kilogram to the Moon; this is without payload, which may include astronauts and their compact astronaut resources. Astronauts are quite heavy pieces of equipment in view of the human endeavour, the national prestige and the emotion they contribute. Of course, the *Star Trek* series is entertainment as well as American cultural propaganda.

Although there is a strong similarity between science fiction and what really happens, the differences are striking too. Science fiction movies depict adventures in space with vehicles that usually are much closer to what people are familiar with than to what would be realistic. Spaceship interiors are often spacious, which means more drag in gaseous planetary atmospheres and a lot of extra mass to accelerate when you need to escape for whatever narrative reason. Their structures tend to have a steam punk appeal. Steam punk, for those who don't know, is a boyish nostalgic design style related to sturdy cast iron and bronze, winches, cogwheels and large switches. Spaceships have bulky steel frames, metal walls and thick doors, which invariably are automatic and open with a buzz. A future in space screams heaviness. One quirky exception could be *Star Trek IV: The Voyage Home* (1986), in which the crew build a huge fish tank to carry two humpback whales (named George and Gracie) back to the future of the twenty-third century for enemy drone communication purposes. For this they use 'transparent aluminium'. The amount of belief an audience seems willing to suspend is positively alienating.

Space contraptions are bound to look very fragile and sloppy.

The fact remains that real space contraptions are very different from what audiences expect. To begin with, these are bound to look very fragile and sloppy. This comes from the absence of gravity. In general space gear can go through four stages: launch, orbit, landing and telepresence. Everything has to pass through launch and orbit. During the launch there has to be some mechanical protection against acceleration and the ever-growing amount of space debris, and there has to be an aerodynamic shield. In orbit, all forces are absent. There is only radiation, which could harm circuits and instruments. And people: even a Concorde crew had to wear radiation badges, like X-ray personnel. Protection is required, which

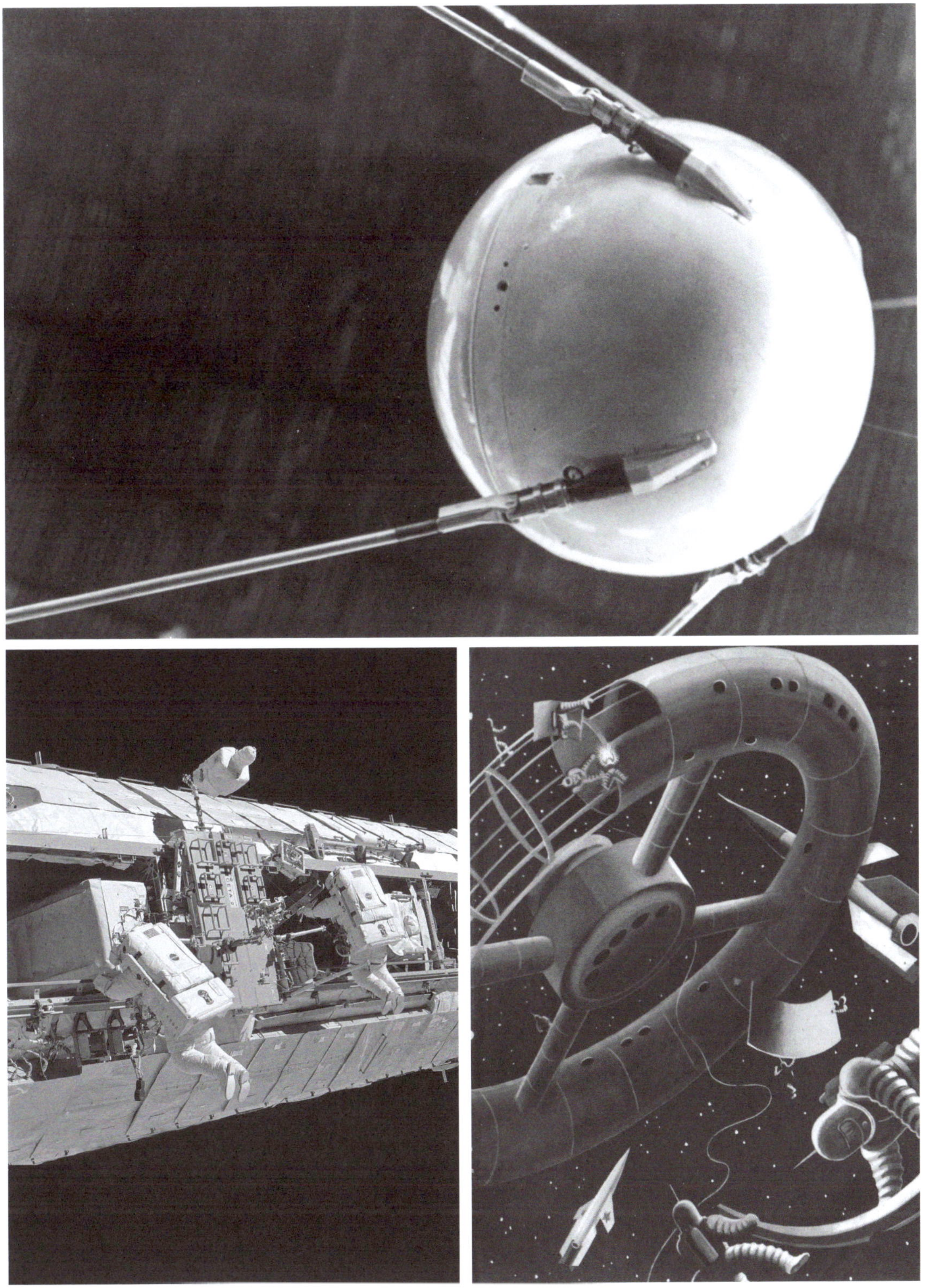

Top: Sputnik. Bottom left: Space walk. Bottom right: Klushantsev visual space station

Top: Soyuz spacecraft. Bottom: Launch of small satellites

just means covering devices where necessary with layers of special radiation reflecting foil. Once again, saving weight is priority number one.

SpaceX, an Elon Musk initiative, makes use of refillable boosters, which significantly lowers the costs of launching, from $54,500 per kilogram in NASA Space Shuttle times to, currently, less than $3,000 per kilogram. Space transportation is becoming affordable in current economics. Musk's system upgrade allowed him to send a red Tesla Roadster with a mannequin behind the wheel into space, as a test payload for the Falcon Heavy, a launch vehicle that can lift 64 tonnes into orbit and 17 tonnes to the Moon or Mars, which is roughly half of what NASA's Saturn V could do but now costing a good deal less.

Humans are regularly conveyed to and from the ISS. This space station doesn't look as immaculate and smooth as you might be led to expect. The interior is a mess, because the floor is all around and everything is strapped to it. The outside is not all that orthogonal either. Since 2006, two experimental inflatable habitats have been circling the Earth. Genesis 1 and Genesis 2 were developed for Bigelow Aerospace by Thin Red Line, the Canadian company established by Maxim de Jong, a hands-on expert in the development and fabrication of exotic lightweight structures. De Jong succeeded in stitching together carbon heat shield panels with carbon fibre. Inflatables like the BEAM (Bigelow Expandable Activity Module as Genesis is called now) are the structures of choice for orbiting in space, because the only force they have to handle is pressure from the atmosphere inside. They have to be able to withstand impact as well, and layers of resilient materials are much better at that than metals, particularly because of oblique layering, here used in a different context than FiberCore Europe's bridges.

Space transportation has evolved due to our ever-increasing knowledge. Twelve men have landed on the Moon, and until now there have been 24 probes by impactors, landers and rovers of Russian, American and Chinese design. There have been many more orbiting probes. These include satellites like Sputnik 1, boosted into orbit by a rocket. Thanks to technological refinement, composite thinking if you like, today's satellites can be tiny. They are now classified according to size.

Small satellites are not really small and can weigh up to 500 kilograms. Traditionally they have been launched together with a larger payload as a kind of 'supporting actor'. Some companies, like Richard Branson's Virgin, are planning dedicated launch vehicles for 'SmallSats'. Microsatellites weigh up to 100 kilograms. Two of these accompanied the Mars InSight lander and orbited Mars. They were CubeSat pioneers, the first in space to fit within a modular system for launching satellites simultaneously.

Already there are warnings of overcrowding space.

That is the direction in which space exploitation is moving. There are nanosatellites up to 10 kilograms that are already available to students. Picosatellites are even smaller and the smallest of all are femtosatellites. With their numbers rapidly increasing, it is hard to keep track of failures and successes. There have been attempts to launch hundreds of these chip satellites. In March 2019 over one hundred CubeSat femtosatellites were deployed into orbit.

Tiny satellites don't come alone. SpaceX is currently working on Starlink, a swarm of satellites that orbit as a global network of communication nodes. So far 182 satellites have been launched and there are plans to extend that number to 12,000 in the mid 2020s and maybe reach 42,000 later on. This constellation is to support global broadband Internet.

Already there are warnings of overcrowding space, because SpaceX won't be the only communications contender. It may obstruct space observation and turn into a clash between communication convenience and orbiting waste, an extra-terrestrial continuation of the impact of human life on Earth, with 'space slides' far above the clouds. The second emerging effect may well be the rapidly growing energy consumption among data centres. The latest estimate for Ireland, an important gateway between the US and Europe, is that soon between 25 and 30 per cent of Irish energy will drive the country's data storage and transfer. Communication support is likely to influence social drama through media enrichment, with the spread of cheap space consumption even presenting the possibility of the 'space selfie'. Emergent effects may very well bring drama back from space. Fritz Lang's *Frau im Mond* could backfire on us yet. ■

22.3 BALLOONING AWAY

You must have been wondering what the vertical stack on the cover of *Designing Lightness* is all about. This is the moment to explain. In 2014 the ISTAR Group in Bend, Oregon, together with Thin Red Line run by Maxim de Jong, mentioned elsewhere in this chapter when discussing Genesis 1 and 2, designed a mid-altitude (50 kilometres) balloon to be used on, or rather above, the planet Venus.

The intelligent principle behind it is that the volume can be made larger or smaller, which will change the lift without the need to adjust the mass. The amount of gas inside is fixed and no ballast is required. The device, which would be 5.5 metres wide, can be manoeuvred up and down simply by adjusting the height of the stack. It is a ballooning idea that maybe should have been conceived in 1783, when the Montgolfier brothers flew the first hot air balloon.

THINGS TO COME

23. SHIFTING TECHNO-LOGICAL BOUNDARIES

We're talking the 1950s. Raised voices can be heard coming from the design room of Erres, the Dutch electrical appliance factory. They're having a terrible row. The CEO, who is passing by, goes in to ask what all the shouting is about. The cause appears to be the colour of the new vacuum cleaner. The company produces the Blue Range and now the designer says that the vacuum cleaner has to be red. 'Well', says the CEO, 'if that's what the designer says, that's what it's going to be'. And so it is decided. Except that a few weeks later, in trial runs, the red paint clearly isn't covering the metal surface well enough after spraying. So it's back to blue. Remember, this is just about colour and still it concerns the triad of concept (Blue Range house-cleaning appliance), materials (steel and paint) and process (spray painting).

Yes, and back in the present the design triad is as valid as ever. In fact, its importance has grown. We design ever more sophisticated lightweight structures and devices and are beginning to focus on cultivating their value in time, with the aim of decreasing the flow of both materials and energy. These considerations scarcely existed in the 1950s. In those days progress was synonymous with technology working for economic growth by producing and consuming more materials and energy, with very little attention to the side effects. Complete villages were demolished and the villagers accepted this, because it was progress. All dreams were believed to come true some day, even the dream of a fully automatic, perfectly red vacuum cleaner.

It is becoming increasingly clear that the ramifications of each and every decision, even as seemingly trivial as a coating, or 'let's stop riveting, we'll weld it', have much wider repercussions for design and implementation than had once been assumed. Our increased understanding tells us that whatever we design and make is much larger than we thought and has a more profound impact. This takes place on two main levels that are intertwined through the concept of the products we make.

The first level is that of the object in question and its direct use against the background of all the transportation required. There are several examples in *Designing Lightness*: change the material and the processing and the concept changes along with them. Losing sight of the whole raises the risk of failure. The second level is that of value cultivation, the ability to maintain value and control handling of the used parts and materials to keep optimum quality as long as possible. Although the first ideas of what is currently called circular design (tacitly including transportation) emerged in the 1970s, it hasn't been until now that a true understanding of their implications is beginning to sink in. The most radical, but nevertheless logical consequence of containing all materials in circular flows and suppressing the emergence of waste may come as quite a shock to some, namely that there should be no more mining. This is not likely to happen overnight, nor does it mean that

mined materials will disappear altogether: one can keep on using what has been dug up and processed and one can mine existing artefacts. But there is nothing wrong with keeping this major challenge in mind to be forced to explore different options. It does mean that products, parts and materials have to remain accessible for different kinds of continuous use over time, in order to keep them in circulation at the highest possible value. Circularity is not a matter of reusing or recycling parts of a given product when its life is over, which currently seems to be the epitome of greenness, but of trying to plan decades into the future and keep things going, which requires a different approach.

The other consequence of no more mining is renewability. Newness is a property that plant materials in particular can introduce over and over again. Today their potential is somewhat hesitantly being explored. There is a dilemma, however. Wood and plants have the right kind of reputation, but it is no simple matter to provide them with high-grade properties and turn them into composites required for many existing technical applications, nor is it easy to develop their particular kind of circularity and overcome negative qualities such as lagging behind in compostability, as mentioned earlier. Value cultivation is an option for plant products too. Some can be recycled, which requires energy, and some can be burned or digested, which may produce greenhouse gases.

Some may compete with food in terms of soil area. Lastly, biomaterials need their own flow control. The goals are being set but reaching them will take time.

The stage we have now reached, where the key role played by energy and the all-encompassing organization of transportation are becoming clear – more than anything we are a logistics animal – shows that refinement of design must include movement and change as a given context. Structures have a dynamic character that can deal with complicated stress scenarios and that may actively and passively include all kinds of physical and chemical changes. For this expanding field, thinking in composite structures is inevitable and currently it is really beginning to make its mark in technological development.

Composites have hit the colonization trail with a vengeance, and we can already discern a sequence of waves that sees design refinement seeping into technological considerations, with adjustments made to rule out unwanted environmental effects. Fibre reinforced thermosets are much better known than they were 25 years ago and getting well accepted, apart from the disadvantages in continued use and recycling that come with mass production. But now we have the follow-up of thermoplastics as a composite matrix and the potentials of melting for welding as well as for easier separation. And the next jump in the development

of bio-composites, for example with lignin-based carbon fibres, is already in the run-up. The first steps have also been taken to combine functions so as to replenish structural and speed enhancing properties with insulation, energy generation, tactility, electronic networking and whatever else may arrive.

These changes, particularly the step towards thermoplastics, are ushering in a 'compositization' of manufacturing, and doing it almost imperceptibly, in line with the general inclination of technology to become invisible and exclusively show itself as magic. The assembly of relatively simple parts is, very slowly, being replaced by the shared manufacture of complex products. Overmoulding and overprinting, whereby extra features are added to larger parts so as to combine refined details with strong and stiff function carriers, mark the beginning of manufacturing refinement that inevitably comes with composite design.

With the integration of technologies immediately comes the challenge of reversal. The more complex the parts, the more difficult it becomes to guarantee continued use and eventually complete or partial recycling. Suppose, for instance, that the toaster redone by Thomas Thwaites described at the start were to consist of four extremely advanced parts instead of 400 simple ones. There is no general rule to get around this issue, except that in each case an optimum balance needs making between manufacturing and value cultivation, and between the logistics of construction and reverse logistics of disassembly and recycling. The implication is that every design will have to be defined at the broad level of systems within which it exists and not merely as itself, to be sold or rented in a particular market. This means breaking down functions into system components and rearranging these into better functioning products. Rearrangement is tricky. It takes time and it will also take time to reach this level of technological discretion.

The term 'sufficiency' directly relates to discretion. In a TV interview Marleen Stikker, director of Waag in Amsterdam and initiator of 'De Digitale Stad' (The Digital City), a very early (1998) version of what is now called 'social media', said that not every idea needs to be implemented. She was referring to the unfolding dark side of the Internet, which she considers broken, but not irreparable. It holds true for structure design as well, the dark side of which is overproduction of the unwanted. (Both the digital and the material world keep on tucking into energy supplies as if these were free). We don't have to fulfil our every dream. No matter in which field we make things, sports, warfare, networks, transportation, fashion, architecture or exploration, we have to remember they all boil down to making things easier for ourselves, and to the essence of who we are, a species that longs for recognition of the self in context and is easily impressed by a little touch of magic ■

24. BEHAVIOURS AND POLICIES

What kind of people are people anyway? A simple newspaper article gives us some idea. It concerns a very picturesque UNESCO protected village in the mountains of Austria called Hallstatt. It has 780 inhabitants and gets about a million visitors a year. Flocks of tourists visit Hallstatt, simply because this small town bears a strong resemblance to a very picturesque village in the Disney blockbuster *Frozen* (2013). The movie does feature a village, but it was modelled on another very picturesque place in Norway. Nevertheless, tourism in Hallstatt soared, particularly after someone in China built an equally picturesque full-size replica.

Here we have a simple illustration of our longing for the feast of recognition. It also points to the fact that material and energy overflow is not just a technological issue we can resolve by weight reduction. People fly across the globe to stare at things, take selfies and buy souvenirs made elsewhere. We understand technology far better than we understand ourselves, as individuals, as groups and as nations. Apart from travelling the world to recognize stuff, we humans like to wait for things to go wrong and clear up the mess afterwards. Evidently, the prevention of anything from small accidents to huge catastrophes takes years, decades, or even centuries of learning.

Changing harmful habits is probably the most demanding task for humans. In this respect the individual habit of eating too many cookies is not that different from the cultural habit of commuting, or the consumerist habit of always looking for ultimate convenience 'at a fair price'. Most of us know this all too well, and simply accept it.

Just as damaging as gathering convenience is the pursuit of identity. Wearing certain brands has fragmented into following certain influencers who, for purposes of identifiability, look surprisingly similar. British artist Grayson Perry did a wonderful project on taste and style in lower, middle and upper English social classes. He interviewed people and designed six tapestries to tell the story. The title is particularly appropriate here, as it gives a name to the main force that defines human behaviour: 'Vanity of Small Differences'.

Flying with a particular company, driving an SUV of a certain brand, or a nondescript car for that matter, going to shops or websites of our choice: everything from toilet paper to a dummy in a Tesla launched into outer space contributes to our self-image. Whatever we purchase, some part of the money spent goes to identification. If that's the case, we may wonder why it has to cost so much material and energy.

Where does this awareness come from? Well, the limits to the metabolism of humanity have been under suspicion for a long time, but we only began to actually experience them quite recently. Humankind had no idea of its impact on the environment and, let's be honest, preferred it that way. As a consequence, our knowledge acquisition and way of reasoning followed a matching path of exploiting

We should first learn to understand ourselves much better, as individuals, as groups and as nations. Energy and material overload is caused by us humans doing too much.

abundance and pricing it according to models derived from the opposite concept of scarcity, because scarcity inflates value.

Economics evolved as a rather staid set of social models based on crude and often superficial assumptions about human behaviour, expressed in monetary transactions to suggest mathematical precision. Dutch author and computer linguist Hugo Brandt Corstius wrote a mock encyclopaedia, in which he defines an economist as 'someone who disagrees with another economist'. The point is that the true power of economics doesn't justify its reputation as the strongly preferred policy development tool. Economics' predictive capacities are meagre, its understanding of human behaviour is naive, and its principles of value allocation fall short. Moreover, the decreasing availability of resources may be a less important criterion for economic functioning than the increase in side effects detrimental to the living environment.

Nevertheless, economics can serve as a foundation for further development, provided its elements and assumptions are used openly and critically but never dogmatically. Indeed, improvements to economics as a toolbox are continually being developed and tested. Importantly, the meaning of the word capital has been defined (Wikipedia) as the collection of assets that can be put to economic use, in which 'economic' has its original everyday meaning. This includes everything humans develop, make and use (tools, infrastructure, etc) but leaves out everything that is taken for granted but indispensable: air, clean water, landscape, even life itself.

There are many other definitions, such as the 'five capitals' framework identified by the non-profit sustainability programme 'Forum of the Future'. This distinguishes between Natural, Human, Social, Financial and Manufactured capital and adds Man-Made, Cultural and Symbolic capital. It isn't the strongest subdivision, since the categories overlap. The point is that the different capitals are interdependent and that the growth of one can mean the decline of one or more of the others. Economic growth in particular is a third rail. Some say it is crucial, others say it is unsustainable. In fact, it depends on the cluster of capitals that constitute growth at a certain moment and the capitals that decline because of this. It is also

Klima-Paket: Zurück an Absender
PILLE-PALLE!
CLIMATE JUSTICE
=
SOCIAL JUSTICE
FRIDAYS FOR FUTURE
HOW DARE YOU?
NO More Pillepalle

important to be aware that not all capital needs to be expressed in monetary terms.

Value is only an assumption anyway. On the Pacific island of Yap, the inhabitants use giant round stones, sometimes 2.5 metres in diameter, to express the worth of abstract items, such as a dowry. These Rai stones are carved on another island. Once, one was lost overboard on the way to Yap but this didn't affect the value of the sunken supercoins. In essence that is how money works, including Bitcoin. It is a matter of trust.

One of the observations on economic strangeness in the first *Lightness* book, by economist Wim Hafkamp, is that economic forces make us trade more for less money instead of what one would expect to be profitable, which is to trade less for more money. This emerges from the phenomenon that the affordability of products requires investments in machines that force the investors to sell more so as to earn back what they invested.

This implies that lightness as a way to save materials and energy hasn't really been that much of an economic issue. However, when we consider lightness as a kind of capital the story changes. It agrees with the assertion made by Adriaan Beukers et al. in *Future Aircraft Structures*: 'So, in general, major improvements can only be achieved by the introduction of more potent material families,

with better specific properties and more attractive manufacturing possibilities to build structures with higher added value.'

The rebound effect is another caveat that always turns up when sustainability is linked to profitability. In the corridors one often hears: 'We should be able to convince entrepreneurs that sustainable development can save money.' If only it were that simple. Economic activity doesn't stop at one transaction, so the next question is: what will the money saved be spent on? The answer must itself become part of the road to sustainability.

Lightness can contribute. It can also help to demonstrate the causes of the stalemate of ecological warnings from the world of science leading to disputes about responsibility, power, organization and blame games. As stated earlier, it isn't easy to outgrow habits. Enterprises claim they depend on what customers want, which is convenience, identity and magic. Customers, or consumers, want what they can get, which is different from what they say they want, but they appear willing to pay by weight, even when they buy candy. Democratic governments want votes, which prevents them from making choices that curb consumer desires.

The advantage of weight reduction as part of a policy is that it is quite clear. And it is not uncommon either. Weight as a criterion for taxes, for instance, has been used for decades. It is politically dangerous, however, to make rules much stricter and, say, no longer allow cars beyond a certain weight. These things do happen, but they take time to get used to. The reasoning behind it is that change through commercial choice is extremely difficult when it collides with 'business as usual'. Governments can enforce change, and they do, but this requires persuasive skills that are not always present.

More than anything else, a change for the lighter requires cooperation. It is clear that we need sophisticated machinery to make composites. And that this process needs organizing, which means combining professionals with specialist skills and knowledge with conceptualists who understand how designed elements fit together. Culturally lightness will require a convincing narrative. It may be a while before people take pride in saying: 'Look! I can lift my car with one hand!' And yet, lightness has the ability to become normal, because of its relationship with convenience. ■

CAR BOOT

INDEX

LIST OF ABBREVIATIONS

ABS Acrylonitile Butadiene Styrene
AFP Automated Fibre Placement
BWB Blended Wing Body
BYD Build Your Dream
CFRP Carbon Fibre Reinforced Polymer
CNG Compressed Natural Gas
EPS Expanded Polystyrene
FRP Fibre Reinforced Polymer
GFRP Glass Fibre Reinforced Polymer
LCA Life Cycle Assessment
LED Light Emitting Diode
LPG Liquefied Petroleum Gas
PA Polyamide
PAI Polyamide-im§ide
PC Polycarbonate
PE Polyethylene
PEEK Polyether Ester Ketone
PEI Polyetherimide
PEK Polyetherketone
PES Polyethersulfone
PET Polyethylene Terephthalate
PLA Polylactic Acid
PMMA Polymethyl Metacrylate
POM Polyoxymethylene
PP Polypropylene
PPA Polyphthalamide
PPE Polyphenylene Ether
PPS Polyphenylene Sulfide
PPSU Polyphenylsulfone
PSU Polysulfone
PUR Polyurethane
PVC Polyvinyl Chloride
RIM Reaction Injection Moulding
RTM Resin Transfer Moulding
RRIM Reinforced Reaction Injection Moulding
SRIM Structured Reaction Injection Moulding
SAN Styrene Acrylonitrile
SMC Sheet Moulding Compound
SPS Syndiotactic Polystyrene
SRIM Structured Reaction Injection Moulding
SUV Sports Utility Vehicle
TED Technology Entertainment and Design
UD Unidirectional

FOR READING AND SEARCHING

Bakker, C., Hollander, M. den, Hinte, E. van & Zijlstra, Y., *Products that Last: Product Design for Circular Business Models*. BIS Publishers, Amsterdam 2014

Beukers, A. & Hinte, E.J. van, *Flying Lightness: Promises for Structural Elegance*. 010 Publishers, Rotterdam 2005

Beukers, A. & Hinte, E.J. van, *Lightness: The Inevitable Renaissance of Minimum Energy Structures*. 010 Publishers, Rotterdam 1998

Beukers, A., Bersee, H., Bergsma, O., Koussios, S. & Tooren, M. van, *Future Aircraft Structures: From Metal to Composite Structures*. IMAST, Capri 2008

Gordon, J.E., *Structures: Or Why Things Don't Fall Down*. Penguin Books, London 1991

Haffmans, S., Gelder, M. van, Hinte, E. van & Zijlstra, Y., *Products that Flow: Circular Business Models and Design Strategies for Fast-Moving Consumer Goods*. BIS Publishers, Amsterdam 2018

Hirt, M.R., Jetz, W., Rall, B.C. & Brose, U., *'Universal scaling of maximum speed with body mass: Why the largest animals are not the fastest'*. bioRxiv preprint, first posted online 17 December 2016

Wikipedia has been invaluable in the writing of *Designing Lightness*. Payment to Wikipedia would be very much appreciated. And remember: Designing Lightness is a portal.

IMAGE CREDITS

AeroVelo: 119/4;
Adem Altan/AFP: 36;
Alan Welner/AP: 10/1;
Anne de Henning/Aga Khan Trust for Culture: 3/2;
DUTCHPHOTO/ANP: 129;
Anthony Quintano/Flickr: 348;
Armel/Flickr: 60/2;
Bill Allen/Mountain Trip: 4/2, 16/2;
Bob Peterson: 104/3;
Clouds Architecture Office: 35;
Damen Group: 290, 294, 298/2;
Daniel Alexander/Thomas Thwaites: 48;
Delft Hyperloop: 123/1;
Dick Teske: 161/1;
Didier Boy de la Tour/Shigeru Ban: 286;
Jeff Wall, *Morning Cleaning, Mies van der Rohe Foundation, Barcelona:* 63/3;
KOGA: 248/1;
Kreuzschnabel: 109/1;
Maggie Starbard/Adam Cole/Ben De La Cruz: 119/2, 119/3;
Mari/Flickr: 30;
Matthew Lamb: 40;
NASA: 8/1;
Ogannes/Flickr: 103/3;
Port of Rotterdam/Paul Martens: 55/4;
Reuters/China Stringer Network: 141;
Royal Huisman: 97;
Stanley Kubrick, *2001: A Space Odyssey,* TM & © Turner Entertainment Co: 44;
Sergio Souza/@serjosoza/Unsplah: 12;
Thanassis Stavrakis/ASSOCIATED PRESS/AP: 52/1;
The Buckminster Fuller Institute: 66;
Todd Reichert: 119/1;
United States Air Force: 4/2, 10/2;
Vincent Dubois/Flickr: 270;

CREDITS

Texts: Ed van Hinte, Adriaan Beukers
Foreword: Conny Bakker
Copy editing: John Kirkpatrick
Design: Studio Renate Boere
Lithography and Printing: NPN Drukkers
Paper: Edixion 100gr
Publisher: Marcel Witvoet, nai010 publishers

This publication was made possible by financial support from CompositesNL, NL in Business, topsector High Tech Systems and Materials, topsector Holland Chemistry and private contributors.

Thanks to:
Conny Bakker, Renate Boere, Paula Dekkers, Quirine Dob, Demi Horsman, Pia Jacques de Dixmude, Pepijn de Jonge, Marc Lamain, John Kirkpatrick, Eva Knollenburg, Paul Kortman, Jonathan Tams, Macarena Torres Puga, Bouke Veldman, Marcel Witvoet, Mahtab Zamanifar

nai010 publishers is an internationally orientated publisher specialized in developing, producing and distributing books in the fields of architecture, urbanism, art and design. www.nai010.com

nai010 books are available internationally at selected bookstores and from the following distribution partners:

North, Central and South America - Artbook | D.A.P., New York, USA, dap@dapinc.com

Rest of the world - Idea Books, Amsterdam, the Netherlands, idea@ideabooks.nl

For general questions, please contact nai010 publishers directly at sales@nai010.com or visit our website www.nai010.com for further information.

Printed and bound in the Netherlands
ISBN: 978-94-6208-546-6
NUR: 656
BISAC: DES009000

Designing Lightness is also available as e-book:
ISBN: 978-94-6208-559-6 (e-book)